D1096067

NATIONAL SAFETY COUNCIL
INJURY FACTS®
2015 EDITION

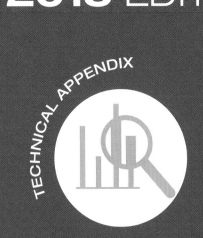
TECHNICAL APPENDIX

ALL INJURIES

OCCUPATIONAL

STATE DATA

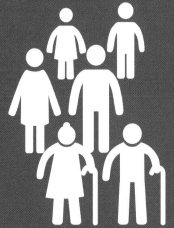

MOTOR VEHICLE

INTERNATIONAL

HOME AND COMMUNITY

FORMERLY
ACCIDENT FACTS®

See page ii for information on your free downloadable book

i

The National Safety Council, chartered by an act of Congress, is a nongovernmental, not-for-profit, public service organization. The mission of the National Safety Council is to save lives by preventing injuries and deaths at work, in homes and communities, and on the roads through leadership, research, education, and advocacy.

Injury Facts®, the Council's annual statistical report on unintentional injuries and their characteristics and costs, was prepared by:

Research and Safety Management Solutions Group:
Terry Miller, Senior Director, Research and Safety Management Solutions
Kenneth P. Kolosh, Manager, Statistics Department
Kevin T. Fearn, Sr. Statistical Associate
Kathleen T. Porretta, Technical Editor

Questions or comments about the content of *Injury Facts* should be directed to the Research and Safety Management Solutions Group, National Safety Council, 1121 Spring Lake Drive, Itasca, IL, 60143, by phone at (630) 775-2322, fax at (630) 285-0242, or email *rssdept@nsc.org*.

For price and ordering information, visit *www.nsc.org* or write:

Customer Service
National Safety Council, 1121 Spring Lake Drive, Itasca, IL, 60143, call (800) 621-7619, or fax (630) 285-0797.

Acknowledgments
The information presented in *Injury Facts* was made possible by the cooperation of many organizations and individuals, including state vital and health statistics authorities, state traffic authorities, state workers' compensation authorities, trade associations, Bureau of the Census, Bureau of Labor Statistics, Consumer Product Safety Commission, Federal Highway Administration, Federal Railroad Administration, International Labour Organization, National Center for Health Statistics, National Fire Protection Association, National Highway Traffic Safety Administration, National Transportation Safety Board, National Weather Service, Mine Safety and Health Administration, and the World Health Organization. Specific contributions are acknowledged in footnotes and source notes throughout the book.

Visit the National Safety Council website:
nsc.org
nsc.org/learn/safety-knowledge/Pages/injury-facts.aspx

Access your free downloadable copy of Injury Facts: nsc.org/getinjuryfacts2015

PDF

Table of Contents

Since 1991, unintentional injuries have ranked as the fifth leading cause of death behind heart disease, cancer, chronic lower respiratory disease, and stroke. As shown in the top graph on the facing page, deaths in the United States are dominated by heart disease and cancer. The next three causes, chronic lower respiratory disease, stroke, and unintentional injuries, look almost insignificant in comparison. These three causes combined account for fewer deaths than cancer alone. Given this reality, why are organizations like the National Safety Council focused on preventing unintentional injuries?

The use of a single metric such as fatalities does not adequately quantify the devastating impact of unintentional injuries on individuals, their families, and society. Compared to other leading causes of death, unintentional injuries impact younger victims who are often raising families and otherwise contributing to society through work and other activities. Compare the average age of victim for each cause of death:

• heart disease – age 77
• cancer – age 71
• chronic lower respiratory disease – age 77
• stroke – age 78
• unintentional injuries – 45

The average age of 45 for unintentional injury death is the only age in the list that is not in the 70s. Because of this age disparity, an alternative metric, years of potential life lost (YPLL), can be helpful to quantify the impact of unintentional injury deaths. YPLL is an estimate of the average years a person would have lived if he or she had not died prematurely. As shown on the bottom graph on the facing page, in 2012 unintentional injuries accounted for the third most YPLL (3,503,000) behind cancer (6,320,000) and heart disease (4,300,000).

Because injury events occur suddenly without notice and because victims are often young, the loss seems especially senseless. The typical unintentional injury death occurs more than 30 years earlier than national life expectancy averages. YPLL is used in an attempt to partially quantify this loss. But because all lives have equal value, young and old, YPLL fails to fully capture the impact.

Neither fatality data nor YPLL alone presents the whole picture of unintentional injury deaths. For this reason, *Injury Facts*® tracks unintentional injury data using a variety of metrics. This publication is intended to educate and encourage people to take action to prevent unintentional injuries. This promise, that individual actions can improve safety and save lives, is perhaps the most accurate explanation of why the National Safety Council has been working for more than 100 years to saves lives by preventing injuries and deaths at work, in homes and communities, and on the roads through leadership, research, education and advocacy.

The latest estimates show a continuation of the recent negative trend with over a 2% increase in unintentional-injury deaths in 2013 compared to the revised 2012 total.

Unintentional-injury deaths were estimated to total 130,800 in 2013 and 127,792 in 2012.

The resident population of the United States was 316,160,000 in 2013, an increase of less than 1% from 2012. The unintentional death rate in 2013 was 41.4 per 100,000 population – an increase of nearly 2% from 2012 and 22% greater than the lowest rate on record, which was 34.0 in 1992.

A more complete summary of the situation in 2013 and recent trends is given on page 2.

Changes in the 2015 edition

For the first time, a downloadable electronic version of *Injury Facts*® is being made available FREE with each hard copy book! Please see page ii for additional information on how to download your copy today.

Look for new data on…
• Occupational injury and illness undercount
• Driveway and parking lot crashes
• Distracted walking
• Falls
• Smoke alarms

And updated or expanded data on…
• General mortality
• Occupational injury and illness incidence rates by industry
• Occupational injury and illness profile data by industry sector
• Forklift injury trends
• Workers' compensation claims and costs
• Disasters
• Distracted driving
• Young drivers
• Comparing safety of transportation modes
• Traffic safety issues – alcohol, occupant protection, speeding, and others
• Consumer product-related injuries
• Unintentional deaths by states

We also continue to receive questions regarding a change made three years ago. Editions of *Injury Facts*® prior to 2011 included estimates of disabling injuries. Starting with the 2011 edition, NSC transitioned to the concept of "medically consulted injury" in place of "disabling injury." This new definition was adopted from the National Health Interview Survey, a household survey conducted by the National Center for Health Statistics (NCHS). A medically consulted injury is defined by NCHS as an injury serious enough that a medical professional was consulted. Moving *Injury Facts*® estimates from disabling injuries to medically consulted injuries provides several advantages. First and foremost, a medically consulted injury is a more inclusive definition that allows for more comprehensive estimates of the true burden of unintentional injuries. Second, medically consulted injury estimates are updated each year by NCHS allowing NSC to provide the most timely and accurate data possible. Finally, the previous definition of disabling injury was often misinterpreted as a workers' compensation injury. Using the term medically consulted injuries should help eliminate this confusion. For more information on medically consulted injuries, please see the technical appendix.

For more information on *Injury Facts®* and other products, visit the NSC's web site (nsc.org), call Customer Service at 800-621-7619, or contact your local council.

Your comments and suggestions on how to improve *Injury Facts®* are welcome. Contact information is given on page ii.

Five leading causes of death, United States, 2012

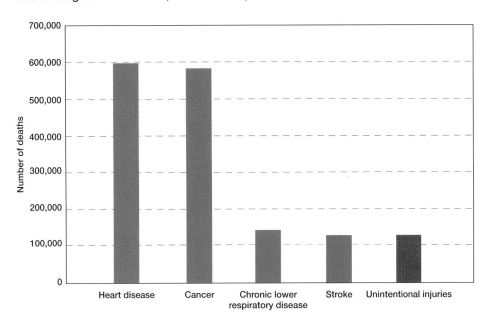

Five leading causes of years of potential life lost, United States, 2012

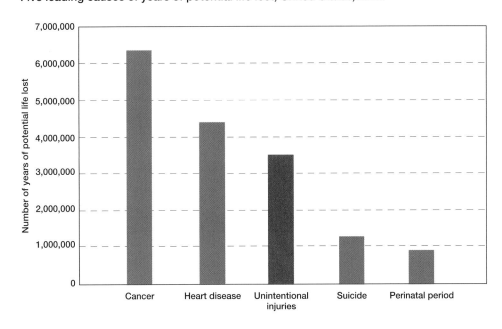

All Injuries

Lifetime odds of death for selected causes, United States, 2011ᵃ

Total, any cause
1 in 1

Heart disease
and cancer
1 in 7

Chronic lower
respiratory disease
1 in 28

Intentional
self-harm
1 in 100

Unintentional poisoning by and
exposure to noxious substances
1 in 109

Motor vehicle incidents
1 in 112

Falls 1 in 144

Lightning
1 in 164,968

Legal execution
1 in 127,717

Bitten or struck by dog
1 in 116,448

Contact with heat
and hot substances
1 in 59,093

Contact with hornets,
wasps, and bees
1 in 55,764

Health Statistics–Mortality Data for 2011 as compiled from
Population and life expectancy data are from the U.S. Ce
tion codes based on the Tenth Revision of the World Health
ages 41-42.

NATIONAL SAFETY C

The collection, analysis and dissemination of unintentional injury and fatality statistics have been a focus for the National Safety Council since its inception. The first comprehensive statistical compendium ever produced relating to unintentional injuries and deaths was published in the early 1920s, shortly after the Council was formed. Since the 1920s, as a testament to its reliance on data as a measure of progress and guidance, statistical information has been published by the Council on an annual basis without interruption – first as Accident Facts® and more recently as Injury Facts®.

INJURY FACTS® **2015**

National Safety Council

All Unintentional Injuries, 2013

Unintentional-injury-related deaths were up 2.4% in 2013, compared to the revised 2012 estimate. Unintentional-injury-related deaths were estimated to total 130,800 in 2013 and 127,792 in 2012. The 2013 estimate is 51% greater than the 1992 total of 86,777 (the lowest annual total since 1924).

The death rate in 2013 was 41.4 per 100,000 population – 22% greater than the lowest rate on record, which was 34.0 in 1992. The 2013 death rate increased 1.7% from the 2012 revised rate.

Comparing 2013 to 2012, work deaths and motor vehicle deaths decreased while home and public deaths both increased. The population death rate for motor vehicle and work decreased, and increased for the public and home classes.

The motor vehicle death total was down 2.5% in 2013. The 2013 mileage death rate of 1.20 per 100,000,000 vehicle miles was down 11% from the revised 2012 rate of 1.35. The 2013 rate was unchanged from the revised 2011 rate of 1.20.

According to the latest final data (2012), unintentional injuries continued to be the fifth leading cause of death, exceeded only by heart disease, cancer, chronic lower respiratory diseases, and stroke.

Nonfatal injuries also affect millions of Americans. In 2013, 39 million people – about 1 out of 8 – sought medical attention.

The economic impact of these fatal and nonfatal unintentional injuries amounted to $820.6 billion in 2013. This is equivalent to about $2,600 per capita, or about $6,700 per household. These are costs that every individual and household pays whether directly out of pocket, through higher prices for goods and services, or through higher taxes.

Between 1912 and 2013, unintentional-injury-related deaths per 100,000 population were reduced 50% (after adjusting for the classification change in 1948) from 82.5 to 41.4. The reduction in the overall rate during a period when the nation's population tripled has resulted in 6,100,000 fewer people being killed due to unintentional injuries than there would have been if the rate had not been reduced.

All unintentional injuries, 2013

Class	Deaths	Change from 2012	Deaths per 100,000 people	Medically consulted injuries[a]
All classes[b]	130,800	2.4%	41.4	39,600,000
Motor vehicle	35,500	-2%	11.2	4,300,000
Public nonwork	33,802			4,200,000
Work	1,498			100,000
Home	200			(c)
Work	3,738	-4%	1.2	4,800,000
Non-motor vehicle	2,240			4,700,000
Motor vehicle	1,498			100,000
Home	66,000	5%	20.9	19,900,000
Non-motor vehicle	65,800			19,900,000
Motor vehicle	200			(c)
Public	27,200	2%	8.6	10,700,000

Source: National Safety Council estimates (rounded) based on data from the National Center for Health Statistics (NCHS), state departments of health, and state traffic authorities, except for the work figures, which are from the Bureau of Labor Statistics, Census of Fatal Occupational Injuries (CFOI). The National Safety Council adopted the CFOI count for work-related unintentional injuries beginning with 1992 data. See the Glossary for definitions and the Technical Appendix for estimating procedures. Beginning with 1999 data, deaths are classified according to the 10th revision of the International Classification of Diseases. Caution should be used in comparing data classified under the two systems.

[a]The totals shown are approximations based on the National Safety Council's analysis of National Health Interview Survey results that is conducted by NCHS. The totals are the best estimates for the current year. They should not, however, be compared with totals shown in previous editions of this book to indicate year-to-year changes or trends. See the Glossary for definitions and the Technical Appendix for estimating procedures.

[b]Deaths and injuries above for the four separate classes add to more than the "All classes" figures due to rounding and because some deaths and injuries are included in more than one class. For example, 1,498 work deaths involved motor vehicles and are in both the work and motor vehicle totals, and 200 motor vehicle deaths occurred on home premises and are in both home and motor vehicle. The total of such duplication amounted to about 1,698 deaths and 100,000 injuries in 2013.

[c]Less than 10,000.

All Injury-Related Deaths, 2011

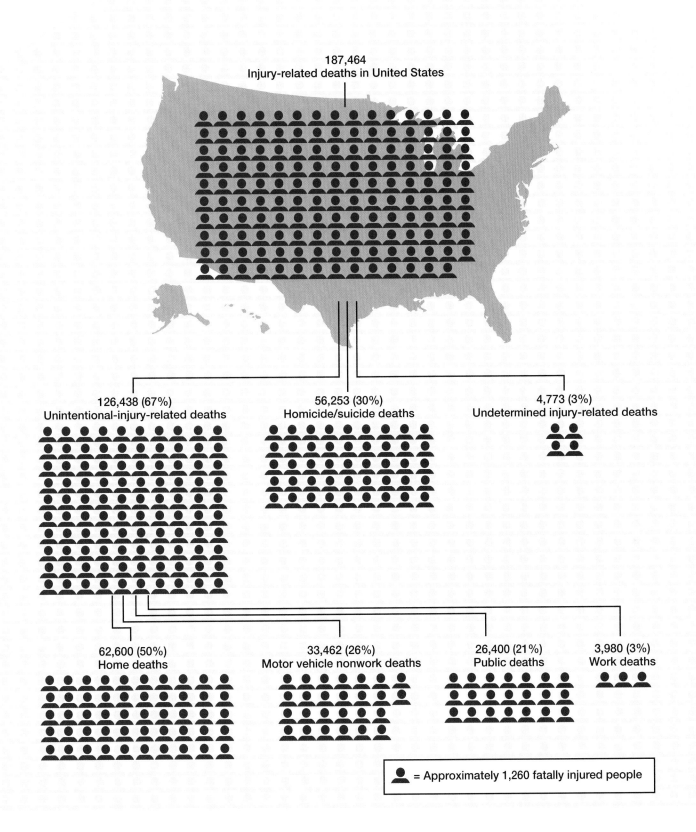

4,000,000
Injury deaths worldwide

187,464
Injury-related deaths in United States

126,438 (67%)
Unintentional-injury-related deaths

56,253 (30%)
Homicide/suicide deaths

4,773 (3%)
Undetermined injury-related deaths

62,600 (50%)
Home deaths

33,462 (26%)
Motor vehicle nonwork deaths

26,400 (21%)
Public deaths

3,980 (3%)
Work deaths

= Approximately 1,260 fatally injured people

All Injury-Related Deaths, 2013 (cont.)

Unintentional-injury-related deaths by class, United States, 2013

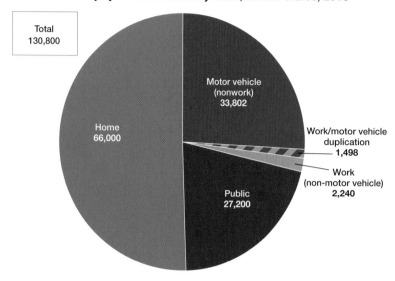

Total
130,800

Home
66,000

Motor vehicle
(nonwork)
33,802

Work/motor vehicle
duplication
1,498

Work
(non-motor vehicle)
2,240

Public
27,200

Unintentional medically consulted injuries by class, United States, 2013

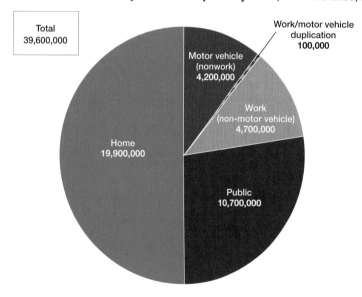

Total
39,600,000

Work/motor vehicle
duplication
100,000

Motor vehicle
(nonwork)
4,200,000

Work
(non-motor vehicle)
4,700,000

Home
19,900,000

Public
10,700,000

In 1912, the First Cooperative Safety Congress met in Milwaukee. The meeting was attended by representatives of industry, government, insurance, and others. The most important result of this Congress was the decision to form a "permanent body devoted to the promotion of safety to human life in the industries of the U.S." One year later, during the Second Safety Congress, the National Safety Council was created. At this same time, unintentional-injury-related deaths were occurring at a staggering pace of 82.4 deaths per 100,000 population. Since then, the "safety movement" has contributed to the 50% reduction (after adjusting for the classification change in 1948) in the unintentional-injury rate to its current level of 41.4. The reduction in the overall rate during a period when the nation's population tripled has resulted in 6,100,000 fewer people being killed due to unintentional injuries than there would have been if the rate had not been reduced.

Lives saved from 1912 to 2013, United States

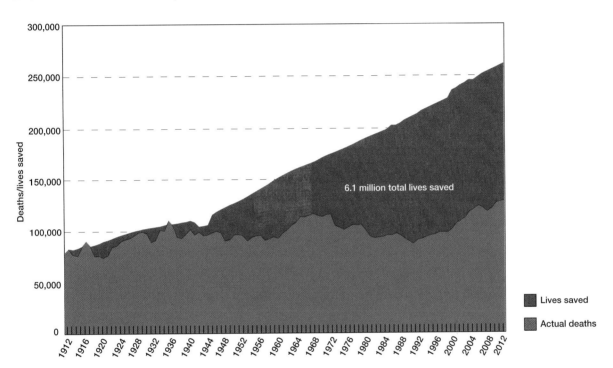

Costs of Unintentional Injuries by Class, 2013

The total cost of unintentional injuries in 2013, $820.6 billion, includes estimates of economic costs of fatal and nonfatal unintentional injuries together with employers' uninsured costs, vehicle damage costs, and fire losses. Wage and productivity losses, medical expenses, administrative expenses, and employers' uninsured costs are included in all four classes of injuries. Cost components unique to each class are identified below.

Motor vehicle crash costs include property damage from motor vehicle incidents. Work costs include the value of property damage in on-the-job motor vehicle incidents and fires. Home and public costs include estimated fire losses, but do not include other property damage costs.

Besides the estimated $820.6 billion in economic losses from unintentional injuries in 2013, lost quality of life from those injuries is valued at an additional $4,253.9 billion, making the comprehensive cost $5,074.5 billion in 2013.

Several cost benchmarks were updated for this edition of *Injury Facts*, making costs not comparable to previous years. The method for estimating the number of medically attended injuries by class was revised to use the latest National Health Interview Survey data. Estimated property damage costs in motor vehicle crashes were re-benchmarked using data from the National Highway Traffic Safety Administration. In addition, the value of a statistical life was updated for this edition, which affects only the comprehensive cost mentioned in the paragraph above.

Certain costs of unintentional injuries by class, 2013 ($ billions)

Cost	Total[a]	Motor vehicle	Work	Home	Public non-motor vehicle
Total	**$820.6**	**$288.1**	**$206.1**	**$226.1**	**$124.2**
Wage and productivity losses	388.4	90.8	91.0	137.7	73.1
Medical expenses	219.8	63.8	57.9	62.9	38.7
Administrative expenses[b]	133.3	86.0	40.6	12.2	7.9
Motor vehicle damage	45.0	45.0	2.3	(c)	(c)
Employers' uninsured costs	22.5	2.5	11.5	6.1	2.9
Fire loss	11.6	(c)	2.8	7.2	1.6

Source: National Safety Council estimates. See the Technical Appendix. Cost-estimating procedures were revised extensively for the 1993, 2005-2006, and 2014 editions of Accident Facts. *In general, cost estimates are not comparable from year to year. As additional data or new benchmarks become available, they are used from that point forward. Previously estimated figures are not revised.*
[a]Duplication between work and motor vehicle, which amounted to $23.9 billion, was eliminated from the total.
[b]Home and public insurance administration costs may include costs of administering medical treatment claims for some motor vehicle injuries filed through health insurance plans.
[c]Not included, see comments above.

Costs of unintentional injuries by class, 2013

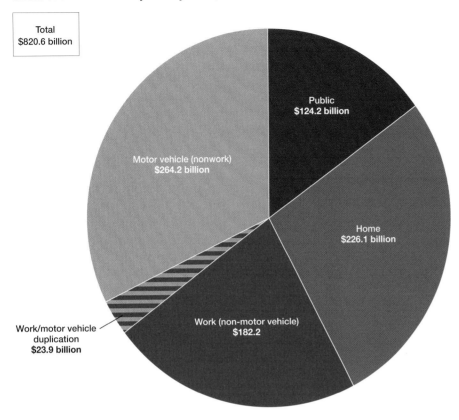

Total
$820.6 billion

Public
$124.2 billion

Motor vehicle (nonwork)
$264.2 billion

Home
$226.1 billion

Work (non-motor vehicle)
$182.2

Work/motor vehicle
duplication
$23.9 billion

Wage and productivity losses

A person's contribution to the wealth of the nation usually is measured in terms of wages and household production. The total of wages and fringe benefits, together with an estimate of the replacement-cost value of household services, provides an estimate of this lost productivity. Also included is travel delay for motor vehicle incidents.

Medical expenses

Doctor fees; hospital charges; the cost of medicines; future medical costs; and ambulance, helicopter, and other emergency medical services are included.

Administrative expenses

Includes the administrative cost of public and private insurance, as well as police and legal costs. Private insurance administrative costs are the difference between premiums paid to insurance companies and claims paid out by them. It is their cost of doing business and a part of the cost total. Claims paid by insurance companies are not identified separately, as every claim is compensation for losses such as wages, medical expenses, property damage, etc.

Motor vehicle damage

Includes the value of damage to vehicles from motor vehicle crashes. The cost of normal wear and tear to vehicles is not included.

Employers' uninsured costs

This is an estimate of the uninsured costs incurred by employers, representing the dollar value of time lost by uninjured workers. It includes time spent investigating and reporting injuries, administering first aid, hiring and training replacement workers, and the extra cost of overtime for uninjured workers.

Fire loss

Includes losses from both structure fires and nonstructure fires, such as vehicles, outside storage, crops, and timber.

Work – motor vehicle duplication

The cost of motor vehicle crashes that involve people in the course of their work is included in both classes, but the duplication is eliminated from the total. The duplication in 2013 amounted to $23.9 billion and consists of $4.2 billion in wage and productivity losses, $3.5 billion in medical expenses, $13.4 billion in administrative expenses, $2.3 billion in vehicle damage, and $0.5 billion in employers' uninsured costs.

Costs of unintentional injuries by component, 2013

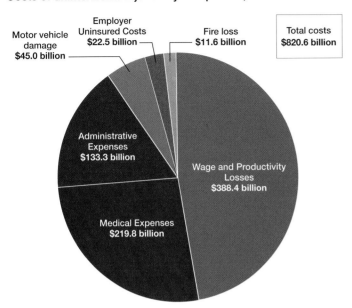

Motor vehicle damage
$45.0 billion

Employer Uninsured Costs
$22.5 billion

Fire loss
$11.6 billion

Total costs
$820.6 billion

Administrative Expenses
$133.3 billion

Wage and Productivity Losses
$388.4 billion

Medical Expenses
$219.8 billion

Cost Equivalents

The costs of unintentional injuries are immense – billions of dollars. Because figures this large can be difficult to comprehend, it is sometimes useful to reduce the numbers to a more understandable scale by relating them to quantities encountered in daily life. The table below shows how the costs of unintentional injuries compare to common quantities such as taxes, corporate profits, or stock dividends.

Cost equivalents, 2013

The cost of...	Is equivalent to...
...All injuries ($820.6 billion)	...64 cents of every dollar paid in federal personal income taxes, **or** ...51 cents of every dollar spent on food in the United States.
...Motor vehicle crashes ($288.1 billion)	...purchasing 320 gallons of gasoline for each registered vehicle in the United States, **or** ...more than $1,400 per licensed driver.
...Work injuries ($206.1 billion)	...23 cents of every dollar of corporate dividends to stockholders, **or** ...9 cents of every dollar of pre-tax corporate profits, **or** ...exceeds the combined profits reported by the 12 largest Fortune 500 companies.
...Home injuries ($226.1 billion)	...a $364,200 rebate on each new single-family home built, **or** ...51 cents of every dollar of property taxes paid.
...Public injuries ($124.2 billion)	...a $13.9 million grant to each public library in the United States, **or** ...a $107,000 bonus for each police officer and firefighter.

Source: National Safety Council estimates.

Deaths Due to Unintentional Injuries, 2013

Type of event and age of victim

All unintentional injuries

The term "unintentional" covers most deaths from injury and poisoning. Excluded are homicides (including legal intervention), suicides, deaths for which none of these categories can be determined, and war deaths.

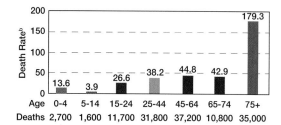

	Total	Change from 2012	Death rate[a]
Deaths	130,800	+2.4%	41.4

Age	0-4	5-14	15-24	25-44	45-64	65-74	75+
Death Rate[b]	13.6	3.9	26.6	38.2	44.8	42.9	179.3
Deaths	2,700	1,600	11,700	31,800	37,200	10,800	35,000

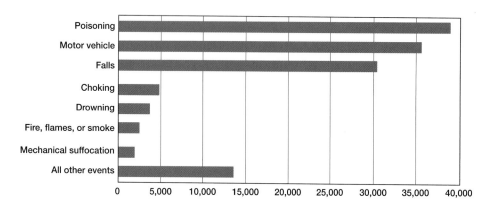

Poisoning

Includes deaths from drugs, medicines, other solid and liquid substances, and gases and vapors. Excludes poisonings from spoiled foods, *Salmonella*, etc., which are classified as disease deaths.

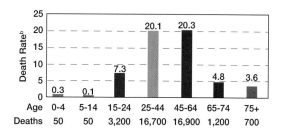

	Total	Change from 2012	Death rate[a]
Deaths	38,800	+7%	12.3

Age	0-4	5-14	15-24	25-44	45-64	65-74	75+
Death Rate[b]	0.3	0.1	7.3	20.1	20.3	4.8	3.6
Deaths	50	50	3,200	16,700	16,900	1,200	700

Motor vehicle incidents

Includes deaths involving mechanically or electrically powered highway-transport vehicles in motion (except those on rails), both on and off the highway or street.

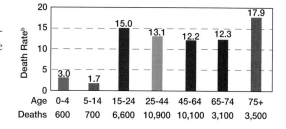

	Total	Change from 2012	Death rate[a]
Deaths	35,500	-2%	11.2

Age	0-4	5-14	15-24	25-44	45-64	65-74	75+
Death Rate[b]	3.0	1.7	15.0	13.1	12.2	12.3	17.9
Deaths	600	700	6,600	10,900	10,100	3,100	3,500

Falls

Includes deaths from falls from one level to another or on the same level. Excludes falls in or from transport vehicles, or while boarding or alighting from them.

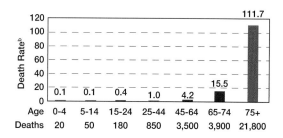

	Total	Change from 2012	Death rate[a]
Deaths	30,300	+5%	9.6

Age	0-4	5-14	15-24	25-44	45-64	65-74	75+
Death Rate[b]	0.1	0.1	0.4	1.0	4.2	15.5	111.7
Deaths	20	50	180	850	3,500	3,900	21,800

See footnotes on page 11.

Type of event and age of victim

Choking

Includes deaths from unintentional ingestion or inhalation of food or other objects resulting in the obstruction of respiratory passages.

	Total	Change from 2012	Death rate[a]
Deaths	4,800	+4%	1.5

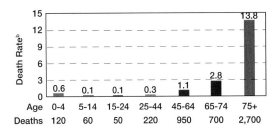

Age	0-4	5-14	15-24	25-44	45-64	65-74	75+
Deaths	120	60	50	220	950	700	2,700

Drowning

Includes non-transport-related drownings such as those resulting from swimming, playing in the water, or falling in. Excludes drownings in floods and other cataclysms, which are classified to the cataclysm, and boating-related drownings.

	Total	Change from 2012	Death rate[a]
Deaths	3,700	+4%	1.2

Age	0-4	5-14	15-24	25-44	45-64	65-74	75+
Deaths	450	230	600	800	1,090	280	250

Fire, flames, or smoke

Includes deaths from exposure to fire, flames, or smoke, and from injuries in fires such as falls and struck by falling objects. Excludes burns from hot objects or liquids.

	Total	Change from 2012	Death rate[a]
Deaths	2,400	-3%	0.8

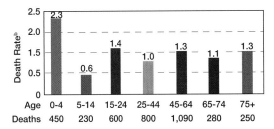

Age	0-4	5-14	15-24	25-44	45-64	65-74	75+
Deaths	120	110	80	340	800	350	600

Mechanical suffocation

Includes deaths from hanging and strangulation, and suffocation in enclosed or confined spaces; cave-ins; or by bed clothes, plastic bags, or similar materials.

	Total	Change from 2012	Death rate[a]
Deaths	1,800	+12%	0.6

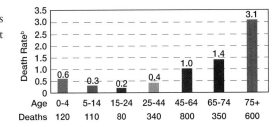

Age	0-4	5-14	15-24	25-44	45-64	65-74	75+
Deaths	1,100	90	70	210	220	40	70

All other types

Most important types included are natural heat or cold; firearms; struck by or against object; machinery; electric current; and air, water, or rail transport.

	Total	Change from 2012	Death rate[a]
Deaths	13,500	-4%	4.3

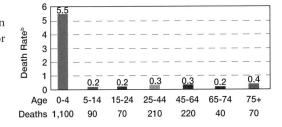

Age	0-4	5-14	15-24	25-44	45-64	65-74	75+
Deaths	230	170	700	2,000	3,800	1,500	5,100

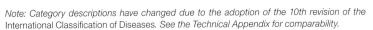

Note: Category descriptions have changed due to the adoption of the 10th revision of the International Classification of Diseases. See the Technical Appendix for comparability.

[a]Deaths per 100,000 population.
[b]Deaths per 100,000 population in each age group.

Unintentional injuries are the fifth leading cause of death overall and first among people in age groups from 1 to 44. By single years of age, unintentional injuries are the leading cause of death from age 1 to 42.

Causes are ranked for both sexes combined. Some leading causes for males and females separately may not be shown. Beginning with 1999 data, deaths are classified according to the 10th revision of the *International Classification of Diseases.* See the Technical Appendix for comparability.

Deaths and death rates by age and sex, 2011

Cause	Number of deaths			Death rates[a]		
	Total	Male	Female	Total	Male	Female
All ages[b]						
All causes	**2,515,458**	**1,254,978**	**1,260,480**	**807.3**	**818.7**	**796.3**
Heart disease	596,577	308,398	288,179	191.5	201.2	182.0
Cancer (malignant neoplasms)	576,691	302,231	274,460	185.1	197.2	173.4
Chronic lower respiratory diseases	142,943	67,521	75,422	45.9	44.0	47.6
Stroke (cerebrovascular disease)	128,932	52,335	76,597	41.4	34.1	48.4
Unintentional injuries	**126,438**	**79,527**	**47,181**	**40.6**	**51.9**	**29.8**
Poisoning	*36,280*	*23,288*	*12,992*	*11.6*	*15.2*	*8.2*
Motor-vehicle	*35,303*	*24,947*	*10,356*	*11.3*	*16.3*	*6.5*
Falls	*27,483*	*13,814*	*13,669*	*8.8*	*9.0*	*8.6*
Choking[c]	*4,708*	*2,474*	*2,234*	*1.5*	*1.6*	*1.4*
Drowning	*3,556*	*2,773*	*783*	*1.1*	*1.8*	*0.5*
All other unintentional injuries	*19,108*	*12,231*	*7,147*	*6.1*	*8.0*	*4.5*
Alzheimer's disease	84,974	25,677	59,297	27.3	16.8	37.5
Diabetes mellitus	73,831	38,324	35,507	23.7	25.0	22.4
Influenza and pneumonia	53,826	25,401	28,425	17.3	16.6	18.0
Nephritis and nephrosis	45,591	22,649	22,942	14.6	14.8	14.5
Suicide	39,518	31,003	8,515	12.7	20.2	5.4
Younger than 1						
All causes	**23,985**	**13,327**	**10,658**	**600.1**	**652.1**	**545.8**
Congenital anomalies	5,013	2,630	2,383	125.4	128.7	122.0
Short gestation, low birth weight, n.e.c.	4,106	2,273	1,833	102.7	111.2	93.9
Sudden infant death syndrome	1,910	1,108	802	47.8	54.2	41.1
Maternal complications of pregnancy	1,591	904	687	39.8	44.2	35.2
Unintentional injuries	**1,163**	**647**	**516**	**29.1**	**31.7**	**26.4**
Mechanical suffocation	*825*	*464*	*361*	*20.6*	*22.7*	*18.5*
Motor-vehicle	*95*	*58*	*37*	*2.4*	*2.8*	*1.9*
Choking[c]	*71*	*38*	*33*	*1.8*	*1.9*	*1.7*
Drowning	*52*	*25*	*27*	*1.3*	*1.2*	*1.4*
Fire, flames, or smoke	*21*	*8*	*13*	*0.5*	*0.4*	*0.7*
All other unintentional injuries	*99*	*54*	*45*	*2.5*	*2.6*	*2.3*
Complications of placenta, cord, or membranes	1,004	548	456	25.1	26.8	23.4
Bacterial sepsis	526	293	233	13.2	14.3	11.9
Respiratory distress	513	276	237	12.8	13.5	12.1
Circulatory system disease	500	268	232	12.5	13.1	11.9
Neonatal hemorrhage	456	266	190	11.4	13.0	9.7
1-4 years						
All causes	**4,246**	**2,405**	**1,841**	**26.3**	**29.1**	**23.3**
Unintentional injuries	**1,377**	**839**	**538**	**8.5**	**10.2**	**6.8**
Drowning	*438*	*300*	*138*	*2.7*	*3.6*	*1.7*
Motor-vehicle	*425*	*219*	*206*	*2.6*	*2.7*	*2.6*
Fire, flames, or smoke	*129*	*73*	*56*	*0.8*	*0.9*	*0.7*
Choking[c]	*82*	*56*	*26*	*0.5*	*0.7*	*0.3*
Mechanical suffocation	*62*	*40*	*22*	*0.4*	*0.5*	*0.3*
All other unintentional injuries	*241*	*151*	*90*	*1.5*	*1.8*	*1.1*
Congenital anomalies	493	266	227	3.0	3.2	2.9
Homicide	412	239	173	2.5	2.9	2.2
Cancer (malignant neoplasms)	353	183	170	2.2	2.2	2.1
Heart disease	165	84	81	1.0	1.0	1.0
Influenza and pneumonia	112	55	57	0.7	0.7	0.7
Septicemia	61	26	35	0.4	0.3	0.4
Chronic lower respiratory diseases	53	37	16	0.3	0.4	0.2
Benign neoplasms	45	26	19	0.3	0.3	0.2
Stroke (cerebrovascular disease)	42	29	13	0.3	0.4	0.2

See source and footnotes on page 14.

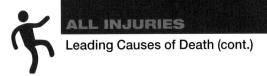

Deaths and death rates by age and sex, 2011 (cont.)

Cause	Number of deaths			Death rates[a]		
	Total	Male	Female	Total	Male	Female
5-14 years						
All causes	**5,401**	**3,179**	**2,222**	**13.2**	**15.2**	**11.1**
Unintentional injuries	**1,635**	**1,033**	**602**	**4.0**	**4.9**	**3.0**
Motor-vehicle	*881*	*526*	*355*	*2.1*	*2.5*	*1.8*
Drowning	*235*	*174*	*61*	*0.6*	*0.8*	*0.3*
Fire, flames, or smoke	*123*	*80*	*43*	*0.3*	*0.4*	*0.2*
Mechanical suffocation	*53*	*39*	*14*	*0.1*	*0.2*	*0.1*
Poisoning	*50*	*29*	*21*	*0.1*	*0.1*	*0.1*
All other unintentional injuries	*293*	*185*	*108*	*0.7*	*0.9*	*0.5*
Cancer (malignant neoplasms)	860	483	377	2.1	2.3	1.9
Congenital anomalies	358	198	160	0.9	0.9	0.8
Suicide	287	201	86	0.7	1.0	0.4
Homicide	283	178	105	0.7	0.8	0.5
Heart disease	203	95	108	0.5	0.5	0.5
Chronic lower respiratory diseases	136	87	49	0.3	0.4	0.2
Influenza and pneumonia	118	63	55	0.3	0.3	0.3
Stoke (cerebrovascular disease)	87	46	41	0.2	0.2	0.2
Benign neoplasms	70	37	33	0.2	0.2	0.2
15-24 years						
All causes	**29,667**	**21,924**	**7,743**	**67.7**	**97.7**	**36.2**
Unintentional injuries	**12,330**	**9,172**	**3,158**	**28.2**	**40.9**	**14.8**
Motor-vehicle	*7,105*	*5,106*	*1,999*	*16.2*	*22.8*	*9.4*
Poisoning	*3,440*	*2,587*	*853*	*7.9*	*11.5*	*4.0*
Drowning	*543*	*492*	*51*	*1.2*	*2.2*	*0.2*
Falls	*205*	*173*	*32*	*0.5*	*0.8*	*0.1*
Fire, flames, or smoke	*135*	*76*	*59*	*0.3*	*0.3*	*0.3*
All other unintentional injuries	*902*	*738*	*164*	*2.1*	*3.3*	*0.8*
Suicide	4,822	3,959	863	11.0	17.6	4.0
Homicide	4,554	3,941	613	10.4	17.6	2.9
Cancer (malignant neoplasms)	1,611	966	645	3.7	4.3	3.0
Heart disease	998	684	314	2.3	3.0	1.5
Congenital anomalies	432	275	157	1.0	1.2	0.7
Influenza and pneumonia	220	123	97	0.5	0.5	0.5
Stroke (cerebrovascular disease)	186	104	82	0.4	0.5	0.4
Complicated pregnancy	172	0	172	0.4	0.0	0.8
Chronic lower respiratory diseases	170	117	53	0.4	0.5	0.2
25-34 years						
All causes	**43,748**	**30,085**	**13,663**	**104.7**	**143.0**	**65.9**
Unintentional injuries	**15,518**	**11,426**	**4,092**	**37.1**	**54.3**	**19.7**
Poisoning	*7,652*	*5,429*	*2,223*	*18.3*	*25.8*	*10.7*
Motor-vehicle	*5,742*	*4,287*	*1,455*	*13.7*	*20.4*	*7.0*
Drowning	*442*	*381*	*61*	*1.1*	*1.8*	*0.3*
Falls	*279*	*225*	*54*	*0.7*	*1.1*	*0.3*
Fire, flames, or smoke	*174*	*111*	*63*	*0.4*	*0.5*	*0.3*
All other unintentional injuries	*1,229*	*993*	*236*	*2.9*	*4.7*	*1.1*
Suicide	6,100	4,862	1,238	14.6	23.1	6.0
Homicide	4,185	3,499	686	10.0	16.6	3.3
Cancer (malignant neoplasms)	3,499	1,713	1,786	8.4	8.1	8.6
Heart disease	3,301	2,210	1,091	7.9	10.5	5.3
Diabetes mellitus	686	388	298	1.6	1.8	1.4
Human immunodeficiency virus infection	666	428	238	1.6	2.0	1.1
Stroke (cerebrovascular disease)	530	284	246	1.3	1.3	1.2
Influenza and pneumonia	515	290	225	1.2	1.4	1.1
Chronic liver disease and cirrhosis	505	306	199	1.2	1.5	1.0
35-44 years						
All causes	**69,893**	**43,215**	**26,678**	**172.0**	**213.7**	**130.7**
Unintentional injuries	**15,230**	**10,459**	**4,771**	**37.5**	**51.7**	**23.4**
Poisoning	*8,075*	*5,089*	*2,986*	*19.9*	*25.2*	*14.6*
Motor-vehicle	*4,610*	*3,385*	*1,225*	*11.3*	*16.7*	*6.0*
Falls	*524*	*407*	*117*	*1.3*	*2.0*	*0.6*
Drowning	*414*	*340*	*74*	*1.0*	*1.7*	*0.4*
Fire, flames, or smoke	*200*	*133*	*67*	*0.5*	*0.7*	*0.3*
All other unintentional injuries	*1,407*	*1,105*	*302*	*3.5*	*5.5*	*1.5*
Cancer (malignant neoplasms)	11,717	5,034	6,683	28.8	24.9	32.8
Heart disease	10,635	7,393	3,242	26.2	36.6	15.9
Suicide	6,599	5,044	1,555	16.2	24.9	7.6
Homicide	2,519	1,940	579	6.2	9.6	2.8
Chronic liver disease and cirrhosis	2,449	1,572	877	6.0	7.8	4.3
Stroke (cerebrovascular disease)	1,718	906	812	4.2	4.5	4.0
Human immunodeficiency virus infection	1,619	1,060	559	4.0	5.2	2.7
Diabetes mellitus	1,842	1,120	722	4.5	5.5	3.5
Influenza and pneumonia	859	456	403	2.1	2.3	2.0

See source and footnotes on page 14.

Deaths and death rates by age and sex, 2011 (cont.)

Cause	Number of deaths			Death rates[a]		
	Total	Male	Female	Total	Male	Female
45-54 years						
All causes	**183,247**	**111,709**	**71,538**	**409.8**	**507.3**	**315.2**
Cancer (malignant neoplasms)	48,897	24,372	24,525	109.3	110.7	108.0
Heart disease	36,100	25,691	10,409	80.7	116.7	45.9
Unintentional injuries	**20,749**	**13,917**	**6,832**	**46.4**	**63.2**	**30.1**
Poisoning	10,379	6,190	4,189	23.2	28.1	18.5
Motor-vehicle	5,485	4,097	1,388	12.3	18.6	6.1
Falls	1,368	1,009	359	3.1	4.6	1.6
Drowning	479	377	102	1.1	1.7	0.4
Fire, flames, or smoke	413	264	149	0.9	1.2	0.7
All other unintentional injuries	2,625	1,980	645	5.9	9.0	2.8
Chronic liver disease and cirrhosis	8,864	5,868	2,996	19.8	26.6	13.2
Suicide	8,858	6,637	2,221	19.8	30.1	9.8
Diabetes mellitus	6,012	3,743	2,269	13.4	17.0	10.0
Stroke (cerebrovascular disease)	5,705	3,201	2,504	12.8	14.5	11.0
Chronic lower respiratory diseases	4,634	2,173	2,461	10.4	9.9	10.8
Human immunodeficiency virus infection	2,781	2,052	729	6.2	9.3	3.2
Septicemia	2,461	1,296	1,165	5.5	5.9	5.1
55-64 years						
All causes	**323,315**	**196,641**	**126,674**	**849.4**	**1,071.1**	**642.9**
Cancer (malignant neoplasms)	112,572	62,499	50,073	295.8	340.4	254.1
Heart disease	69,742	48,388	21,354	183.2	263.6	108.4
Unintentional injuries	**15,158**	**10,441**	**4,717**	**39.8**	**56.9**	**23.9**
Poisoning	5,048	3,126	1,922	13.3	17.0	9.8
Motor-vehicle	4,381	3,255	1,126	11.5	17.7	5.7
Falls	2,141	1,487	654	5.6	8.1	3.3
Choking[c]	562	350	212	1.5	1.9	1.1
Fire, flames, or smoke	513	313	200	1.3	1.7	1.0
All other unintentional injuries	2,513	1,910	603	6.6	10.4	3.1
Chronic lower respiratory diseases	15,044	7,890	7,154	39.5	43.0	36.3
Diabetes mellitus	12,688	7,624	5,064	33.3	41.5	25.7
Stroke (cerebrovascular disease)	11,205	6,405	4,800	29.4	34.9	24.4
Chronic liver disease and cirrhosis	10,749	7,589	3,160	28.2	41.3	16.0
Suicide	6,521	5,018	1,503	17.1	27.3	7.6
Septicemia	4,953	2,648	2,305	13.0	14.4	11.7
Nephritis and nephrosis	4,754	2,701	2,053	12.5	14.7	10.4
65-74 years						
All causes	**415,052**	**234,276**	**180,776**	**1,846.2**	**2,236.2**	**1,505.8**
Cancer (malignant neoplasms)	145,593	80,223	65,370	647.6	765.8	544.5
Heart disease	89,708	56,609	33,099	399.0	540.4	275.7
Chronic lower respiratory diseases	32,433	16,497	15,936	144.3	157.5	132.7
Stroke (cerebrovascular disease)	17,584	9,228	8,356	78.2	88.1	69.6
Diabetes mellitus	16,189	9,181	7,008	72.0	87.6	58.4
Unintentional injuries	**10,014**	**6,295**	**3,719**	**44.5**	**60.1**	**31.0**
Falls	3,149	1,926	1,223	14.0	18.4	10.2
Motor-vehicle	2,913	1,905	1,008	13.0	18.2	8.4
Poisoning	945	513	432	4.2	4.9	3.6
Choking[c]	652	361	291	2.9	3.4	2.4
Fire, flames, or smoke	389	228	161	1.7	2.2	1.3
All other unintentional injuries	1,966	1,362	604	8.7	13.0	5.0
Nephritis and nephrosis	7,682	4,083	3,599	34.2	39.0	30.0
Septicemia	6,636	3,379	3,257	29.5	32.3	27.1
Influenza and pneumonia	6,488	3,585	2,903	28.9	34.2	24.2
Chronic liver disease and cirrhosis	5,905	3,676	2,229	26.3	35.1	18.6
75 years or older[b]						
All causes	**1,416,904**	**598,217**	**818,687**	**7,491.9**	**8,011.4**	**7,153.0**
Heart disease	385,416	167,082	218,334	2,037.9	2,237.6	1,907.6
Cancer (malignant neoplasms)	251,519	126,719	124,800	1,329.9	1,697.0	1,090.4
Stroke (cerebrovascular disease)	91,741	32,058	59,683	485.1	429.3	521.5
Chronic lower respiratory diseases	89,439	40,203	49,236	472.9	538.4	430.2
Alzheimer's disease	79,709	23,396	56,313	421.5	313.3	492.0
Influenza and pneumonia	38,898	16,987	21,911	205.7	227.5	191.4
Diabetes mellitus	36,213	16,152	20,061	191.5	216.3	175.3
Unintentional injuries	**33,264**	**15,028**	**18,236**	**175.9**	**201.3**	**159.3**
Falls	19,754	8,547	11,207	104.4	114.5	97.9
Motor-vehicle	3,666	2,109	1,557	19.4	28.2	13.6
Choking[c]	2,634	1,247	1,387	13.9	16.7	12.1
Fire, flames, or smoke	649	347	302	3.4	4.6	2.6
Poisoning	642	295	347	3.4	4.0	3.0
All other unintentional injuries	5,919	2,483	3,436	31.3	33.3	30.0
Nephritis and nephrosis	30,114	14,100	16,014	159.2	188.8	139.9
Septicemia	20,111	8,345	11,766	106.3	111.8	102.8

Source: National Safety Council analysis of National Center for Health Statistics–Mortality Data for 2011 as compiled from data provided by the 57 vital statistics jurisdictions through the Vital Statistics Cooperative Program. Rates are National Safety Council estimates based on data from the National Center for Health Statistics and the U.S. Census Bureau.
[a]Deaths per 100,000 population in each age group. [b]Includes 134 deaths for which the age was unknown. [c]Inhalation or ingestion of food or other objects.

The rank of unintentional injuries as a cause of death varies with race and Hispanic origin. While ranking fifth overall (following heart disease, cancer, stroke, and chronic lower respiratory diseases), unintentional injuries rank third for Hispanics after heart disease and cancer.

By race, unintentional injuries rank fourth for whites and for other non-black groups including Asians, Pacific Islanders, American Indians, and Alaskan Natives (after heart disease, cancer, and chronic lower respiratory diseases or stroke), and fifth for blacks.

Unintentional-injury-related deaths and death rates by race, Hispanic origin, and sex, United States, 2011

Race and sex	Total			Hispanic origin					
				Non-Hispanic			Hispanic		
	Rank	Number	Rate	Rank	Number	Rate	Rank	Number	Rate
All races	5	126,438	40.6	5	114,873	44.2	3	11,166	21.5
Males	3	79,257	51.7	3	70,874	55.8	3	8,098	30.7
Females	6	47,181	29.8	6	43,999	33.1	5	3,068	12.0
White	4	109,751	45.1	5	98,605	49.9	3	10,852	(b)
Males	3	68,123	56.5	3	60,043	61.8	3	7,872	(b)
Females	6	41,628	33.9	6	38,562	38.4	5	2,980	(b)
Black	5	12,531	30.7	5	12,299	32.1	3	137	(b)
Males	3	8,387	43.1	3	8,219	44.9	3	99	(b)
Females	7	4,144	19.5	7	4,080	20.3	4	38	(b)
Not white or black[a]	4	4,156	15.1	4	3,969	16.7	3	177	(b)
Males	3	2,747	20.6	3	2,612	22.8	3	127	(b)
Females	5	1,409	10.0	5	1,357	11.0	3	50	(b)

Source: National Safety Council analysis of National Center for Health Statistics (NCHS)–Mortality Data for 2011, as compiled from data provided by the 57 vital statistics jurisdictions through the Vital Statistics Cooperative Program. Rates are National Safety Council estimates based on data from NCHS and the U.S. Census Bureau.
Note: Rates are deaths per 100,000 population in each race/sex/Hispanic origin group. Total column includes 399 deaths for which Hispanic origin was not determined.
[a]Includes American Indian, Alaskan Native, Asian, Native Hawaiian, and Pacific Islander.
[b]Race is not well-reported for persons of Hispanic origin. Population death rates are unreliable.

Leading causes of unintentional-injury-related death by race, Hispanic origin, and sex, United States, 2011

Cause of death	All races			White			Black			Not white or black[a]		
	Both	Male	Female	Both	Male	Female	Both	Male	Female	Both	Male	Female
Total	126,438	79,257	47,181	109,751	68,123	41,628	12,531	8,387	4,144	4,156	2,747	1,409
Motor vehicle	35,303	24,947	10,356	29,315	20,725	8,590	4,492	3,231	1,261	1,496	991	505
Poisoning	36,280	23,288	12,992	32,075	20,565	11,510	3,310	2,127	1,183	895	596	299
Fall	27,483	13,814	13,669	25,510	12,644	12,866	1,186	708	478	787	462	325
Choking[b]	4,708	2,474	2,234	4,045	2,123	1,922	523	275	248	140	76	64
Drowning	3,556	2,773	783	2,729	2,085	644	603	503	100	224	185	39
Fires, flames, or smoke	2,746	1,633	1,113	2,108	1,259	849	563	326	237	75	48	27
Population (thousands)	311,588	153,261	158,326	243,342	120,466	122,877	40,775	19,472	21,303	27,470	13,324	14,147

Cause of death	Non-Hispanic			Hispanic			Unknown		
	Both	Male	Female	Both	Male	Female	Both	Male	Female
Total	114,873	70,874	43,999	11,166	8,098	3,068	399	285	114
Motor vehicle	30,665	21,475	9,190	4,544	3,401	1,143	94	71	23
Poisoning	33,125	20,966	12,159	2,980	2,197	783	175	125	50
Fall	25,982	12,884	13,098	1,451	901	550	50	29	21
Choking[b]	4,463	2,337	2,126	230	130	100	15	7	8
Drowning	3,039	2,350	689	510	416	94	7	7	0
Fires, flames, or smoke	2,547	1,503	1,044	187	120	67	12	10	2
Population (thousands)	259,707	126,923	132,783	51,881	26,338	25,543	–	–	–

Source: National Safety Council analysis of National Center for Health Statistics (NCHS)–Mortality Data for 2011, as compiled from data provided by the 57 vital statistics jurisdictions through the Vital Statistics Cooperative Program. Rates are National Safety Council estimates based on data from NCHS and the U.S. Census Bureau.
Note: Dashes (–) indicate not applicable.
[a]Includes American Indian, Alaskan Native, Asian, Native Hawaiian, and Pacific Islander.
[b]Suffocation by inhalation or ingestion.

Leading Causes of Unintentional-Injury-Related Death by Age, 2011

Unintentional-injury-related deaths by age and event, United States, 2011

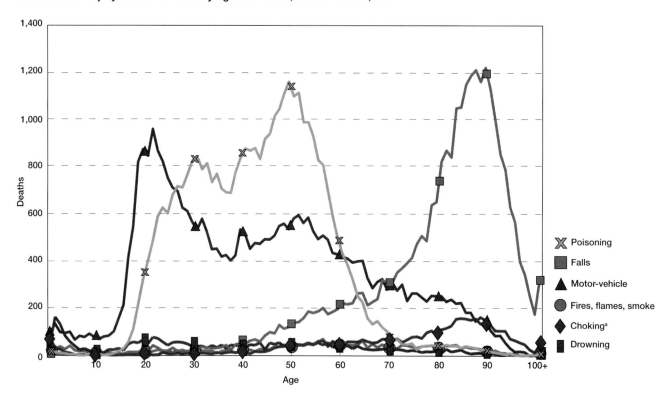

Poisonings, motor vehicle crashes; falls; choking (suffocation by inhalation or ingestion of food or other object); drownings; and fire, flames, or smoke were the six leading causes of unintentional-injury-related death in the United States in 2011. The graph above depicts the number of deaths attributed to the top six causes by single years of age through age 99 and an aggregate age group of people 100 and older.

In 2011, poisonings overtook motor vehicle crashes for the first time as the leading cause of unintentional-injury-related death for all ages combined and were the leading cause of unintentional-injury-related death for each single year of age from 26 to 60. Among infants younger than 1, mechanical suffocation was the leading cause of death, followed by motor vehicle deaths. Motor vehicle deaths also were the second leading cause of death among 1- and 2-year-olds, after drowning.

The distribution of 2011 poisoning fatalities shows a sharp increase during early adulthood into middle age, rising from 217 for 18-year-olds to 1,160 for 49-year-olds. The greatest number of poisoning fatalities in 2011 occurred among people 49 years old.

The second leading cause of unintentional-injury-related death overall in 2011 was motor vehicle crashes. Motor vehicle fatalities reached a high of 958 for 21-year-olds, and were the leading cause of unintentional-injury-related death for people age 3 to 25, 61 to 68, and age 70. Poisoning was the second leading cause of unintentional-injury-related death for every single year of age from 15 to 25 and from 61 to 62. Motor vehicle fatalities were the second most common cause for every

single year of age from less than age 1 to 2, 26 to 60, 69, 71 to 86, and from ages 88 to 89.

Falls were the third leading cause of unintentional-injury-related death in the United States in 2011. Falls were the leading cause of unintentional-injury-related death of people age 69 and those 71 and older, and the second leading cause each single year of age from age 63-68 and for those age 70. Deaths resulting from falls peaked at 1,219 for individuals age 89.

The fourth leading cause of unintentional-injury-related death in 2011 was choking.[a] Choking deaths peaked at age 84 with 159 deaths. Choking was the second leading cause of unintentional-injury-related death for people age 87 and those age 90 and older.

Drowning was the fifth leading cause of unintentional-injury-related death in 2011 and peaked at 163 fatalities for 1-year-olds, resulting in the leading cause of death for this age group as well as people age 2. Drownings were the second leading cause of unintentional-injury-related death for children ages 3-8 and 10-14 in 2011.

Fire, flames, or smoke was the sixth leading cause of unintentional-injury-related death in 2011. Fatalities due to fires, flames, or smoke peaked at 70 deaths among 56-year-olds.

Source: National Safety Council analysis of National Center for Health Statistics (NCHS)–Mortality Data for 2011, as compiled from data provided by the 57 vital statistics jurisdictions through the Vital Statistics Cooperative Program. Rates are National Safety Council estimates based on data from NCHS and the U.S. Census Bureau. See the Technical Appendix for ICD-10 codes for the leading causes and comparability with prior years.
[a]Inhalation or ingestion of food or other objects.

Unintentional-Injury-Related Death Rates by Age, 2011

Unintentional-injury-related deaths per 100,000 population by age and event, United States, 2011

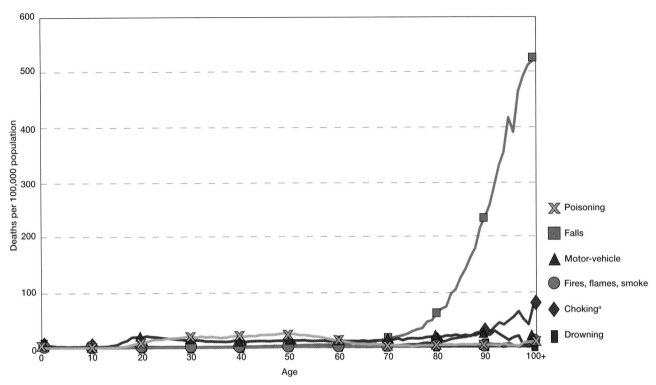

The graph above depicts U.S. death rates per 100,000 population for the six leading causes of unintentional-injury-related deaths in 2011 by age, through age 99 and an aggregate age group of people 100 and older.

Unintentional poisoning fatalities had the highest overall death rate, with an average of 11.6 deaths per 100,000 population. The poisoning death rate remained low until about age 16, when it started to increase steadily up to its peak rate of 25.7 at age 49 before it fell again.

Motor vehicle crashes had the second highest overall death rate from unintentional injury in the United States, with an average rate of 11.3 deaths per 100,000 population. Historically, motor vehicle death rates peak for people in the 18-20 age group and, in 2011, there was such a peak among persons age 18-23 that reached a high of 20.9 for people age 21. However, in 2011 the death rate was highest among people age 92, at a rate of 29.2. This peak rate is followed by a rate of 26.8 occurring at age 89, 25.2 for 88-year-olds, 23.4 for 93-year-olds, 22.6 for 90-year-olds, 22.2 for 84-year-olds, and 21.8 for both 86- and 91-year-olds.

Although motor vehicle crashes were a significant problem for all ages, deaths resulting from falls for certain older ages had even higher death rates. Beginning at about age 68, the death rate from falls increased dramatically. The falls death rate surpassed that for motor vehicle for the first time at age 69 and then again at age 71 as it continued to rise steeply with increasing age, peaking for those age 100 and over with a rate of 519.7. Based on 100,000 population, falls had an overall fatality rate of 8.8.

Death rates due to choking on inhaled or ingested food or other objects were quite low for most ages. Rates rise rapidly beginning at about age 74. While relatively stable and low for all ages, the death rates for drownings showed peaks in the first few years of life and again at some very old ages. Death rates for fire, flames, or smoke were only slightly elevated at very young ages and began to climb at about age 72. The overall death rates per 100,000 U.S. population for choking; drowning; and fire, flames, or smoke did not exceed 1.5.

Source: National Safety Council analysis of National Center for Health Statistics (NCHS)–Mortality Data for 2011, as compiled from data provided by the 57 vital statistics jurisdictions through the Vital Statistics Cooperative Program. Rates are National Safety Council estimates based on data from NCHS and the U.S. Census Bureau. See the Technical Appendix for ICD-10 codes for the leading causes and comparability with prior years.
aInhalation or ingestion of food or other objects.

Unintentional-Injury-Related Deaths by Sex and Age, 2011

Unintentional-injury-related deaths by sex and age, United States, 2011

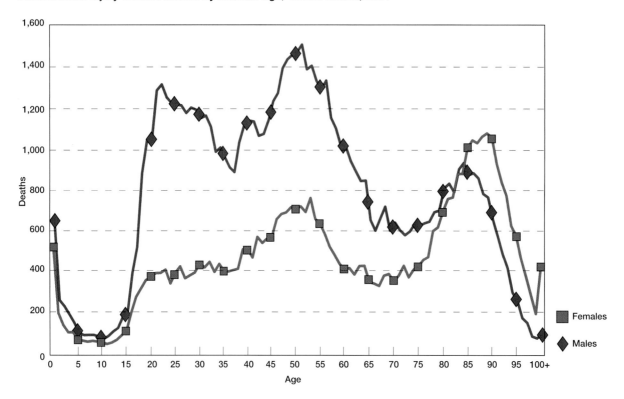

Males incurred more deaths due to unintentional injuries than females at all ages from birth to age 85 in 2011. The difference between the unintentional-injury-related death totals ranged from 19 more male deaths than female deaths at age 10 to 924 more deaths at age 22. The excess number of deaths for males compared to females was most evident from the late teen years to the mid-50s, when the gap begins to narrow. From age 85 on, deaths of females exceeded those of males by as little as 117 at age 99 to as much as 398 deaths nationwide at age 90.

Unintentional-injury-related deaths are at their lowest level for both sexes from about age 5 to about age 13. For males, the highest number of deaths (1,511) occurred at age 51, with high totals occurring from the late teens until about age 60. For females, however, the highest totals occurred among the elderly throughout the 80s and into the early 90s. The greatest number of female deaths (1,074) occurred at age 89.

The graph above shows the number of unintentional-injury-related deaths in the United States during 2011 for each sex by single year of age from younger than 1 to age 99 and an aggregate age group of people 100 and older. It is based on death certificate data from the National Center for Health Statistics.

Source: National Safety Council analysis of National Center for Health Statistics (NCHS)–Mortality Data for 2011, as compiled from data provided by the 57 vital statistics jurisdictions through the Vital Statistics Cooperative Program. Rates are National Safety Council estimates based on data from NCHS and the U.S. Census Bureau. See the Technical Appendix for ICD-10 codes for the leading causes and comparability with prior years.

Unintentional-injury-related deaths per 100,000 population by sex and age, United States, 2011

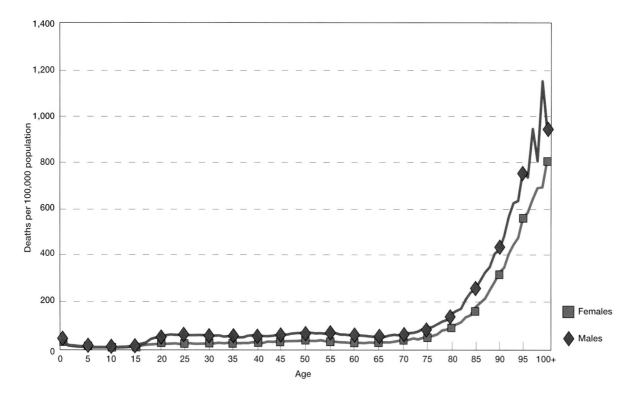

Males have greater unintentional-injury-related death rates for each year of age compared to females. The graph above shows the unintentional-injury-related death rates for males and females by single year of age from younger than 1 to age 99 and an aggregate age group of people 100 and older. It is based on National Center for Health Statistics mortality data and U.S. Census Bureau population data.

Death rates for both sexes are lowest from birth until the mid-teen years, where rates rise rapidly. Rates then remain fairly constant until the early 70's, where they again rise steadily with increasing age. Across all ages, males had an overall death rate of 51.7 unintentional-injury-related deaths per 100,000 males, while the rate among females in the United States was 29.8. The overall unintentional-injury-related death rate for all ages and both sexes was 40.6 deaths per 100,000 population.

Source: National Safety Council analysis of National Center for Health Statistics (NCHS)–Mortality Data for 2011, as compiled from data provided by the 57 vital statistics jurisdictions through the Vital Statistics Cooperative Program. Rates are National Safety Council estimates based on data from NCHS and the U.S. Census Bureau. See the Technical Appendix for ICD-10 codes for the leading causes and comparability with prior years.

Mortality by selected external causes, United States, 2009-2011

Type of accident or manner of injury	2011[a]	2010	2009
All external causes of mortality, V01-Y89, *U01, *U03[b]	190,048	183,301	179,770
Deaths due to unintentional (accidental) injuries, V01-X59, Y85-Y86	126,438	120,859	118,021
Transport accidents, V01-V99, Y85	38,023	37,961	39,031
Motor vehicle accidents, V02-V04, V09.0, V09.2, V12-V14, V19.0-V19.2, V19.4-V19.6, V20-V79, V80.3-V80.5, V81.0-V81.1, V82.0-V82.1, V83-V86, V87.0-V87.8, V88.0-V88.8, V89.0, V89.2	35,303	35,332	36,216
Pedestrian, V01-V09	5,622	5,457	5,219
Pedalcyclist, V10-V19	873	793	785
Motorcycle rider, V20-V29	4,344	4,278	4,310
Occupant of three-wheeled motor vehicle, V30-V39	4	10	12
Car occupant, V40-V49	8,415	8,009	9,415
Occupant of pick-up truck or van, V50-V59	1,929	1,755	2,449
Occupant of heavy transport vehicle, V60-V69	273	257	246
Bus occupant, V70-V79	50	39	22
Animal rider or occupant of animal-drawn vehicle, V80	129	118	118
Occupant of railway train or railway vehicle, V81	23	16	22
Occupant of streetcar, V82	1	1	2
Other and unspecified land transport accidents, V83-V89	14,590	15,628	14,649
Occupant of special industrial vehicle, V83	*2*	*12*	*14*
Occupant of special agricultural vehicle, V84	*120*	*109*	*87*
Occupant of special construction vehicle, V85	*15*	*19*	*21*
Occupant of all-terrain or other off-road motor vehicle, V86	*913*	*906*	*1,004*
Other and unspecified person, V87-V89	*13,540*	*14,582*	*13,523*
Water transport accidents, V90-V94	533	398	462
Drowning, V90, V92	*405*	*256*	*329*
Other and unspecified injuries, V91, V93-V94	*128*	*142*	*133*
Air and space transport accidents, V95-V97	494	472	541
Other and unspecified transport accidents and sequelae, V98-V99, Y85	743	730	779
Other specified transport accidents, V98	*0*	*0*	*1*
Unspecified transport accidents, V99	*0*	*5*	*2*
Nontransport unintentional (accidental) injuries, W00-X59, Y86	88,415	82,898	78,990
Falls, W00-W19	27,483	26,009	24,792
Fall on same level from slipping, tripping, and stumbling, W01	*800*	*785*	*788*
Other fall on same level, W00, W02-W03, W18	*8,661*	*7,986*	*7,439*
Fall involving bed, chair, other furniture, W06-W08	*1,113*	*1,045*	*1,090*
Fall on and from stairs and steps, W10	*2,101*	*1,991*	*1,960*
Fall on and from ladder or scaffolding, W11-W12	*465*	*437*	*448*
Fall from out of or through building or structure, W13	*452*	*484*	*476*
Other fall from one level to another, W09, W14-W17	*623*	*599*	*635*
Other and unspecified fall, W04-W05, W19	*13,268*	*12,682*	*11,956*
Exposure to inanimate mechanical forces, W20-W49	2,496	2,439	2,353
Struck by or striking against object, W20-W22	*827*	*779*	*755*
Caught between objects, W23	*137*	*107*	*140*
Contact with machinery, W24, W30-W31	*610*	*590*	*608*
Contact with sharp objects, W25-W29	*106*	*105*	*121*
Firearms discharge, W32-W34	*591*	*606*	*554*
Explosion and rupture of pressurized devices, W35-W38	*19*	*26*	*29*
Fireworks discharge, W39	*5*	*1*	*4*
Explosion of other materials, W40	*118*	*151*	*78*
Foreign body entering through skin or natural orifice, W44-W45	*31*	*29*	*29*
Other and unspecified inanimate mechanical forces, W41-W43, W49	*52*	*45*	*35*
Exposure to animate mechanical forces, W50-W64	130	134	146
Struck by or against another person, W50-W52	*10*	*9*	*21*
Bitten or struck by dog, W54	*34*	*38*	*32*
Bitten or struck by other mammals, W53, W55	*72*	*71*	*68*
Bitten or stung by nonvenomous insect and other arthropods, W57	*7*	*5*	*10*
Bitten or crushed by other reptiles, W59	*0*	*1*	*0*
Other and unspecified animate mechanical forces, W56, W58, W60, W64	*7*	*10*	*15*
Accidental drowning and submersion, W65-W74	3,556	3,782	3,517
Drowning and submersion while in or falling into bath-tub, W65-W66	*431*	*424*	*438*
Drowning and submersion while in or falling into swimming-pool, W67-W68	*652*	*680*	*705*
Drowning and submersion while in or falling into natural water, W69-W70	*1,782*	*1,844*	*1,656*
Other and unspecified drowning and submersion, W73-W74	*691*	*834*	*718*
Other accidental threats to breathing, W75-W84	6,242	6,165	5,939
Accidental suffocation and strangulation in bed, W75	*692*	*684*	*717*
Other accidental hanging and strangulation, W76	*233*	*257*	*259*
Threat to breathing due to cave-in, falling earth and other substances, W77	*16*	*30*	*34*
Inhalation of gastric contents, W78	*327*	*301*	*264*
Inhalation and ingestion of food causing obstruction of respiratory tract, W79	*1,173*	*1,081*	*1,018*
Inhalation and ingestion of other objects causing obstruction of respiratory tract, W80	*3,208*	*3,188*	*3,088*
Confined to or trapped in a low-oxygen environment, W81	*4*	*12*	*6*
Other and unspecified threats to breathing, W83-W84	*589*	*612*	*553*

See source and footnotes on page 21.

Mortality by selected external causes, United States, 2009-2011

Type of accident or manner of injury	2011[a]	2010	2009
Exposure to electric current, radiation, temperature, and pressure, W85-W99	324	324	322
Electric transmission lines, W85	72	63	71
Other and unspecified electric current, W86-W87	236	248	232
Radiation, W88-W91	0	0	0
Excessive heat or cold of man-made origin, W92-W93	4	3	8
High and low air pressure and changes in air pressure, W94	12	10	11
Other and unspecified man-made environmental factors, W99	0	0	0
Exposure to smoke, fire, and flames, X00-X09	2,746	2,782	2,756
Uncontrolled fire in building or structure, X00	2,176	2,168	2,219
Uncontrolled fire not in building or structure, X01	40	44	52
Controlled fire in building or structure, X02	19	36	23
Controlled fire not in building or structure, X03	38	44	27
Ignition of highly flammable material, X04	42	61	39
Ignition or melting of nightwear, X05	4	4	5
Ignition or melting of other clothing and apparel, X06	83	69	97
Other and unspecified smoke fire and flames, X08-X09	344	356	294
Contact with heat and hot substances, X10-X19	67	63	67
Contact with hot tap-water, X11	27	30	23
Other and unspecified heat and hot substances, X10, X12-X19	40	33	44
Contact with venomous animals and plants, X20-X29	94	80	80
Contact with venomous snakes and lizards, X20	9	9	5
Contact with venomous spiders, X21	3	7	6
Contact with hornets, wasps and bees, X23	71	52	55
Contact with other and unspecified venomous animal or plant, X22, X24-X29	11	12	14
Exposure to forces of nature, X30-X39	1,944	1,342	1,084
Exposure to excessive natural heat, X30	587	474	352
Exposure to excessive natural cold, X31	672	710	616
Lightning, X33	24	29	31
Earthquake and other earth movements, X34-X36	22	33	19
Cataclysmic storm, X37	584	47	31
Flood, X38	25	39	15
Exposure to other and unspecified forces of nature, X32, X39	30	10	20
Accidental poisoning by and exposure to noxious substances, X40-X49	36,280	33,041	31,758
Nonopioid analgesics, antipyretics, and antirheumatics, X40	220	224	252
Antiepileptic, sedative-hypnotic, antiparkinsonism, and psychotropic drugs n.e.c., X41	2,080	1,916	1,681
Narcotics and psychodysleptics [hallucinogens] n.e.c., X42	13,214	12,280	12,458
Other and unspecified drugs, medicaments, and biologicals, X43-X44	17,557	15,586	14,363
Alcohol, X45	2,155	2,107	2,014
Gases and vapors, X46-X47	866	753	784
Other and unspecified chemicals and noxious substances, X48-X49	188	175	206
Overexertion, travel, and privation, X50-X57	35	26	28
Accidental exposure to other and unspecified factors and sequelae, X58-X59, Y86	7,018	6,711	6,148
Intentional self-harm, X60-X84, Y87.0, *U03	**39,518**	**38,364**	**36,909**
Intentional self-poisoning, X60-X69	6,564	6,599	6,398
Intentional self-harm by hanging, strangulation, and suffocation, X70	9,913	9,493	9,000
Intentional self-harm by firearm, X72-X74	19,990	19,392	18,735
Other and unspecified means and sequelae, X71, X75-X84, Y87.0	3,051	2,880	2,776
Terrorism, *U03	0	0	0
Assault, X85-Y09, Y87.1, *U01	**16,238**	**16,259**	**16,799**
Assault by firearm, X93-X95	11,068	11,078	11,493
Assault by sharp object, X99	1,797	1,799	1,874
Other and unspecified means and sequelae, X85-X92, X96-X98, Y00-Y09, Y87.1	3,373	3,382	3,432
Terrorism, *U01	0	0	0
Event of undetermined intent, Y10-Y34, Y87.2, Y89.9	**4,773**	**4,908**	**5,005**
Poisoning, Y10-Y19	3,098	3,197	3,349
Hanging, strangulation, and suffocation, Y20	151	160	163
Drowning and submersion, Y21	287	278	264
Firearm discharge, Y22-Y24	248	252	232
Exposure to smoke, fire, and flames, Y26	111	125	117
Falling, jumping, or pushed from a high place, Y30	62	50	67
Other and unspecified means and sequelae, Y25, Y27-Y29, Y31-Y34,Y87.2, Y89.9	816	846	813
Legal intervention, Y35, Y89.0	**492**	**412**	**395**
Legal intervention involving firearm discharge, Y35.0	454	344	333
Legal execution, Y35.5	31	41	49
Other and unspecified means and sequelae, Y35.1-Y35.4, Y35.6-Y35.7, Y89.0	7	27	13
Operations of war and sequelae, Y36, Y89.1	**5**	**9**	**25**
Complications of medical and surgical care and sequelae, Y40-Y84, Y88.0-Y88.3	**2,584**	**2,490**	**2,616**

Source: National Center for Health Statistics–Mortality Data for 2011, as compiled from data provided by the 57 vital statistics jurisdictions through the Vital Statistics Cooperative Program. Deaths are classified on the basis of the 10th revision of The International Classification of Diseases *(ICD-10), which became effective in 1999.*
Note: "n.e.c." means not elsewhere classified.
[a]*Latest official figures.*
[b]*Numbers following titles refer to external cause of injury and poisoning classifications in ICD-10.*

Unintentional-injury-related deaths by age, sex, and type, United States, 2011[a]

Age and sex	Total[b]	Poisoning	Motor vehicle	Falls	Choking[c]	Drowning[d]	Fire, flames, or smoke	Mechanical suffocation	Natural heat or cold	All types	
										Males	Females
Total	126,438	36,280	35,303	27,483	4,708	3,556	2,746	1,534	1,259	79,257	47,181
Younger than 5	2,540	49	520	35	153	490	150	887	27	1,486	1,054
5-14	1,635	50	881	28	24	235	123	53	4	1,033	602
15-24	12,330	3,440	7,105	205	48	543	135	79	37	9,172	3,158
25-44	30,748	15,727	10,352	803	228	856	374	188	172	21,885	8,863
45-64	35,907	15,427	9,866	3,509	969	891	926	211	476	24,358	11,549
65-74	10,014	945	2,913	3,149	652	258	389	41	188	6,295	3,719
75 or older	33,264	642	3,666	19,754	2,634	283	649	75	355	15,028	18,236
Males	79,257	23,288	24,947	13,814	2,474	2,773	1,633	997	841		
Females	47,181	12,992	10,356	13,669	2,234	783	1,113	537	418		

Source: National Safety Council analysis of National Center for Health Statistics–Mortality Data for 2011, as compiled from data provided by the 57 vital statistics jurisdictions through the Vital Statistics Cooperative Program.
[a]Latest official figures.
[b]Includes types not shown separately.
[c]Inhalation or ingestion of food or other object obstructing breathing.
[d]Excludes water transport drownings.

Of the 126,438 unintentional-injury-related deaths in 2011, males accounted for 63% of all deaths. Females had the greatest share of deaths only in the 75 and older age group (55% female). Other than for falls, which is roughly split evenly between women and men, males are disproportionably repre-sented over females. The largest differences in the proportion of fatalities were drowning (78% male) and motor vehicle deaths (71% male). The smallest difference between the proportion of male and female fatalities was choking (53% male).

Unintentional-injury-related death rates by type and sex, United States, 2011[a]

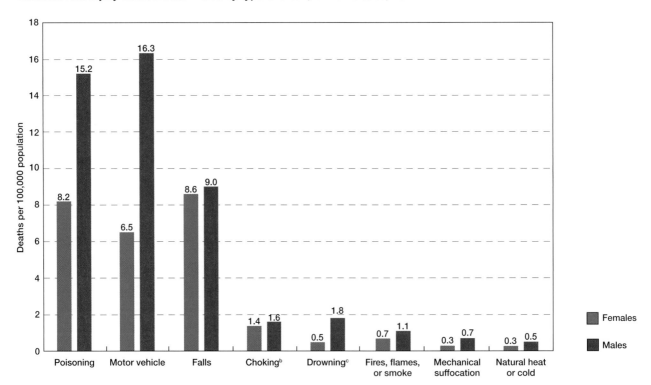

[a]Latest official figures.
[b]Inhalation or ingestion of food or other objects.
[c]Excludes water transport drownings.

Unintentional-injury-related deaths by month and type, United States, 2011[a]

Month	All types	Poisoning	Motor vehicle	Falls	Choking[b]	Drowning[c]	Fire, flames, or smoke	Mechanical suffocation	Natural heat or cold	Struck by or against	All other types
Total	**126,438**	**36,280**	**35,303**	**27,483**	**4,708**	**3,556**	**2,746**	**1,534**	**1,259**	**827**	**12,742**
January	10,214	3,096	2,471	2,373	444	117	377	132	195	66	943
February	9,500	3,059	2,236	2,142	399	138	323	124	166	51	862
March	10,262	3,117	2,662	2,339	455	185	282	121	64	49	988
April	10,589	3,058	2,805	2,238	408	260	226	116	28	73	1,377
May	10,893	3,130	3,030	2,260	374	390	199	134	37	60	1,279
June	10,553	2,778	3,130	2,181	371	567	145	128	94	91	1,068
July	11,704	3,034	3,417	2,270	352	759	162	128	270	71	1,241
August	10,955	2,952	3,288	2,293	364	415	174	154	173	84	1,058
September	10,176	2,864	3,080	2,184	332	280	166	128	35	83	1,024
October	10,767	3,056	3,336	2,443	398	169	174	139	29	69	954
November	10,311	3,023	2,962	2,322	397	132	241	122	60	72	980
December	10,514	3,113	2,886	2,438	414	144	277	108	108	58	968
Average	**10,537**	**3,023**	**2,942**	**2,290**	**392**	**296**	**229**	**128**	**105**	**69**	**1,062**

Source: National Safety Council analysis of National Center for Health Statistics–Mortality Data for 2011, as compiled from data provided by the 57 vital statistics jurisdictions through the Vital Statistics Cooperative Program.
[a]*Latest official figures.*
[b]*Inhalation or ingestion of food or other object obstructing breathing.*
[c]*Excludes water transport drownings.*

Unintentional-injury-related deaths by month and type, United States, 2011[a]

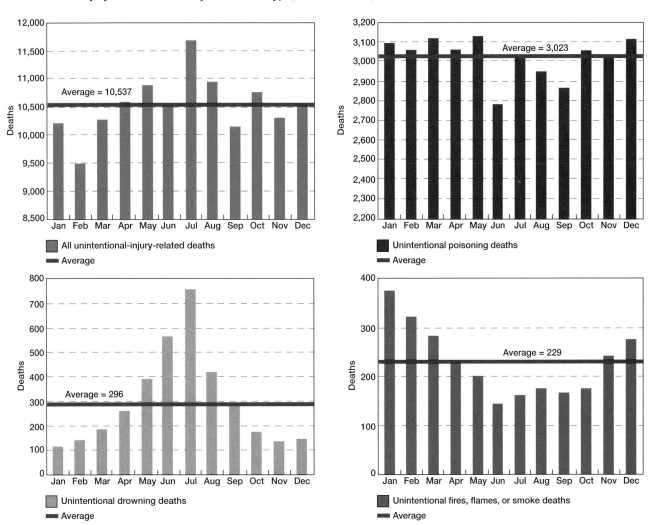

Cross-reference: See page 129 for motor vehicle deaths by month and page 165 for pedalcycle deaths by month.

The National Health Interview Survey, 2012

The National Health Interview Survey (NHIS), conducted by the National Center for Health Statistics, is a continuous, personal-interview sampling of households to obtain information about the health status of household members, including injuries experienced during the five weeks prior to the interview. Responsible family members residing in the household supplied the information used in the survey. In 2012, interviews were completed for 108,131 people living in 42,366 households throughout the United States. See page 25 for definitions.

Number of leading external causes of medically consulted injury and poisoning episodes by age, United States, 2012

	Population[a] (000)	External cause of injury and poisoning (number in thousands)						
		Falls	Struck by or against person or object	Transportation[b]	Overexertion	Cutting-piercing instruments	Other injury causes[b]	Poisoning[b]
All ages	**308,699**	**13,402**	**3,809**	**3,684**	**4,911**	**3,164**	**7,914**	**518**
Younger than 12	48,647	2,330	758	310	245[c]	127[c]	1,134	[d]
12-17 years	24,938	1,292	845	340[c]	450	[d]	1,411	[d]
18-44 years	111,197	2,405	1,249	1,632	2,094	1,583	2,241	208[c]
45-64 years	82,067	3,828	571	1,157	1,453	1,157	2,350	[d]
65-74 years	23,759	1,359	219[c]	[d]	633	[d]	628	[d]
75 and older	18,091	2,187	167[c]	[d]	[d]	[d]	[d]	[d]

[a]Civilian noninstitutionalized population.
[b]"Transportation" includes motor vehicle, bicycle, motorcycle, pedestrian, train, boat, or airplane. "Poisoning" does not include food poisoning or allergic reaction. "Other injury causes" includes fire/burn/scald-related, animal or insect bites, machinery, and unspecified causes.
[c]Estimate does not meet standard of reliability or precision and should be used with caution.
[d]Estimate is not shown because it does not meet standard of reliability or precision.

Leading external causes of injury and poisoning episodes by sex, United States, 2012

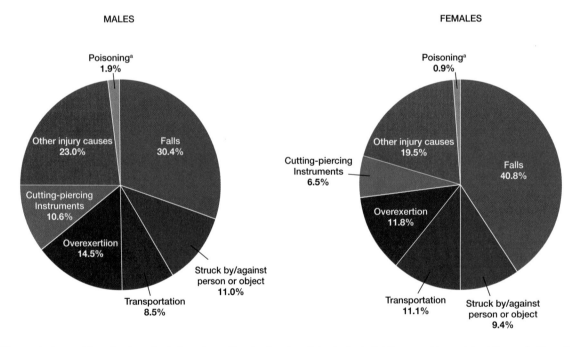

MALES

Poisoning[a] 1.9%
Other injury causes 23.0%
Falls 30.4%
Cutting-piercing Instruments 10.6%
Overexertiion 14.5%
Struck by/against person or object 11.0%
Transportation 8.5%

FEMALES

Poisoning[a] 0.9%
Other injury causes 19.5%
Cutting-piercing Instruments 6.5%
Falls 40.8%
Overexertion 11.8%
Transportation 11.1%
Struck by/against person or object 9.4%

[a]The standard error of the poisoning estimate for males and females do not meet standards of reliability or precision and should be used with caution.

Source: Adams, P.F., Kirzinger W.K., & Martinez, M.E. (2013, December). Summary of health statistics for the U.S. population: National Health Interview Survey, 2012. National Center for Health Statistics. Vital and Health Statistics, Series 10 (No. 259).

In 2012, an estimated 37.4 million medically consulted injury and poisoning episodes were recorded, of which 48.2% were among males and 51.8% among females. The overall injury rate was 120.27 episodes per 1,000 population, with males experiencing slightly higher rates (121.17 per 1,000 males) than females (119.32 per 1,000 females). Most injuries occurred in or around the home (51.9%), followed by injuries on streets, highways, sidewalks, and in parking lots (12.6%), and injuries at sport facilities, recreation areas, lakes, rivers, and pools (12.0%). Nationwide, injuries in public areas such as schools, hospitals, streets, recreational facilities, industrial and trade areas, and public buildings together accounted for 41.8% of the total injuries.

Among the 18.0 million injuries reported for males, the single most common place of injury occurrence was at home, with 24.7% occurring inside the home while injuries occurring outside contributed an additional 22.5%. More than half of the injuries among females occurred at home. More than twice as many injuries to females occurred inside the home than outside, consistent with past findings. Streets, parking lots, sidewalks, and highways, along with sport facility, recreation area, lake, river, or pools, were the next most common locations for injuries among females, accounting for 14.4% and 8.1% of injuries, respectively. For males, sport facilities and recreational areas were the most common nonhome places for injuries to occur (16.2%), followed by streets, parking lots, sidewalks, and highways (10.7%).

The 2012 NHIS injury definitions are listed below for comparability with prior years and other injury figures published in *Injury Facts*.

Number and percent of injury episodes by place of occurrence and sex, United States, 2012

Place of occurrence of injury episode	Both sexes No. of episodes (000)	Percent	Male No. of episodes (000)	Percent	Female No. of episodes (000)	Percent
Total episodes[a]	37,401	100.0	18,016	100.0	19,385	100.0
Home (inside)	11,816	31.6	4,455	24.7	7,362	38.0
Home (outside)	7,604	20.3	4,054	22.5	3,549	18.3
School, child care center, or preschool	2,622	7.0	1,381	7.7	1,241	6.4
Hospital or residential institution	836	2.2	161[b]	0.9[b]	675	3.5
Street, highway, sidewalk, or parking lot	4,720	12.6	1,919	10.7	2,801	14.4
Sport facility, recreational area, lake, river, or pool	4,489	12.0	2,924	16.2	1,566	8.1
Industrial, construction, or farm	945	2.5	777	4.3	(c)	(c)
Trade or service area	913	2.4	373[b]	2.1[b]	540	2.8
Other public building	1,099	2.9	498	2.8	600	3.1
Other (unspecified)	2,420	6.5	1,546	8.6	874	4.5

Source: Adams, P.F., Kirzinger W.K., & Martinez, M.E. (2013, December). Summary of health statistics for the U.S. population: National Health Interview Survey, 2012. National Center for Health Statistics. Vital and Health Statistics, Series 10 (No. 259).
[a]*Numbers and percentages may not sum to respective totals due to rounding and unknowns.*
[b]*Estimate does not meet standard of reliability or precision and should be used with caution.*
[c]*Estimate is not shown because it does not meet standard of reliability or precision.*

Injury definitions

National Health Interview Survey definitions. The 2012 National Health Interview Survey (NHIS) figures include medically consulted injury and poisoning episodes (e.g., call to a poison control center; use of an emergency vehicle or emergency room; visit to a doctor's office or other health clinic; or phone call to a doctor, nurse, or other health care professional) that reportedly occurred during the three months prior to the date of the interview and resulted in one or more conditions. Beginning in 2004, injury and poisoning estimates were calculated using only those episodes that occurred five weeks or less before the interview date. This reflects a change from 1997 to 2003, when NHIS data contained injury and poisoning episodes that were reported to occur within four months of the interview, and estimates were calculated using a three-month recall period. Also, an imputation procedure was performed for injury and poisoning episodes to assign a date of occurrence if it was not reported. Therefore, figures for 2004 and subsequent years are not comparable to estimates from prior years.

In the 2012 NHIS Injury and Poisoning file, an injury episode refers to the traumatic event in which the person was injured one or more times from an external cause (e.g., a fall or a motor vehicle traffic incident). An injury condition is the acute condition or the physical harm caused by the traumatic event. Likewise, a poisoning episode refers to the event resulting from ingestion of or contact with harmful substances, as well as overdoses or wrong use of any drug or medication, while a poisoning condition is the acute condition or the physical harm caused by the event. Each episode must have at least one injury condition or poisoning classified according to the nature-of-injury codes 800-909.2, 909.4, 909.9, 910-994.9, 995.5-995.59, and 995.80-995.85 in the Ninth Revision of the International Classification of Diseases (ICD-9-CM). Poisoning episodes exclude food poisoning, sun poisoning, or poison ivy rashes.

National Safety Council definition of injury. A medically consulted injury is defined as one that is serious enough that a medical professional was consulted or is a recordable work injury based on OSHA definitions (see Glossary). All injury totals labeled "medically consulted" in *Injury Facts* are based on this definition.

Of the 37.4 million medically consulted injuries in 2012, 35.6% were related to sports and leisure activities. Sports and leisure injuries accounted for 60.0% of all injury episodes among children younger than 12 and 69.2% of injury episodes among 12- to 17-year-olds.

The rate of injuries occurring during sports and leisure activities was substantially higher for males (49 cases per 1,000 males) than for females (39 cases per 1,000 females). The charts on this page illustrate these gender differences in terms of percentages and rates.

Number of injury episodes by age and activity at time of injury, United States, 2012

	Total episodes[a] (000)	Activity at time of injury[b] (number in thousands)						
		Driving[c]	Working at paid job	Working around house or yard	Attending school	Sports	Leisure activities	Other[d]
All ages	**37,401**	**2,576**	**4,247**	**5,401**	**1,043**	**6,062**	**7,263**	**10,849**
Younger than 12	4,976	203[f]	0	(e)	465	978	2,006	1,301
12-17 years	4,540	(e)	(e)	(e)	441	2,268	874	609
18-44 years	11,413	899	2,342	1,639	(e)	1,939	1,802	2,579
45-64 years	10,621	1,065	1,775	2,257	0	653	1,461	3,439
65-74 years	3,074	191[f]	(e)	664	0	(e)	610	1,314
75 or older	2,777	(e)	0	649	0	0	510	1,607

Percent and rates of injury episodes by sex and activity at time of injury, United States, 2012

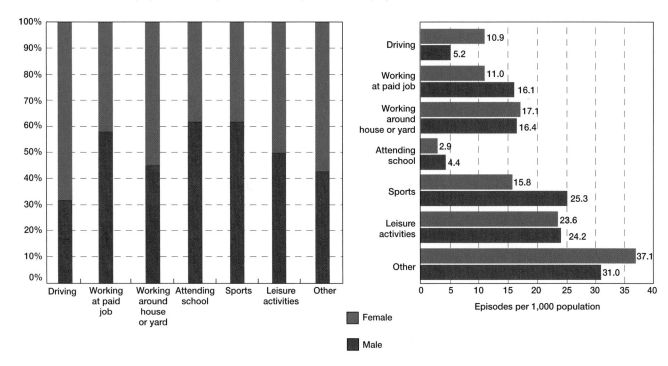

Source: Adams, P.F., Kirzinger W.K., & Martinez, M.E. (2013, December). Summary of health statistics for the U.S. population: National Health Interview Survey, 2012. National Center for Health Statistics. Vital and Health Statistics, Series 10 (No. 259).

[a]Numbers may not sum to respective totals due to rounding and unknowns.

[b]Activity at time of injury and poisoning episodes is based on the question, "What was [person] doing when the injury/poisoning happened?" Respondents could indicate up to two activities.

[c]Driving includes both drivers and passengers.

[d]"Other" includes unpaid work such as housework, shopping, volunteer work, sleeping, resting, eating, drinking, cooking, hands-on care from another person, and other unspecified activities.

[e]Estimate is not shown because it does not meet standard of reliability or precision.

[f]Estimate does not meet standard of reliability or precision and should be used with caution.

A wealth of research demonstrates the role of socioeconomic status in the etiology of medical conditions and disease. In general, people with the highest levels of income and education are healthier than those with median income and education, who, in turn, tend to be in better health than the poor and least educated.[a]

Lower socioeconomic status is known to contribute to increased rates of fatal injuries. Although research provides some evidence of links between socioeconomic status and nonfatal injuries, studies based on morbidity data provide results somewhat less consistent than those of mortality studies. Nonetheless, numerous studies show considerable differences between socioeconomic groups even for nonfatal injuries.[b] The National Health Interview Survey provides an opportunity to look at the occurrence of unintentional injuries in the U.S. population as a function of socioeconomic position using two socioeconomic status measures – family income and education.[c]

Although NHIS data indicate that all people are affected by injuries, families whose poverty status was poor (below the poverty threshold) had substantially higher injury rates than families whose poverty status was near poor (100% to less than 200% of the poverty threshold) and not poor (200% of the poverty threshold and greater). Similarly, those with a bachelor's degree or higher had the lowest medically consulted injury rate in 2012 (96.83 injuries per 1,000 population). In contrast, those with some college had the highest injury rate (155.74 per 1,000 population). The finding that individuals with some college education have the highest rate of medically consulted injuries is consistent with past NHIS findings but does not seem to support the typical socioeconomic status pattern.

[a]Banks, J., Marmot, M., Oldfield, Z., & Smith, J.P. (2006). Disease and disadvantage in the United States and in England. Journal of American Medical Association, Issue 295, No. 17, pp. 2037-2045.
[b]Laflamme, L., Burrows, S., & Hasselberg, M. (2009). Socioeconomic differences in injury risks--A review of findings and a discussion of potential countermeasures. Denmark: World Health Organization--Europe.
[c]Education data are shown for people 25 and older

Percentages and rates of medically consulted injuries by poverty status, United States, 2012

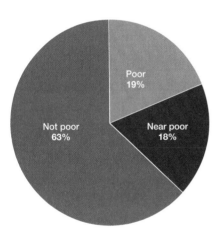

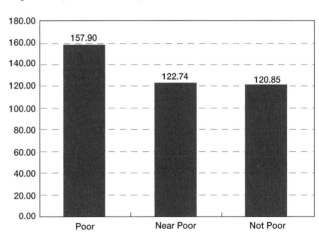

Percentages and rates of medically consulted injuries by level of education, United States, 2012

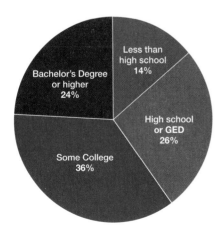

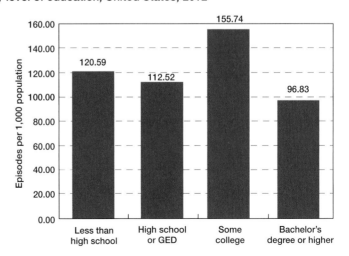

Source: Adams, P.F., Kirzinger W.K., & Martinez, M.E. (2013, December). Summary of health statistics for the U.S. population: National Health Interview Survey, 2012. National Center for Health Statistics. Vital and Health Statistics, Series 10 (No. 259).

Injury-Related Hospital Emergency Department Visits, 2011

■ *Over 40 million visits to hospital emergency departments in 2011 were due to injuries.*

About 29% of all hospital emergency department visits in the United States were injury-related, according to information from the 2011 National Hospital Ambulatory Medical Care Survey conducted for the National Center for Health Statistics. Approximately 136.3 million visits were made to emergency departments in 2011, of which about 40.2 million were injury-related. This resulted in an annual rate of about 44.5 emergency department visits per 100 people, of which about 13.1 visits per 100 people were injury-related.

Males had a higher overall rate of injury-related visits than females. For males, about 14.2 visits per 100 people were recorded; for females, the rate was 12.1 per 100 people. Males also had higher rates of injury-related visits than females for those younger than 15 through age 64, while females had higher rates for age groups beginning at age 65. Those ages 15-24 had the highest rate of injury-related visits for males, while those 75 and older had the highest rate for females.

Falls and motor vehicle incidents were the leading causes of injury-related emergency department visits, accounting for

26% and 10% of the total, respectively. In total, over 11.3 million visits to emergency departments were made in 2011 due to unintentional falls, and over 4.1 million were made due to motor vehicle incidents. The next leading types were struck against or struck accidentally by objects or people, with nearly 3.5 million visits (8% of the total), and incidents involving cutting or piercing instruments or objects, which accounted for about 2.4 million visits (over 5% of the total).

The upper extremities were the most frequent body site of injuries treated in hospital emergency departments, followed by injuries to the lower extremities and those to the head and neck. These three body sites accounted for about 42% of injury-related visits. Injury visits with multiple injury diagnoses accounted for another 2%. The most commonly mentioned specific body sites for injuries were wrist, hand, and fingers, followed by the vertebral column, lower leg and ankle, and foot and toes.

Number and percent distribution of emergency department visits by cause of injury, United States, 2011

Cause of injury and E-code[a]	No. of visits (000)	Percent
All visits related to injury, poisoning, and adverse effects	**42,997**	**100.0**
All injury visits	**40,220**	**93.5**
Unintentional injuries, E800-E848, E850-E869, E880-E929	**31,013**	**72.1**
Falls, E880.0-E886.9, E888	11,324	26.3
Total motor vehicle, E810-E819, E820-E825 (.0-.5, .7-.9)	4,142	9.6
Motor vehicle traffic, E810-E819	*3,828*	*8.9*
Motor vehicle, nontraffic, E820-E825(.0-.5, .7-.9)	*314*	*0.7*
Struck against or struck accidentally by objects or persons, E916-E917	3,482	8.1
Cutting or piercing instruments or objects, E920	2,369	5.5
Overexertion and strenuous movements, E927	2,210	5.1
Natural and environmental factors, E900-E909, E928.0-E928.2	2,091	4.9
Poisoning, E850-E869	946	2.2
Foreign body, E914-E915	780	1.8
Caught accidentally in or between objects, E918	405	0.9
Pedalcycle, nontraffic, and other, E800-E807(.3), E820-E825(.6), E826.1, E826.9	400	0.9
Fire and flames, hot substances or object, caustic or corrosive material, and steam, E890-E899, E924	393	0.9
Other transportation, E800-807(.0-.2, .8-.9), E826(.0, .2-.8), E827-E829, E831, E833-E845	(b)	(b)
Suffocation, E911-E913	(b)	(b)

Cause of injury and E-code[a]	No. of visits (000)	Percent
Machinery, E919	179	0.4
Other mechanism[c], E830, E832, E846-E848, E910, E921-E923, E925-E926, E928(.3-.5, .8), E929(.0-.5, .8)	2,046	4.8
Mechanism unspecified, E887, E928.9, E929.9	(b)	(b)
Intentional injuries, E950-E979, E990-E999	**2,984**	**6.9**
Assault, E960-E969, E979	2,061	4.8
Unarmed fight or brawl, striking by blunt or thrown object, E960.0, E968.2	*1,240*	*2.9*
Cutting or piercing instrument, E966	*127*	*0.3*
Other and unspecified mechanism[d], E960.1, E961-E964, E965, E967-E968.1, E968.3-E969, E979	*693*	*1.6*
Self-inflicted injury, E950-E959	836	1.9
Poisoning by solid or liquid substances, gases, and vapors, E950-E952	*509*	*1.2*
Other and unspecified mechanism[e], E953-E959	*327*	*0.8*
Other causes of violence, E970-E978, E990-E999	(b)	(b)
Injuries of undetermined intent, E980-E989	**510**	**1.2**
Adverse effects of medical treatment, E870-E879, E930-E949	**1,888**	**4.4**
Medical and surgical complications, E870-E879	1,157	2.7
Adverse drug effects, E930-E949	731	1.7
Alcohol and drug use[f]	**134**	**0.3**
Unknown[g]	**6,468**	**15.0**

Source: National Hospital Ambulatory Medical Care Survey: 2011 Emergency Department Summary Tables. Accessed December 2, 2014, at www.cdc.gov/nchs/data/ahcd/nhamcs_emergency/2011_ed_web_tables.pdf. Note: Sum of parts may not add to total due to rounding.
[a]Based on "Supplementary Classification of External Causes of Injury and Poisoning" in the International Classification of Diseases, 9th Revision, Clinical Modification (ICD-9-CM).
[b]Figure did not meet standard of reliability or precision.

[c]Includes drowning, firearms, and other mechanism.
[d]Includes assault by firearms and explosives, and other mechanism.
[e]Includes injury by cutting and piercing instruments, suffocation, and other and unspecified mechanism.
[f] Alcohol and drug abuse are not contained in the "Supplementary Classification of External Causes of Injury and Poisoning," but are frequently recorded as a cause of injury or poisoning.
[g]Includes illegible entries and blanks.

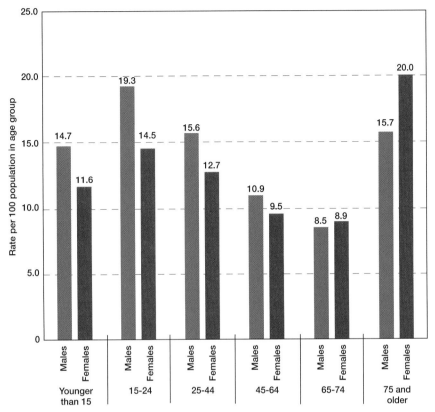
Rate[a] of injury-related[b] visits to emergency departments by patient age and sex, 2011

Rate per 100 population in age group

	Males	Females
Younger than 15	14.7	11.6
15-24	19.3	14.5
25-44	15.6	12.7
45-64	10.9	9.5
65-74	8.5	8.9
75 and older	15.7	20.0

[a]Number of visits per 100 population in each age group.
[b]Injury-related includes injuries or poisoning; adverse effects and complications are excluded.

Percent of injury-related[a] emergency department visits by body site of primary diagnosis, United States, 2011

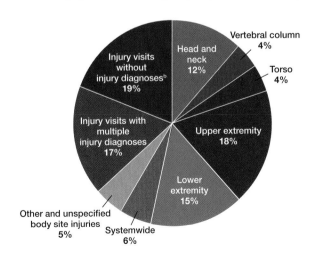

- Injury visits without injury diagnoses[b] 19%
- Head and neck 12%
- Vertebral column 4%
- Torso 4%
- Upper extremity 18%
- Injury visits with multiple injury diagnoses 17%
- Lower extremity 15%
- Other and unspecified body site injuries 5%
- Systemwide 6%

[a] Injury-related includes injuries or poisoning; adverse effects and complications are excluded.
[b]"Injury visits without injury diagnoses" includes musculoskeletal conditions; skin conditions; symptoms, signs, and ill-defined conditions; mental disorders; observation and evaluation; all other diagnoses; and unknown diagnoses.

Leading Causes of Fatal Unintentional Injuries

Poisoning is the leading cause of fatal unintentional injuries in the United States, according to the latest data from the National Center for Health Statistics. A total of 36,280 poisoning fatalities occurred in 2011, accounting for about 29% of all unintentional-injury-related deaths and exceeding the total of motor vehicle traffic fatalities for the first time. Poisoning fatalities were the leading cause of unintentional-injury-related deaths in age groups from 25-34 through 55-64. Suffocation was the leading cause of unintentional-injury-related deaths for people younger than 1, while drowning was the leading cause for those 1-4

years old. Motor vehicle traffic fatalities were the leading cause of death in the 5-9 through 15-24 age groups. The leading cause of unintentional-injury-related deaths among age groups from 25-34 through 55-64 was poisoning, and the leading cause for those age 65 and older was falls. Taken together, poisoning, motor vehicle traffic, and falls accounted for more than three-quarters of all unintentional-injury-related deaths. In addition to these three causes, drowning was a leading cause of unintentional-injury-related deaths for most age groups.

Leading causes of fatal unintentional injuries by age group, United States, 2011

Rank	All ages	Age group									
		Younger than 1	1-4	5-9	10-14	15-24	25-34	35-44	45-54	55-64	65 or older
1	Poisoning 36,280	Suffocation 896	Drowning 438	Motor vehicle traffic 350	Motor vehicle traffic 437	Motor vehicle traffic 6,926	Poisoning 7,652	Poisoning 8,075	Poisoning 10,379	Poisoning 5,048	Falls 22,901
2	Motor vehicle traffic 33,783	Motor vehicle traffic 93	Motor vehicle traffic 330	Drowning 128	Drowning 107	Poisoning 3,440	Motor vehicle traffic 5,569	Motor vehicle traffic 4,425	Motor vehicle traffic 5,240	Motor vehicle traffic 4,184	Motor vehicle traffic 6,225
3	Falls 27,483	Drowning 52	Suffocation 144	Fire/burn 81	Other land transport 47	Drowning 543	Drowning 442	Falls 524	Falls 1,368	Falls 2,141	Unspecified 4,360
4	Suffocation 6,242	Unspecified 28	Fire/burn 130	Suffocation 34	Suffocation 43	Falls 205	Falls 279	Drowning 414	Suffocation 536	Suffocation 644	Suffocation 3,402
5	Unspecified 5,871	Fire/burn 24	Pedestrian, other 88	Other land transport 31	Fire/burn 42	Other land transport 177	Other specified 212	Suffocation 240	Drowning 479	Fire/burn 522	Poisoning 1,581
6	Drowning 3,556	Natural/ environment 21	Struck by/ against 56	Natural/ environment 28	Poisoning 35	Fire/burn 136	Suffocation 176	Other specified 209	Fire/burn 425	Unspecified 496	Fire/burn 1,073
7	Fire/burn 2,813	Poisoning 15	Natural/ environment 40	Firearms 16	Other transport 32	Firearms 130	Fire/burn 175	Fire/burn 201	Natural/ environment 401	Natural/ environment 424	Natural/ environment 825
8	Natural/ environment 2,193	Falls 11	Poisoning 34	Pedetrian, other 16	Firearms 29	Suffocation 127	Other land transport 173	Natural/ environment 182	Other specified 345	Drowning 412	Other specified, n.e.c.[a] 604
9	Other specified 1,409	Other specified 10	Firearms 25	Other transport 15	Natural/ environment 21	Other specified 122	Natural/ environment 155	Unspecified 175	Unspecified 336	Other specified 240	Drowning 540
10	Other land transport 1,301	Struck by/ against 6	Falls 24	Poisoning 15	Falls 19	Pedetrian, other 109	Other transport 152	Other land transport 166	Other land transport 232	Other transport 181	Other land transport 285
All causes of fatal unintentional injury											
Number	126,438	1,163	1,377	761	874	12,330	15,518	15,230	20,479	15,158	43,278[b]
Per 100,000 population	39.0	29.3	8.5	3.7	4.2	28.1	37.1	37.5	46.4	39.8	104.6[b]

Source: Centers for Disease Control and Prevention, National Center for Injury Prevention and Control. Web-based Injury Statistics Query and Reporting System (WISQARS), data accessed July 16, 2014, at www.cdc.gov/injury/wisqars/index.html.
[a]*"n.e.c." means not elsewhere classified.*
[b]*Includes 20 cases with age unknown.*

KEY

☐ Poisoning ☐ Falls ☐ Drowning ☐ Overexertion
☐ Motor vehicle traffic/occupant ☐ Suffocation ☐ Stuck by/against ☐ Cut/pierce

Leading Causes of Nonfatal Unintentional Injuries

Falls are the leading cause of nonfatal unintentional injuries that are treated in hospital emergency departments, according to data from the All Injury Program, a cooperative program involving the National Center for Injury Prevention and Control, the Centers for Disease Control and Prevention, and the Consumer Product Safety Commission. More than 8.9 million people were treated in an emergency department for fall-related injuries in 2012. Falls were the leading cause of nonfatal injuries for all age groups except for the 10- to 14 and 15- to 24-year-old age groups, for which struck by or against an object or person was the leading cause. Struck by or against, overexertion, and motor vehicle crashes involving vehicle occupants also were leading causes for most age groups (please see color key at the bottom of the opposite page).

Leading causes of nonfatal unintentional injuries treated in hospital emergency departments by age group, United States, 2012[a]

Rank	All ages	Age group									
		Younger than 1	1-4	5-9	10-14	15-24	25-34	35-44	45-54	55-64	65 or older
1	Falls 8,974,762	Falls 145,406	Falls 928,693	Falls 682,972	Struck by/ against 612,890	Struck by/ against 1,015,214	Falls 781,424	Falls 723,904	Falls 925,945	Falls 881,178	Falls 2,422,463
2	Struck by/ against 4,533,417	Struck by/ against 33,070	Struck by/ against 385,146	Struck by/ against 427,701	Falls 600,403	Falls 882,214	Struck by/ against 648,632	Overexertion 552,464	Overexertion 480,093	Stuck by/ against 269,407	Stuck by/ against 280,326
3	Overexertion 3,385,128	Other bite/ sting[b] 14,293	Other bite/ sting[b] 172,438	Cut/pierce 119,092	Overexertion 318,459	Overexertion 728,819	Overexertion 643,571	Struck by/ against 467,962	Struck by/ against 412,908	Overexertion 259,092	Overexertion 213,553
4	Motor vehicle occupant 2,564,003	Foreign body 11,245	Foreign body 145,117	Other bite/ sting[b] 111,305	Cut/pierce 126,902	Motor vehicle occupant 666,833	Motor vehicle occupant 539,425	Motor vehicle occupant 392,071	Motor vehicle occupant 358,304	Motor vehicle occupant 232,972	Motor vehicle occupant 197,951
5	Cut/pierce 2,145,927	Fire/burn 10,837	Cut/pierce 90,907	Overexertion 93,654	Pedalcyclist 98,448	Cut/pierce 444,644	Cut/pierce 415,539	Cut/pierce 310,662	Other specified[c] 318,190	Cut/pierce 186,182	Cut/pierce 152,185
6	Other specified[c] 1,580,574	Inhalation/ suffocation 9,658	Overexertion 89,007	Pedalcyclist 82,935	Unknown/ unspecified 88,748	Other specified[c] 320,844	Other specified[c] 294,541	Other specified[c] 264,926	Cut/pierce 293,852	Other specified[c] 175,130	Poisoning 99,618
7	Other bite/ sting[b] 1,250,916	Other specified[c] 9,120	Other specified[c] 68,237	Foreign body 64,755	Motor vehicle occupant 77,363	Other bite/ sting[b] 191,062	Other bite/ sting[b] 193,519	Poisoning 162,002	Poisoning 216,942	Poisoning 128,260	Other bite/ sting[b] 90,300
8	Poisoning 972,923	Overexertion 6,416	Fire/burn 56,711	Motor vehicle occupant 60,056	Other bite/ sting[b] 69,914	Unknown/ unspecified 154,866	Poisoning 156,817	Other bite/ sting[b] 148,512	Other bite/ sting[b] 155,748	Other bite/ sting[b] 103,825	Other specified[c] 79,395
9	Unknown/ unspecified 734,164	Cut/pierce 5,963	Unknown/ unspecified 45,276	Dog bite 46,565	Other transport[d] 49,358	Poisoning 147,636	Unknown/ unspecified 113,467	Unknown/ unspecified 90,213	Unknown/ unspecified 85,383	Other transport[d] 52,056	Other transport[d] 68,167
10	Foreign body 588,322	Unknown/ unspecified 5,020	Dog bite 38,556	Unknown/ unspecified 38,208	Dog bite 32,629	Pedalcyclist 110,202	Other transport[d] 88,454	Other transport[d] 64,831	Other transport[d] 67,466	Unknown/ unspecified 50,631	Unknown/ unspecified 62,327
All causes of unintentional injury											
Number	29,437,493	263,625	2,164,954	1,831,910	2,199,215	5,148,641	4,258,303	3,497,700	3,650,019	2,567,222	3,855,902[e]
Per 100,000 population	9,377.6	6,685.8	13,483.5	8,946.8	10,640.0	11,716.4	10,064.7	8,632.8	8,245.1	6,653.2	8,937.0[e]

Source: NEISS All Injury Program, Office of Statistics and Programming, National Center for Injury Prevention and Control, the Centers for Disease Control and Prevention, and Consumer Product Safety Commission.
[a]See color key on bottom of page 30.
[b]Other than dog bite.
[c]Injury associated with any other specified cause that does not fit another category. Includes electric current, explosions, fireworks, radiation, animal scratch, etc. Excludes all causes listed in the table and bb/pellet gunshot, drowning and near drowning, firearm gunshot, suffocation, machinery, natural and environmental conditions, pedestrians, and motorcyclists.
[d]Includes occupant of any transport vehicle other than a motor vehicle or motorcycle (e.g., airplane, space vehicle, railcar, boat, all-terrain vehicle, animal and animal-drawn conveyances, battery-powered carts, ski lifts, and other cable cars not on rails).
[e]Includes 3,772 cases with age unknown.

Disasters are front-page news, even though the lives lost in the United States are relatively few when compared to the day-to-day life losses from unintentional injuries (see "While You Speak!" on page 37). Listed below are the U.S. disasters, of which the National Safety Council is aware, that occurred in 2013 and took five or more lives.

Disaster deaths, United States, 2013

Type and location	No. of deaths	Date of disaster
Major disasters (25 or more deaths)		
Excessive Heat, Nevada	38	July 1-5
Other disasters (5-24 deaths)		
Tornado, Oklahoma	24	May 20
Tornado and flash flood, Oklahoma	21	May 31
Wildfire, Arizona	19	June
West Fertilizer plant explosion, Texas	15	April 17
Aircraft crash, Alaska	10	July 7
Excessive heat, New York	8	July 19-21
Motor vehicle traffic crash, Tennessee	8	October 2
Winter storm, Texas	8	December 5-6
Blizzard, New York	7	February 8-9
Flash flood, Texas	7	October 31
Motor vehicle traffic crash, Indiana	7	August 15
Motor vehicle traffic crash, New York	7	May 29
Three-story duplex fire, Pennsylvania	7	July
Tornado and flash flood, Arkansas	7	May 30-31
Blizzard, Nebraska	6	March 10
Excessive heat, Illinois	6	July 16-20
Flash flood, Colorado	6	September 11-12
Motor vehicle traffic crash, Georgia	6	February 8
Motor vehicle traffic crash, Kentucky	6	March 2
Motor vehicle traffic crash, North Carolina	6	January 18
Motor vehicle traffic crash, Ohio	6	March 10
Motor vehicle traffic crash, Ohio	6	October 18
Motor vehicle traffic crash, Pennsylvania	6	August 31
Motor vehicle traffic crash, Texas	6	August 12
Single-family home fire, Ohio	6	September
Single-family home fire, Pennsylvania	6	May
Single-family home fire, West Virginia	6	October
Tornado, Texas	6	May 15
Aircraft crash, Georgia	5	February 20

Type and location	No. of deaths	Date of disaster
Other disasters (5-24 deaths)		
Aircraft crash, Idaho	5	December 1
Aircraft crash, Pennsylvania	5	July 27
Avalanche, Colorado	5	April 20
Excessive heat, Nevada	5	July 18-20
Motor vehicle traffic crash, Arizona	5	April 20
Motor vehicle traffic crash, California	5	April 6
Motor vehicle traffic crash, California	5	May 27
Motor vehicle traffic crash, California	5	May 4
Motor vehicle traffic crash, California	5	September 28
Motor vehicle traffic crash, California	5	October 22
Motor vehicle traffic crash, Florida	5	December 14
Motor vehicle traffic crash, Florida	5	April 13
Motor vehicle traffic crash, Illinois	5	May 20
Motor vehicle traffic crash, Illinois	5	November 23
Motor vehicle traffic crash, Missouri	5	July 4
Motor vehicle traffic crash, Montana	5	June 15
Motor vehicle traffic crash, Nevada	5	March 30
Motor vehicle traffic crash, Pennsylvania	5	October 19
Motor vehicle traffic crash, Texas	5	March 10
Motor vehicle traffic crash, Texas	5	June 30
Motor vehicle traffic crash, Texas	5	August 12
Motor vehicle traffic crash, Texas	5	September 29
Motor vehicle traffic crash, Virginia	5	April 2
Single-family home fire, Georgia	5	April
Single-family home fire, Idaho	5	April
Single-family home fire, Illinois	5	March
Single-family home fire, Indiana	**5**	February
Single-family home fire, Kentucky	**5**	January
Single-family home fire, Oregon	**5**	September
Vehicle fire, California	**5**	May

Source: The National Climatic Data Center, National Fire Protection Association, National Transportation Safety Board, and National Highway Traffic Safety Administration.
Note: Some death totals are estimates and may differ among sources.

Provided below is a timeline of disasters[a] resulting in substantial loss of life from 1900 to the present. As can be seen, while some sources of disasters, such as steamships and coal mines, become less prevalent toward the end of the timeline, other disaster types, such as hurricanes, are represented throughout the timeline.

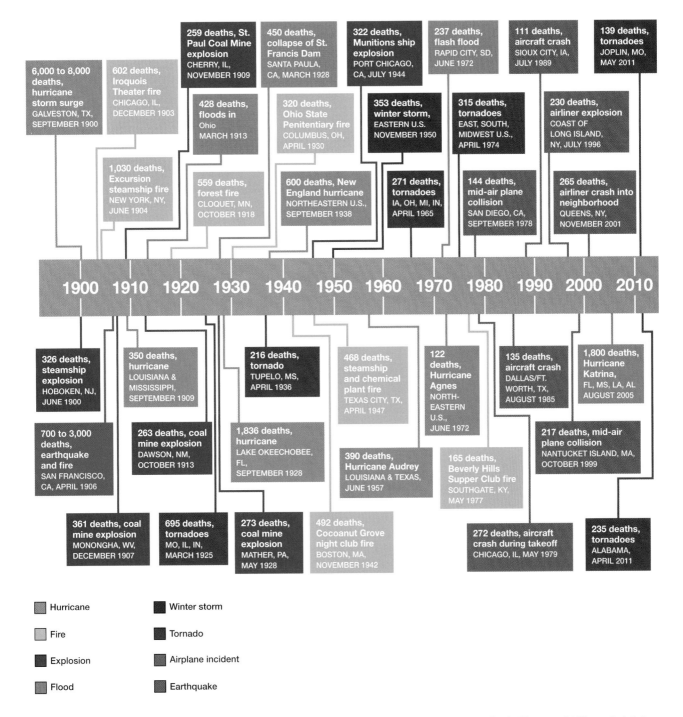

Above timeline:

- 6,000 to 8,000 deaths, hurricane storm surge GALVESTON, TX, SEPTEMBER 1900
- 602 deaths, Iroquois Theater fire CHICAGO, IL, DECEMBER 1903
- 259 deaths, St. Paul Coal Mine explosion CHERRY, IL, NOVEMBER 1909
- 450 deaths, collapse of St. Francis Dam SANTA PAULA, CA, MARCH 1928
- 322 deaths, Munitions ship explosion PORT CHICAGO, CA, JULY 1944
- 237 deaths, flash flood RAPID CITY, SD, JUNE 1972
- 111 deaths, aircraft crash SIOUX CITY, IA, JULY 1989
- 139 deaths, tornadoes JOPLIN, MO, MAY 2011
- 428 deaths, floods in Ohio MARCH 1913
- 320 deaths, Ohio State Penitentiary fire COLUMBUS, OH, APRIL 1930
- 353 deaths, winter storm, EASTERN U.S. NOVEMBER 1950
- 315 deaths, tornadoes EAST, SOUTH, MIDWEST U.S., APRIL 1974
- 230 deaths, airliner explosion COAST OF LONG ISLAND, NY, JULY 1996
- 1,030 deaths, Excursion steamship fire NEW YORK, NY, JUNE 1904
- 559 deaths, forest fire CLOQUET, MN, OCTOBER 1918
- 600 deaths, New England hurricane NORTHEASTERN U.S., SEPTEMBER 1938
- 271 deaths, tornadoes IA, OH, MI, IN, APRIL 1965
- 144 deaths, mid-air plane collision SAN DIEGO, CA, SEPTEMBER 1978
- 265 deaths, airliner crash into neighborhood QUEENS, NY, NOVEMBER 2001

Timeline axis: 1900 1910 1920 1930 1940 1950 1960 1970 1980 1990 2000 2010

Below timeline:

- 326 deaths, steamship explosion HOBOKEN, NJ, JUNE 1900
- 350 deaths, hurricane LOUISIANA & MISSISSIPPI, SEPTEMBER 1909
- 216 deaths, tornado TUPELO, MS, APRIL 1936
- 468 deaths, steamship and chemical plant fire TEXAS CITY, TX, APRIL 1947
- 122 deaths, Hurricane Agnes NORTH-EASTERN U.S., JUNE 1972
- 135 deaths, aircraft crash DALLAS/FT. WORTH, TX, AUGUST 1985
- 1,800 deaths, Hurricane Katrina, FL, MS, LA, AL AUGUST 2005
- 700 to 3,000 deaths, earthquake and fire SAN FRANCISCO, CA, APRIL 1906
- 263 deaths, coal mine explosion DAWSON, NM, OCTOBER 1913
- 1,836 deaths, hurricane LAKE OKEECHOBEE, FL, SEPTEMBER 1928
- 390 deaths, Hurricane Audrey LOUISIANA & TEXAS, JUNE 1957
- 165 deaths, Beverly Hills Supper Club fire SOUTHGATE, KY, MAY 1977
- 217 deaths, mid-air plane collision NANTUCKET ISLAND, MA, OCTOBER 1999
- 361 deaths, coal mine explosion MONONGHA, WV, DECEMBER 1907
- 695 deaths, tornadoes MO, IL, IN, MARCH 1925
- 273 deaths, coal mine explosion MATHER, PA, MAY 1928
- 492 deaths, Cocoanut Grove night club fire BOSTON, MA, NOVEMBER 1942
- 272 deaths, aircraft crash during takeoff CHICAGO, IL, MAY 1979
- 235 deaths, tornadoes ALABAMA, APRIL 2011

Legend:

- Hurricane
- Fire
- Explosion
- Flood
- Winter storm
- Tornado
- Airplane incident
- Earthquake

[a]Timeline does not include epidemics or acts of terrorism. Because of space limitations, only a sample of disasters resulting in 100 or more fatalities are included.
Source: Info Please: www.infoplease.com, retrieved June 27, 2014; the National Centers for Environmental Prediction; U.S. Geological Survey; and the National Fire Protection Association.

Injuries may be divided into three broad groups – unintentional, intentional, and undetermined intent. Most of *Injury Facts* presents data on unintentional injuries. This page and the next two present data on intentional injuries.

Under the World Health Organization's Safe Communities initiative, for which the National Safety Council is the affiliate support center in the United States, injury prevention is not limited to unintentional injuries. Data on intentional injuries are presented here to support Safe Communities and to provide context to the unintentional-injury data provided in *Injury Facts*.

Intentional injuries may be divided into four subgroups – intentional self-harm (suicide), assault (homicide), legal intervention, and operations of war. The diagram below illustrates the injury groupings and shows the death totals for 2011.

Injury deaths by intent, United States, 2011

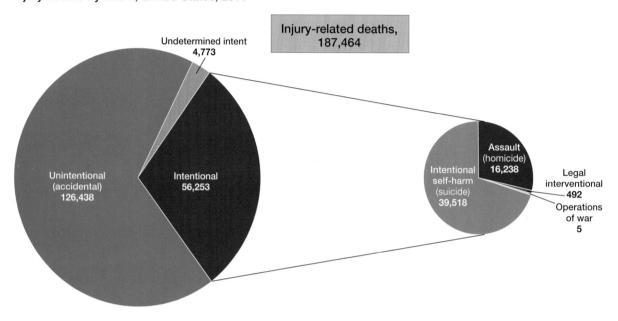

Intentional self-harm includes suicide and attempted suicide by purposely self-inflicted poisoning or injury. The most common methods of intentional self-harm that result in death are firearms; hanging, strangulation, and suffocation; and poisoning.

Assault includes homicide and injuries inflicted by another person with intent to injure or kill (excluding legal intervention and operations of war). The most common means of homicide are firearms; sharp objects; and hanging, strangulation, and suffocation.

Legal intervention includes legal execution. Operations of war include injuries to military personnel and civilians caused by war and civil insurrection. The death must have occurred in the United States. In the vital statistics system, war deaths (and other deaths) occurring outside the United States are counted by the country in which they occurred.

The three most frequent causes of injury death are also among the top 15 causes of all deaths in the United States in 2011. Unintentional (accidental) injuries ranked 5th, intentional self-harm (suicide) ranked 10th, and assault (homicide) ranked 13th.

Intentional self-harm ranked as high as second (after unintentional injuries) for people ages 14-34, and ranked third for those 12 and 13. Suicide deaths were highest at age 51 (951) and ranked fifth at this age after cancer, heart disease, unintentional injuries, and chronic liver disease. Assault ranked as high as second (after unintentional injuries) for people 18-20 years old. It ranked third among people 1, 2, 4, 16, 17, and 21-30 years old. Homicide deaths were highest at age 22 (629). For people 16-30 years old, unintentional, homicide, and suicide are the three leading causes of death. The graph below shows the number of deaths due to injuries by single year of age from 0 to 100.

Injury deaths by age, United States, 2011

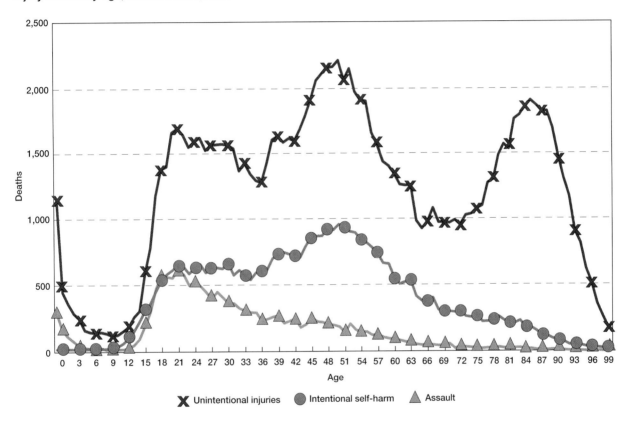

Source: National Safety Council analysis of National Center for Health Statistics–Mortality Data for 2011, as compiled from data provided by the 57 vital statistics jurisdictions through the Vital Statistics Cooperative Program.

Males have higher death rates than females for injuries of all intents. Males also have higher nonfatal injury rates than females for unintentional injuries and assault. Females, however, have a higher injury rate than males for intentional self-harm.

Death and nonfatal injury rates by intent and sex, United States, 2011

Sex	Deaths per 100,000 population			Nonfatal injuries per 100,000 population		
	Unintentional	Homicide	Suicide	Unintentional	Assault	Self-harm
Both sexes	40.6	5.2	12.7	9,636	569	157
Males	51.7	8.3	20.2	10,490	703	132
Females	29.8	2.2	5.4	8,809	439	181
Ratio of male to female	1.7	3.8	3.8	1.2	1.6	0.7

Source: National Safety Council analysis of National Center for Health Statistics (NCHS) – Mortality Data for 2011, as compiled from data provided by the 57 vital statistics jurisdictions through the Vital Statistics Cooperative Program. Rates are National Safety Council estimates based on data from NCHS and the U.S. Census Bureau.

Unintentional and Intentional Injury Trends

The graph below shows the trends from 1992 to 2011 in injury deaths and death rates. Unintentional-injury-related deaths and death rates increased by 50.6% and 24.0%, respectively. Suicide deaths increased 29.6%, while the death rate increased 6.7%. Homicide deaths and death rates decreased 35.4% and 46.8%, respectively, over the 1992-2011 period. Age-adjusted death rates, which remove the effects of the changing age distribution of the population, increased 17.5% for unintentional injuries, increased 3.1% for suicide, and decreased 44.1% for homicide.

Injury deaths and death rates, United States, 1992-2011

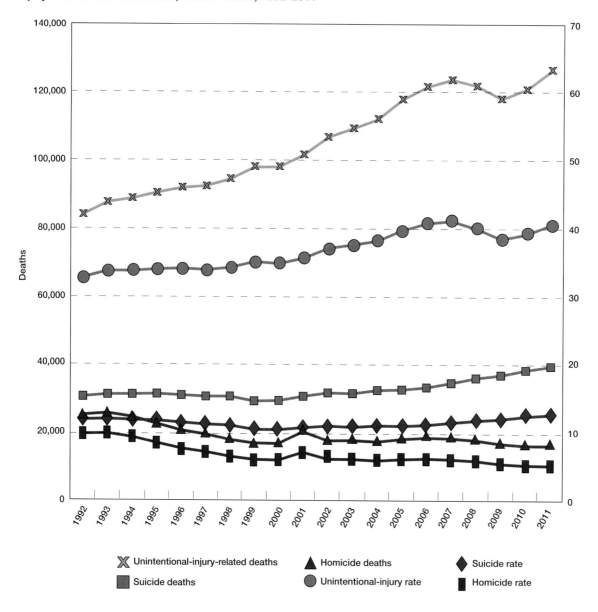

*Deaths per 100,000 population.
Source: National Safety Council analysis of National Center for Health Statistics (NCHS)–Mortality Data for 2011, as compiled from data provided by the 57 vital statistics jurisdictions through the Vital Statistics Cooperative Program. Rates are National Safety Council estimates based on data from NCHS and the U.S. Census Bureau.
Cross-reference: See page 155 for additional information on firearm related deaths.*

While you make a 10-minute safety speech, two people in the United States will be killed and about 753 will suffer an injury severe enough to require a consultation with a medical professional.[a] Costs will amount to $15,610,000. On average, 15 unintentional-injury-related deaths and about 4,520 medically consulted injuries occur every hour during the year. Deaths and medically consulted injuries by class occurred in the nation at the following rates in 2013:

Deaths and medically consulted injuries by class, 2013

| Class | Severity | One every ... | Number per ... | | | 2013 total |
			Hour	Day	Week	
All	Deaths	4 minutes	15	358	2,520	130,800
	Injuries[a]	1 second	4,520	108,500	761,500	39,600,000
Motor vehicle	Deaths	15 minutes	4	97	680	35,500
	Injuries	7 seconds	490	11,800	82,700	4,300,000
Work	Deaths	141 minutes	<1	10	70	3,783
	Injuries	7 seconds	550	13,200	92,300	4,800,000
Workers off the job	Deaths	10 minutes	6	147	1,030	53,600
	Injuries	2 seconds	1,580	37,800	265,400	13,800,000
Home	Deaths	8 minutes	8	181	1,270	66,000
	Injuries	2 second	2,270	54,500	382,700	19,900,000
Public non-motor vehicle	Deaths	19 minutes	3	75	520	27,200
	Injuries	3 seconds	1,220	29,300	205,800	10,700,000

Source: National Safety Council estimates.
[a]Starting with the 2011 edition of Injury Facts, the National Safety Council adopted the definition of "medically consulted injuries" to replace "disabling injuries." For a full description of medically consulted injuries, please see the Technical Appendix.

Deaths every hour...

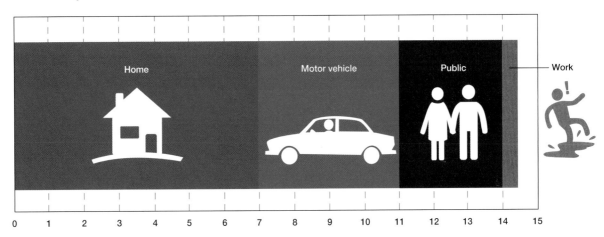

An unintentional-injury-related death occurs every four minutes.

Children and Adolescents

■ *Motor vehicle crashes are the leading cause of injury-related deaths among children.*

Unintentional injuries are a major public health concern affecting children and adolescents in the United States. They are the underlying cause of death in nearly 4 out of 10 childhood mortality cases for people 1-19 years old, and about 41% of the deaths among 15- to 19-year-olds.

Fatal injuries in the first year of life numbered 1,167 in 2011, or approximately 29 deaths per 100,000 population. Mechanical suffocation constituted the majority (71%) of all injury-related mortality cases for infants. Motor vehicle crashes were the second leading cause of injury mortality. In addition, 290 infant deaths that year were attributed to homicide (for more information on intentional injuries, see pages 34-36).

In the second year of life, the risk of fatal injury is reduced by more than half. In 2011, 458 fatal injury cases, or about 11 deaths per 100,000 population, were recorded among 1-year-old children. Drowning was the leading cause of injury death in this age group, followed by motor vehicle crashes.

In the following three-year period (ages 2-4) the injury mortality rate dropped even lower, averaging about 8 deaths per 100,000 population in 2011. Drowning was the leading cause

for 2-year-olds, followed by motor vehicle crashes and fire, flames, or smoke. For 3- and 4-year-olds, motor vehicle crashes were the number one cause of injury mortality, followed by drowning and fires, flames, or smoke.

From the age of 5 to early adolescence (ages 12-14), the injury mortality rate shows a general U-shaped pattern, reaching its lowest level at around age 10. Motor vehicle crashes, unintentional drowning, and incidents related to fire, flames, or smoke were the leading causes of injury mortality for children 5-14 years old in 2011.

Teens (15-19 years) made up 27% of the U.S. population between the ages of 1 and 19 and 59% of all injury mortality cases in that age group. Most importantly, about 67% of teen injury deaths are attributed to motor vehicle crashes. Of the 4,298 injury deaths among teens in 2011, 2,863 occurred in crashes. That same year, the injury mortality rate for 19-year-olds was about 31 deaths per 100,000 population.

For all children and adolescents younger than 19, the injury mortality rate by age can be described as a J-shaped relationship, peaking during infancy and again in the late teen years.

Unintentional injury deaths by event, ages 0-19, United States, 2011

Age	Population (000)	Unintentional injury deaths										
		Total	Rates[a]	Motor vehicle	Drowning	Poisoning	Fire, flames, or smoke	Mechanical suffocation	Firearms	Falls	Choking[b]	All Other
<1 year	3,997	1,167	29.2	95	52	16	22	825	4	12	71	70
1-19 years	78,849	7,310	9.3	4,169	918	823	299	150	136	127	123	565
1 year	3,969	458	11.5	134	163	12	26	39	0	6	32	46
2 years	3,972	370	9.3	98	134	10	37	12	6	7	26	40
3 years	4,102	295	7.2	94	83	8	26	9	11	4	14	46
4 years	4,122	254	6.2	99	58	4	40	2	8	7	10	26
5 years	4,088	167	4.1	66	40	5	21	2	5	4	4	20
6 years	4,075	152	3.7	82	24	1	17	4	3	1	3	17
7 years	4,083	148	3.6	77	29	1	18	3	3	2	4	11
8 years	4,053	152	3.8	91	20	4	10	5	4	0	0	18
9 years	4,035	142	3.5	78	15	4	15	6	1	2	3	18
10 years	4,134	125	3.0	69	16	5	6	8	2	1	2	16
11 years	4,196	131	3.1	79	12	2	11	5	4	3	3	12
12 years	4,124	160	3.9	83	25	3	13	4	5	3	2	22
13 years	4,122	191	4.6	100	24	8	7	12	5	5	1	29
14 years	4,129	267	6.5	156	30	17	5	4	13	7	2	33
15 years	4,157	313	7.5	213	21	30	5	4	8	7	2	23
16 years	4,245	595	14.0	414	48	57	6	5	11	14	3	37
17 years	4,331	796	18.4	543	57	113	12	13	9	14	4	31
18 years	4,396	1,197	27.2	820	53	217	9	7	20	14	4	53
19 years	4,515	1,397	30.9	873	66	322	15	6	18	26	4	67
0-4 years	20,162	2,544	12.6	520	490	50	151	887	29	36	153	228
5-9 years	20,334	761	3.7	394	128	15	81	20	16	9	14	84
10-14 years	20,705	874	4.2	487	107	35	42	33	29	19	10	112
15-19 years	21,644	4,298	19.9	2,863	245	739	47	35	66	75	17	211

Source: National Safety Council analysis of National Center for Health Statistics (NCHS)–Mortality Data for 2011 as compiled from data provided by the 57 vital statistics jurisdictions through the Vital Statistics Cooperative Program. Rates are National Safety Council estimates based on data from NCHS and the U.S. Census Bureau.

Note: Data do not include "age unknown" cases, which totaled 20 in 2011.

[a]*Deaths per 100,000 population in each age group.*

[b]*Suffocation by inhalation or ingestion of food or other object.*

■ *Injury mortality and fall-related mortality rates increase with age.*

Unintentional injuries cause significant mortality among adults in the United States. In 2011 alone, injuries were responsible for nearly 118,000 deaths among Americans 20 and older.

The leading causes of injury mortality include poisoning, motor vehicle crashes, falls, choking, drowning, and fire, flames and smoke. Poisoning (30%), motor vehicle crashes (26%), and falls (23%), the three leading causes of injury mortality, combined to account for nearly four-fifths of all fatal injuries sustained by adults aged 20 and older in 2011.

Age plays an important role in the occurrence of injuries. Motor vehicle crashes are the leading cause of injury mortality through the early to mid-20s. Starting with the mid-20s, incidences of poisoning become the leading cause of death, with prevalence peaking in the mid to late-40s. Beginning in the early 60s, motor vehicle crashes once again take over as the leading cause of injury mortality until superseded by falls beginning in the early 70s.

The increase in the incidence of fatal falls appears to be the driving force behind a surge in the overall injury mortality rate in later life. The highest fall mortality rates occur among adults beginning at age 70 and older. As the table below illustrates, the number of injury-related deaths per 100,000 population in 2011 increased from 52 for 70- to 74-year-olds to 423 for 90- to 94-year-olds – over an eightfold increase.

A 2013 report from the National Trauma Data Bank (NTDB) summarized data from 833,311 records of fatal and nonfatal incidents with valid trauma diagnoses submitted to the NTDB from over 800 hospitals in 2012.[a] By selected mechanism of injury, falls were the only injury type that showed consistent increases in the number of incidents from younger to older adults, increasing nearly 700% from young adults age 20-24 to those older than 84. The motor vehicle traffic; struck by or against; transport, other; firearm; and cut/pierce categories all increased in incidence from the 20-24 to the 25-34 age group, but then generally declined with age, with the average decline in the number of incidents averaging 93% from the 20-24 age group to the older than 84 age group. Case fatality rates generally increased with age for all of the selected mechanisms of injury, with the greatest increases from the youngest to oldest adults observed for the struck by or against, transport or other, and fall categories.

[a]*National Trauma Data Bank 2013 – Annual Report, accessed 7/24/14 at http://www.facs.org/trauma/ntdb/pdf/ntdb-annual-report-2013.pdf*

Unintentional-injury-related deaths by event, age 20 or older, United States, 2011

| Age | Population (000) | Unintentional injury deaths | | | | | | | | | | | |
		Total	Rates[a]	Poisoning	Motor vehicle	Falls	Choking[b]	Drowning	Fire, flames, or smoke	Natural heat or cold	Mechanical suffocation	Firearms	All other
20-24	22,154	8,032	36.3	2,701	4,242	130	31	298	88	25	44	64	409
25-29	21,280	7,961	37.4	3,702	3,207	116	42	255	86	30	37	53	433
30-34	20,511	7,557	36.8	3,950	2,535	163	49	187	88	50	48	33	454
35-39	19,594	7,031	35.9	3,700	2,203	200	65	208	88	35	43	37	452
40-44	21,034	8,199	39.0	4,375	2,407	324	72	206	112	57	60	29	557
45-49	22,158	10,107	45.6	5,266	2,639	559	180	238	184	97	62	46	836
50-54	22,560	10,642	47.2	5,113	2,846	809	227	241	229	132	67	41	937
55-59	20,256	8,556	42.2	3,429	2,356	949	272	232	264	119	48	35	852
60-64	17,807	6,602	37.1	1,619	2,025	1,192	290	180	249	128	34	29	856
65-69	12,874	5,020	39.0	664	1,530	1,311	311	137	198	97	28	24	720
70-74	9,608	4,994	52.0	281	1,383	1,838	341	121	191	91	13	22	713
75-79	7,389	5,867	79.4	195	1,247	2,755	447	92	191	92	21	17	810
80-84	5,787	8,226	142.1	205	1,164	4,632	670	103	210	83	18	13	1,128
85-89	3,706	9,361	252.6	163	826	5,921	741	52	152	82	17	4	1,403
90-94	1,571	6,644	422.9	58	365	4,386	520	27	68	70	11	2	1,137
95-99	398	2,628	660.3	14	53	1,737	209	7	20	26	8	1	553
100 and older	62	518	835.5	1	7	321	47	1	4	1	0	1	135
20 and older	228,749	117,945	51.6	35,436	31,035	27,343	4,514	2,585	2,422	1,215	559	451	12,385
25 and older	206,595	109,913	53.2	32,735	26,793	27,213	4,483	2,287	2,334	1,190	515	387	11,976
35 and older	164,804	94,395	57.3	25,083	21,051	26,934	4,392	1,845	2,160	1,110	430	301	11,089
45 and older	124,176	79,165	63.8	17,008	16,441	26,410	4,255	1,431	1,960	1,018	327	235	10,080
55 and older	79,458	58,416	73.5	6,629	10,956	25,042	3,848	952	1,547	789	198	148	8,307
65 and older	41,395	43,258	104.5	1,581	6,575	22,901	3,286	540	1,034	542	116	84	6,599
75 and older	18,913	33,244	175.8	636	3,662	19,752	2,634	282	645	354	75	38	5,166

Source: National Safety Council analysis of National Center for Health Statistics--Mortality Data for 2011, as compiled from data provided by the 57 vital statistics jurisdictions through the Vital Statistics Cooperative Program. Rates are National Safety Council estimates based on data from NCHS and the U.S. Census Bureau.
Note: Data do not include "age unknown" cases, which totaled 20 in 2011.
[a]*Deaths per 100,000 population in each age group.*
[b]*Suffocation by inhalation or ingestion of food or other object.*

The table on the following pages was prepared in response to frequent inquiries asking questions such as, "What are the odds of being killed by lightning?" or "What are the chances of dying in a plane crash?"

The odds given in the table are statistical averages over the whole U.S. population and do not necessarily reflect the chances of death for a particular person from a particular external cause. Any individual's odds of dying from various external causes are affected by the activities in which they participate, where they live and drive, what kind of work they do, among other factors.

The table has four columns. The first column gives the manner of injury such as motor-vehicle crash, fall, fire, etc. The second column gives the total number of deaths nationwide due to the manner of injury in 2011 (the latest year for which data are available). The third column gives the odds of dying in one year due to the manner of injury. The fourth column gives the lifetime odds of dying from the manner of injury. Statements about the odds or chances of dying from a given cause of death may be made as follows:

- The odds of dying from (manner of injury) in 2011 were 1 in (value given in the one-year odds column).
- The life-time odds of dying from (manner of injury) for a person born in 2011 were 1 in (value given in the lifetime odds column).

For example, referring to the first line of the table:
- The odds of dying from an injury in 2011 were 1 in 1,640.
- The lifetime odds of dying from an injury for a person born in 2011 were 1 in 21.

The one year odds are approximated by dividing the 2011 population (311,591,917) by the number of deaths. The lifetime odds are approximated by dividing the one-year odds by the life expectancy of a person born in 2011 (78.7 years). Please note that odds based on less than 20 deaths are likely to be unstable from year to year and are therefore not included in the table and figure on the following pages.

The figure on page 43 visually represents the lifetime odds of death for selected causes from the odds table. The total lifetime odds of death from any cause are 1 in 1, or 100%, and thus the largest shaded area representing the total odds actually extends off the page to infinity. The circles for selected causes are sized according to their relative lifetime probabilities, with the least probable event – death from lightning – depicted using the smallest circle.

Source: National Safety Council estimates based on data from National Center for Health Statistics—Mortality Data for 2011, as compiled from data provided by the 57 vital statistics jurisdictions through the Vital Statistics Cooperative Program. Population and life expectancy data are from the U.S. Census Bureau. Deaths are classified on the basis of the Tenth Revision of the World Health Organization's "The International Classification of Diseases" (ICD). Numbers following titles refer to External Cause of Morbidity and Mortality classifications in ICD-10.

The Odds of Dying From... (cont.)

Odds of death due to injury, United States, 2011[a]

Type of accident or manner of injury	Deaths	One-year odds	Lifetime odds
All external causes of mortality, V01-Y89, *U01, *U03[b]	**190,048**	**1,640**	**21**
Deaths due to unintentional (accidental) injuries, V01-X59, Y85-Y86	**126,438**	**2,464**	**31**
Transport accidents, V01-V99, Y85	**38,023**	**8,195**	**104**
Motor vehicle accidents, V02-V04, V09.0, V09.2, V12-V14, V19.0-V19.2, V19.4-V19.6, V20-V79, V80.3-V80.5, V81.0-V81.1, V82.0-V82.1, V83-V86, V87.0-V87.8, V88.0-V88.8, V89.0, V89.2	**35,303**	**8,826**	**112**
Pedestrian, V01-V09	5,622	55,424	704
Pedalcyclist, V10-V19	873	356,921	4,535
Motorcycle rider, V20-V29	4,344	71,729	911
Occupant of three-wheeled motor vehicle, V30-V39	4	(c)	(c)
Car occupant, V40-V49	8,415	37,028	470
Occupant of pick-up truck or van, V50-V59	1,929	161,530	2,052
Occupant of heavy transport vehicle, V60-V69	273	1,141,362	14,503
Bus occupant, V70-V79	50	6,231,838	79,185
Animal rider or occupant of animal-drawn vehicle, V80	129	2,415,441	30,692
Occupant of railway train or railway vehicle, V81	23	13,547,475	172,141
Occupant of streetcar, V82	1	(c)	(c)
Other and unspecified land transport accidents, V83-V89	14,590	21,357	271
Occupant of special industrial vehicle, V83	*2*	*(c)*	*(c)*
Occupant of special agricultural vehicle, V84	*120*	*2,596,599*	*32,994*
Occupant of special construction vehicle, V85	*15*	*(c)*	*(c)*
Occupant of all-terrain or other off-road motor vehicle, V86	*913*	*341,284*	*4,337*
Other and unspecified person, V87-V89	*13,540*	*23,013*	*292*
Water transport accidents, V90-V94	533	584,600	7,428
Drowning, V90, V92	*405*	*769,363*	*9,776*
Other and unspecified injuries, V91, V93-V94	*128*	*2,434,312*	*30,932*
Air and space transport accidents, V95-V97	494	630,753	8,015
Other and unspecified transport accidents and sequelae, V98-V99, Y85	743	419,370	5,329
Other specified transport accidents, V98	*0*	*(c)*	*(c)*
Unspecified transport accidents, V99	*0*	*(c)*	*(c)*
Nontransport unintentional (accidental) injuries, W00-X59, Y86	**88,415**	**3,524**	**45**
Falls, W00-W19	27,483	11,338	144
Fall on same level from slipping, tripping, and stumbling, W01	*800*	*389,490*	*4,949*
Other fall on same level, W00, W02-W03, W18	*8,661*	*35,976*	*457*
Fall involving bed, chair, or other furniture, W06-W08	*1,113*	*279,957*	*3,557*
Fall on and from stairs and steps, W10	*2,101*	*148,306*	*1,884*
Fall on and from ladder or scaffolding, W11-W12	*465*	*670,090*	*8,514*
Fall from out of or through building or structure, W13	*452*	*689,363*	*8,759*
Other fall from one level to another, W09, W14-W17	*623*	*500,148*	*6,355*
Other and unspecified fall, W04-W05, W19	*13,268*	*23,484*	*298*
Exposure to inanimate mechanical forces, W20-W49	2,496	124,837	1,586
Struck by or striking against object, W20-W22	*827*	*376,774*	*4,787*
Caught between objects, W23	*137*	*2,274,394*	*28,900*
Contact with machinery, W24, W30-W31	*610*	*510,806*	*6,491*
Contact with sharp objects, W25-W29	*106*	*2,939,546*	*37,351*
Firearms discharge, W32-W34	*591*	*527,228*	*6,699*
Explosion and rupture of pressurized devices, W35-W38	*19*	*(c)*	*(c)*
Fireworks discharge, W39	*5*	*(c)*	*(c)*
Explosion of other materials, W40	*118*	*2,640,609*	*33,553*
Foreign body entering through skin or natural orifice, W44-W45	*31*	*10,051,352*	*127,717*
Other and unspecified inanimate mechanical forces, W41-W43, W49	*52*	*5,992,152*	*76,139*
Exposure to animate mechanical forces, W50-W64	130	2,396,861	30,456
Struck by or against another person, W50-W52	*10*	*(c)*	*(c)*
Bitten or struck by dog, W54	*34*	*9,164,468*	*116,448*
Bitten or struck by other mammals, W53, W55	*72*	*4,327,666*	*54,989*
Bitten or stung by nonvenomous insect and other arthropods, W57	*7*	*(c)*	*(c)*
Bitten or crushed by other reptiles, W59	*0*	*(c)*	*(c)*
Other and unspecified animate mechanical forces, W56, W58, W60, W64	*7*	*(c)*	*(c)*
Accidental drowning and submersion, W65-W74	3,556	87,624	1,113
Drowning and submersion while in or falling into bath-tub, W65-W66	*431*	*722,951*	*9,186*
Drowning and submersion while in or falling into swimming-pool, W67-W68	*652*	*477,902*	*6,072*
Drowning and submersion while in or falling into natural water, W69-W70	*1,782*	*174,855*	*2,222*
Other and unspecified drowning and submersion, W73-W74	*691*	*450,929*	*5,730*
Other accidental threats to breathing, W75-W84	6,242	49,919	634
Accidental suffocation and strangulation in bed, W75	*692*	*450,277*	*5,721*
Other accidental hanging and strangulation, W76	*233*	*1,337,304*	*16,992*
Threat to breathing due to cave-in, falling earth and other substances, W77	*16*	*(c)*	*(c)*
Inhalation of gastric contents, W78	*327*	*952,880*	*12,108*
Inhalation and ingestion of food causing obstruction of respiratory tract, W79	*1,173*	*265,637*	*3,375*
Inhalation and ingestion of other objects causing obstruction of respiratory tract, W80	*3,208*	*97,130*	*1,234*
Confined to or trapped in a low-oxygen environment, W81	*4*	*(c)*	*(c)*
Other and unspecified threats to breathing, W83-W84	*589*	*529,019*	*6,722*

See source and footnotes on page 42.

The Odds of Dying From... (cont.)

Odds of death due to injury, United States, 2011[a] (cont.)

Type of accident or manner of injury	Deaths	One-year odds	Lifetime odds
Exposure to electric current, radiation, temperature, and pressure, W85-W99	324	961,703	12,220
Electric transmission lines, W85	72	4,327,666	54,989
Other and unspecified electric current, W86-W87	236	1,320,305	16,776
Radiation, W88-W91	0	0	0
Excessive heat or cold of man-made origin, W92-W93	4	(c)	(c)
High and low air pressure and changes in air pressure, W94	12	(c)	(c)
Other and unspecified man-made environmental factors, W99	0	0	0
Exposure to smoke, fire, and flames, X00-X09	2,746	113,471	1,442
Uncontrolled fire in building or structure, X00	2,176	143,195	1,820
Uncontrolled fire not in building or structure, X01	40	7,789,798	98,981
Controlled fire in building or structure, X02	19	(c)	(c)
Controlled fire not in building or structure, X03	38	8,199,787	104,190
Ignition of highly flammable material, X04	42	7,418,855	94,268
Ignition or melting of nightwear, X05	4	(c)	(c)
Ignition or melting of other clothing and apparel, X06	83	3,754,119	47,702
Other and unspecified smoke fire and flames, X08-X09	344	905,790	11,509
Contact with heat and hot substances, X10-X19	67	4,650,626	59,093
Contact with hot tap-water, X11	27	11,540,441	146,638
Other and unspecified heat and hot substances, X10, X12-X19	40	7,789,798	98,981
Contact with venomous animals and plants, X20-X29	94	3,314,808	42,120
Contact with venomous snakes and lizards, X20	9	(c)	(c)
Contact with venomous spiders, X21	3	(c)	(c)
Contact with hornets, wasps and bees, X23	71	4,388,619	55,764
Contact with other and unspecified venomous animal or plant, X22, X24-X29	11	(c)	(c)
Exposure to forces of nature, X30-X39	1,944	160,284	2,037
Exposure to excessive natural heat, X30	587	530,821	6,745
Exposure to excessive natural cold, X31	672	463,678	5,892
Lightning, X33	24	12,982,997	164,968
Earthquake and other earth movements, X34-X36	22	14,163,269	179,965
Cataclysmic storm, X37	584	533,548	6,780
Flood, X38	25	12,463,677	158,369
Exposure to other and unspecified forces of nature, X32, X39	30	10,386,397	131,975
Accidental poisoning by and exposure to noxious substances, X40-X49	36,280	8,589	109
Nonopioid analgesics, antipyretics, and antirheumatics, X40	220	1,416,327	17,997
Antiepileptic, sedative-hypnotic, antiparkinsonism, and psychotropic drugs n.e.c., X41	2,080	149,804	1,903
Narcotics and psychodysleptics [hallucinogens] n.e.c., X42	13,214	23,580	300
Other and unspecified drugs, medicaments, and biologicals, X43-X44	17,557	17,747	226
Alcohol, X45	2,155	144,590	1,837
Gases and vapors, X46-X47	866	359,806	4,572
Other and unspecified chemicals and noxious substances, X48-X49	188	1,657,404	21,060
Overexertion, travel, and privation, X50-X57	35	8,902,626	113,121
Accidental exposure to other and unspecified factors and sequelae, X58-X59, Y86	7,018	44,399	564
Intentional self-harm, X60-X84, Y87.0, *U03	**39,518**	**7,885**	**100**
Intentional self-poisoning, X60-X69	6,564	47,470	603
Intentional self-harm by hanging, strangulation, and suffocation, X70	9,913	31,433	399
Intentional self-harm by firearm, X72-X74	19,990	15,587	198
Other and unspecified means and sequelae, X71, X75-X84, Y87.0	3,051	102,128	1,298
Terrorism, *U03	0	(c)	(c)
Assault, X85-Y09, Y87.1, *U01	**16,238**	**19,189**	**244**
Assault by firearm, X93-X95	11,068	28,153	358
Assault by sharp object, X99	1,797	173,396	2,203
Other and unspecified means and sequelae, X85-X92, X96-X98, Y00-Y09, Y87.1	3,373	92,378	1,174
Terrorism, *U01	0	(c)	(c)
Event of undetermined intent, Y10-Y34, Y87.2, Y89.9	**4,773**	**65,282**	**830**
Poisoning, Y10-Y19	3,098	100,578	1,278
Hanging, strangulation, and suffocation, Y20	151	2,063,523	26,220
Drowning and submersion, Y21	287	1,085,686	13,795
Firearm discharge, Y22-Y24	248	1,256,419	15,965
Exposure to smoke, fire, and flames, Y26	111	2,807,134	35,669
Falling, jumping, or pushed from a high place, Y30	62	5,025,676	63,859
Other and unspecified means and sequelae, Y25, Y27-Y29, Y31-Y34, Y87.2, Y89.9	816	381,853	4,852
Legal intervention, Y35, Y89.0	**492**	**633,317**	**8,047**
Legal intervention involving firearm discharge, Y35.0	454	686,326	8,721
Legal execution, Y35.5	31	10,051,352	127,717
Other and unspecified means and sequelae, Y35.1-Y35.4, Y35.6-Y35.7, Y89.0	7	(c)	(c)
Operations of war and sequelae, Y36, Y89.1	**5**	**(c)**	**(c)**
Complications of medical and surgical care and sequelae, Y40-Y84, Y88.0-Y88.3	**2,584**	**120,585**	**1,532**

Source: National Center for Health Statistics–Mortality Data for 2011, as compiled from data provided by the 57 vital statistics jurisdictions through the Vital Statistics Cooperative Program. Deaths are classified on the basis of the Tenth Revision of The International Classification of Diseases *(ICD-10), which became effective in 1999.*

Note: "n.e.c." means not elsewhere classified.

[a]Latest official figures.

[b]Numbers following titles refer to external cause of injury and poisoning classifications in ICD-10.

[c]Rates based on less than 20 deaths are likely to be unstable from year to year and therefore are not included.

The Odds of Dying From... (cont.)

Lifetime odds of death for selected causes, United States, 2011[a]

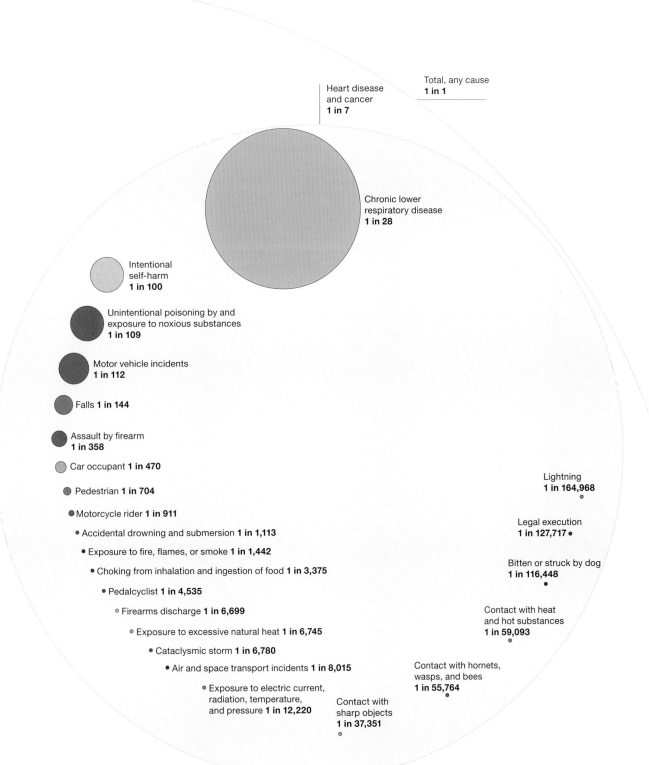

Total, any cause
1 in 1

Heart disease
and cancer
1 in 7

Chronic lower
respiratory disease
1 in 28

Intentional
self-harm
1 in 100

Unintentional poisoning by and
exposure to noxious substances
1 in 109

Motor vehicle incidents
1 in 112

Falls **1 in 144**

Assault by firearm
1 in 358

Car occupant **1 in 470**

Pedestrian **1 in 704**

Motorcycle rider **1 in 911**

Accidental drowning and submersion **1 in 1,113**

Exposure to fire, flames, or smoke **1 in 1,442**

Choking from inhalation and ingestion of food **1 in 3,375**

Pedalcyclist **1 in 4,535**

Firearms discharge **1 in 6,699**

Exposure to excessive natural heat **1 in 6,745**

Cataclysmic storm **1 in 6,780**

Air and space transport incidents **1 in 8,015**

Exposure to electric current,
radiation, temperature,
and pressure **1 in 12,220**

Contact with
sharp objects
1 in 37,351

Lightning
1 in 164,968

Legal execution
1 in 127,717

Bitten or struck by dog
1 in 116,448

Contact with heat
and hot substances
1 in 59,093

Contact with hornets,
wasps, and bees
1 in 55,764

Source: National Safety Council estimates based on data from National Center for Health Statistics–Mortality Data for 2011 as compiled from data provided by the 57 vital statistics jurisdictions through the Vital Statistics Cooperative Program. Population and life expectancy data are from the U.S. Census Bureau. For mortality figures, estimated one-year and lifetime odds, and external cause classification codes based on the Tenth Revision of the World Health Organization's The International Classification of Diseases (ICD) for the causes illustrated, see table on pages 41-42.
[a]*See footnotes on page 42.*

Trends in Unintentional-Injury-Related Death Rates

Age-adjusted rates, which eliminate the effect of shifts in the age distribution of the population, decreased 61% from 1912 to 2013 – from 100.4 to 39.5 deaths per 100,000 population. The adjusted rates, which are shown in the graphs on the opposite page, are standardized to the year 2000 standard U.S. population. The break in the lines at 1948 shows the estimated effect of changes in the International Classification of Diseases (ICD). The break in the lines at 1992 resulted from the adoption of the Bureau of Labor Statistics Census of Fatal Occupational Injuries for work-related deaths. Another change in the ICD in 1999 also affects the trends. See the Technical Appendix for comparability.

The table below shows the change in the age distribution of the population since 1910.

The age-adjusted death rate for all unintentional injuries increased and decreased significantly several times during the period from 1910 to 1940 (top of facing page). Since 1940, there were some setbacks, such as in the early 1960s, but the overall trend through the early 1990s was positive. The age-adjusted death rates for unintentional-injury-related deaths in the work and home classes declined fairly steadily since they became available in the late 1920s, and the home class rates have increased since the early 1990s. The rates in the public class declined for three decades, rose in the 1960s, and then continued declining until leveling out in the 1990s to present. The age-adjusted motor vehicle death rate rose steadily from 1910 to the late 1930s as the automobile became more widely used. A sharp drop in use occurred during World War II and a sharp rise in rates occurred in the 1960s, with death rates reflecting economic cycles and a long-term downward trend since then.

United States population, selected years

Year	All ages	Younger than 15	15-24	25-44	45-64	65 or older
Number (in thousands)						
1910	91,973[a]	29,499	18,121	26,810	13,424	3,950
2000[b]	274,634	58,964	38,077	81,892	60,991	34,710
2013	316,160	61,110	43,960	83,288	83,084	44,718
Percent						
1910	100.0%	32.1%	19.7%	29.2%	14.6%	4.3%
2000[b]	100.0%	21.5%	13.9%	29.8%	22.2%	12.6%
2013	100.0%	19.3%	13.9%	26.3%	26.3%	14.1%

Looking at individual leading causes (bottom chart on next page), at the turn of the last century falls were the leading cause of unintentional-injury-related death, while motor vehicle and poisoning deaths were only minor concerns. Today, although falls continue to be a major concern, poisonings and motor vehicle incidents have become the two leading causes of unintentional-injury-related deaths.

Source: For 1910: U.S. Census Bureau. (1960). Historical Statistics of the United States, Colonial Times to 1957. Series A 71-85. Washington, DC: U.S. Government Printing Office. For 2000: Anderson, R.N., & Rosenberg, H.M. (1998). Age standardization of death rates: Implementation of the year 2000 standard. National Vital Statistics Reports, Issue 47, No. 3 p. 13. For 2013: U.S. Census Bureau.
[a]Includes 169,000 people with age unknown.
[b]This is the population used for standardization (age adjustment) and differs slightly from the actual 2000 population, which totaled 275,306,000.

Age-adjusted death rates by class of injury, United States, 1910-2013

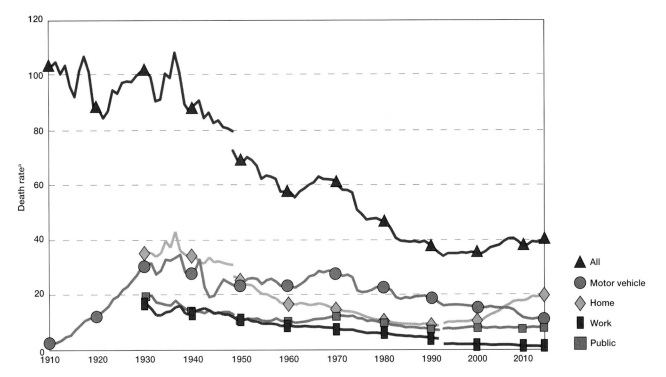

- ▲ All
- ● Motor vehicle
- ◆ Home
- ■ Work
- ■ Public

ᵃ Deaths per 100,000 population adjusted to the year 2000 standard population. The break at 1948 shows the estimated effect of classification changes. The break at 1992 is due to the adoption of the Bureau of Labor Statistics' Census of Fatal Occupational injuries for work-related deaths.

Age-adjusted death rates by leading cause of unintentional injury, United States, 1910-2013

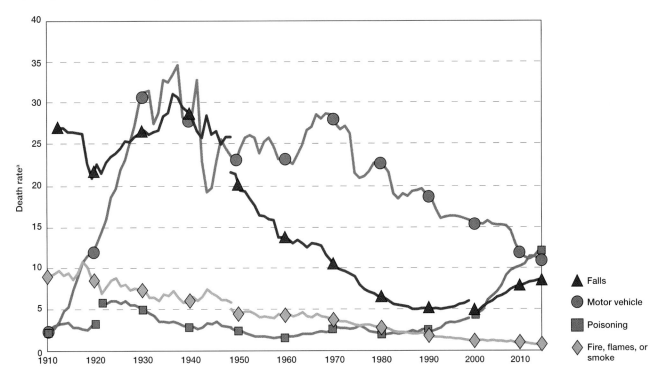

- ▲ Falls
- ● Motor vehicle
- ■ Poisoning
- ◆ Fire, flames, or smoke

ᵃ Deaths per 100,000 population adjusted to the year 2000 standard population. Breaks in graph lines signify changes in fatal injury coding.

Principal Classes of Unintentional-Injury-Related Deaths

Principal classes of unintentional-injury-related deaths, United States, 1903-2013

Year	Total[a] Deaths	Rate[b]	Motor vehicle Deaths	Rate[b]	Work Deaths	Rate[b]	Home Deaths	Rate[b]	Public non-motor vehicle Deaths	Rate[b]
1903	70,600	87.2	(c)	–	(c)	–	(c)	–	(c)	–
1904	71,500	86.6	(c)	–	(c)	–	(c)	–	(c)	–
1905	70,900	84.2	(c)	–	(c)	–	(c)	–	(c)	–
1906	80,000	93.2	400	0.5	(c)	–	(c)	–	(c)	–
1907	81,900	93.6	700	0.8	(c)	–	(c)	–	(c)	–
1908	72,300	81.2	800	0.9	(c)	–	(c)	–	(c)	–
1909	72,700	80.1	1,300	1.4	(c)	–	(c)	–	(c)	–
1910	77,900	84.4	1,900	2.0	(c)	–	(c)	–	(c)	–
1911	79,300	84.7	2,300	2.5	(c)	–	(c)	–	(c)	–
1912	78,400	82.5	3,100	3.3	(c)	–	(c)	–	(c)	–
1913	82,500	85.5	4,200	4.4	(c)	–	(c)	–	(c)	–
1914	77,000	78.6	4,700	4.8	(c)	–	(c)	–	(c)	–
1915	76,200	76.7	6,600	6.6	(c)	–	(c)	–	(c)	–
1916	84,800	84.1	8,200	8.1	(c)	–	(c)	–	(c)	–
1917	90,100	88.2	10,200	10.0	(c)	–	(c)	–	(c)	–
1918	85,100	82.1	10,700	10.3	(c)	–	(c)	–	(c)	–
1919	75,500	71.9	11,200	10.7	(c)	–	(c)	–	(c)	–
1920	75,900	71.2	12,500	11.7	(c)	–	(c)	–	(c)	–
1921	74,000	68.4	13,900	12.9	(c)	–	(c)	–	(c)	–
1922	76,300	69.4	15,300	13.9	(c)	–	(c)	–	(c)	–
1923	84,400	75.7	18,400	16.5	(c)	–	(c)	–	(c)	–
1924	85,600	75.6	19,400	17.1	(c)	–	(c)	–	(c)	–
1925	90,000	78.4	21,900	19.1	(c)	–	(c)	–	(c)	–
1926	91,700	78.7	23,400	20.1	(c)	–	(c)	–	(c)	–
1927	92,700	78.4	25,800	21.8	(c)	–	(c)	–	(c)	–
1928	95,000	79.3	28,000	23.4	19,000	15.8	30,000	24.9	21,000	17.4
1929	98,200	80.8	31,200	25.7	20,000	16.4	30,000	24.6	20,000	16.4
1930	99,100	80.5	32,900	26.7	19,000	15.4	30,000	24.4	20,000	16.3
1931	97,300	78.5	33,700	27.2	17,500	14.1	29,000	23.4	20,000	16.1
1932	89,000	71.3	29,500	23.6	15,000	12.0	29,000	23.2	18,000	14.4
1933	90,932	72.4	31,363	25.0	14,500	11.6	29,500	23.6	18,500	14.7
1934	100,977	79.9	36,101	28.6	16,000	12.7	34,000	26.9	18,000	14.2
1935	99,773	78.4	36,369	28.6	16,500	13.0	32,000	25.2	18,000	14.2
1936	110,052	85.9	38,089	29.7	18,500	14.5	37,000	28.9	19,500	15.2
1937	105,205	81.7	39,643	30.8	19,000	14.8	32,000	24.8	18,000	14.0
1938	93,805	72.3	32,582	25.1	16,000	12.3	31,000	23.9	17,000	13.1
1939	92,623	70.8	32,386	24.7	15,500	11.8	31,000	23.7	16,000	12.2
1940	96,885	73.4	34,501	26.1	17,000	12.9	31,500	23.9	16,500	12.5
1941	101,513	76.3	39,969	30.0	18,000	13.5	30,000	22.5	16,500	12.4
1942	95,889	71.6	28,309	21.1	18,000	13.4	30,500	22.8	16,000	12.0
1943	99,038	73.8	23,823	17.8	17,500	13.0	33,500	25.0	17,000	12.7
1944	95,237	71.7	24,282	18.3	16,000	12.0	32,500	24.5	16,000	12.0
1945	95,918	72.4	28,076	21.2	16,500	12.5	33,500	25.3	16,000	12.1
1946	98,033	70.0	33,411	23.9	16,500	11.8	33,000	23.6	17,500	12.5
1947	99,579	69.4	32,697	22.8	17,000	11.9	34,500	24.1	18,000	12.6
1948 (5th Rev.)[d]	98,001	67.1	32,259	22.1	16,000	11.0	35,000	24.0	17,000	11.6
1948 (6th Rev.)[d]	93,000	63.7	32,259	22.1	16,000	11.0	31,000	21.2	16,000	11.0
1949	90,106	60.6	31,701	21.3	15,000	10.1	31,000	20.9	15,000	10.1
1950	91,249	60.3	34,763	23.0	15,500	10.2	29,000	19.2	15,000	9.9
1951	95,871	62.5	36,996	24.1	16,000	10.4	30,000	19.6	16,000	10.4
1952	96,172	61.8	37,794	24.3	15,000	9.6	30,500	19.6	16,000	10.3
1953	95,032	60.1	37,955	24.0	15,000	9.5	29,000	18.3	16,500	10.4
1954	90,032	55.9	35,586	22.1	14,000	8.7	28,000	17.4	15,500	9.6
1955	93,443	56.9	38,426	23.4	14,200	8.6	28,500	17.3	15,500	9.4
1956	94,780	56.6	39,628	23.7	14,300	8.5	28,000	16.7	16,000	9.6
1957	95,307	55.9	38,702	22.7	14,200	8.3	28,000	16.4	17,500	10.3
1958	90,604	52.3	36,981	21.3	13,300	7.7	26,500	15.3	16,500	9.5
1959	92,080	52.2	37,910	21.5	13,800	7.8	27,000	15.3	16,500	9.3
1960	93,806	52.1	38,137	21.2	13,800	7.7	28,000	15.6	17,000	9.4
1961	92,249	50.4	38,091	20.8	13,500	7.4	27,000	14.8	16,500	9.0
1962	97,139	52.3	40,804	22.0	13,700	7.4	28,500	15.3	17,000	9.2
1963	100,669	53.4	43,564	23.1	14,200	7.5	28,500	15.1	17,500	9.3
1964	105,000	54.9	47,700	25.0	14,200	7.4	28,000	14.6	18,500	9.7
1965	108,004	55.8	49,163	25.4	14,100	7.3	28,500	14.7	19,500	10.1
1966	113,563	58.1	53,041	27.1	14,500	7.4	29,500	15.1	20,000	10.2
1967	113,169	57.3	52,924	26.8	14,200	7.2	29,000	14.7	20,500	10.4
1968	114,864	57.6	54,862	27.5	14,300	7.2	28,000	14.0	21,500	10.8
1969	116,385	57.8	55,791	27.7	14,300	7.1	27,500	13.7	22,500	11.2
1970	114,638	56.2	54,633	26.8	13,800	6.8	27,000	13.2	23,500	11.5
1971	113,439	54.8	54,381	26.3	13,700	6.6	26,500	12.8	23,500	11.4
1972	115,448	55.2	56,278	26.9	14,000	6.7	26,500	12.7	23,500	11.2
1973	115,821	54.8	55,511	26.3	14,300	6.8	26,500	12.5	24,500	11.6

See source and footnotes on page 47.

Principal classes of unintentional-injury-related deaths, United States, 1903-2013 (cont.)

Year	Total[a] Deaths	Total[a] Rate[b]	Motor vehicle Deaths	Motor vehicle Rate[b]	Work Deaths	Work Rate[b]	Home Deaths	Home Rate[b]	Public non-motor vehicle Deaths	Public non-motor vehicle Rate[b]
1974	104,622	49.0	46,402	21.8	13,500	6.3	26,000	12.2	23,000	10.8
1975	103,030	47.8	45,853	21.3	13,000	6.0	25,000	11.6	23,000	10.6
1976	100,761	46.3	47,038	21.6	12,500	5.7	24,000	11.0	21,500	10.0
1977	103,202	47.0	49,510	22.5	12,900	5.9	23,200	10.6	22,200	10.1
1978	105,561	47.5	52,411	23.6	13,100	5.9	22,800	10.3	22,000	9.9
1979	105,312	46.9	53,524	23.8	13,000	5.8	22,500	10.0	21,000	9.4
1980	105,718	46.5	53,172	23.4	13,200	5.8	22,800	10.0	21,300	9.4
1981	100,704	43.9	51,385	22.4	12,500	5.4	21,700	9.5	19,800	8.6
1982	94,082	40.6	45,779	19.8	11,900	5.1	21,200	9.2	19,500	8.4
1983	92,488	39.6	44,452	19.0	11,700	5.0	21,200	9.1	19,400	8.3
1984	92,911	39.4	46,263	19.6	11,500	4.9	21,200	9.0	18,300	7.8
1985	93,457	39.3	45,901	19.3	11,500	4.8	21,600	9.1	18,800	7.9
1986	95,277	39.7	47,865	19.9	11,100	4.6	21,700	9.0	18,700	7.8
1987	95,020	39.2	48,290	19.9	11,300	4.7	21,400	8.8	18,400	7.6
1988	97,100	39.7	49,078	20.1	11,000	4.5	22,700	9.3	18,400	7.5
1989	95,028	38.5	47,575	19.3	10,900	4.4	22,500	9.1	18,200	7.4
1990	91,983	36.9	46,814	18.8	10,100	4.0	21,500	8.6	17,400	7.0
1991	89,347	35.4	43,536	17.3	9,800	3.9	22,100	8.8	17,600	7.0
1992	86,777	34.0	40,982	16.1	4,968[e]	1.9[e]	24,000[e]	9.4[e]	19,000[e]	7.4[e]
1993	90,523	35.1	41,893	16.3	5,035	2.0	26,100	10.1	19,700	7.6
1994	91,437	35.1	42,524	16.3	5,338	2.1	26,300	10.1	19,600	7.5
1995	93,320	35.5	43,363	16.5	5,018	1.9	27,200	10.3	20,100	7.6
1996	94,948	35.8	43,649	16.5	5,058	1.9	27,500	10.4	21,000	7.9
1997	95,644	35.7	43,458	16.2	5,162	1.9	27,700	10.3	21,700	8.1
1998	97,835	36.2	43,501	16.1	5,120	1.9	29,000	10.7	22,600	8.4
1999[f]	97,860	35.9	42,401	15.5	5,185	1.9	30,500	11.2	22,200	8.1
2000	97,900	35.6	43,354	15.7	5,022	1.8	29,200	10.6	22,700	8.2
2001	101,537	35.6	43,788	15.4	5,042	1.8	33,200	11.6	21,800	7.6
2002	106,742	37.1	45,380	15.8	4,726	1.6	36,400	12.6	22,500	7.8
2003	109,277	37.6	44,757	15.4	4,725	1.6	38,800	13.3	23,200	8.0
2004	112,012	38.1	44,933	15.3	5,000	1.7	41,700	14.2	22,700	7.7
2005	117,809	39.7	45,343	15.3	4,987	1.7	46,400	15.6	23,400	7.9
2006	121,599	40.8	45,316	15.2	5,092	1.7	49,600	16.6	23,900	8.0
2007	123,706	41.1	43,945	14.6	4,833	1.6	53,500	17.8	23,700	7.9
2008	121,902	40.0	39,790	13.1	4,425	1.5	55,200	18.1	24,500	8.0
2009	118,046	38.5	36,216	11.8	3,744	1.2	55,800	18.2	24,000	7.8
2010	120,859	39.0	35,332	11.4	3,902	1.3	58,100	18.7	25,300	8.2
2011[g]	126,438	40.6	35,303	11.3	3,975	1.3	62,400	20.0	26,400	8.5
2012[g]	127,792	40.7	36,415	11.6	3,904	1.2	62,800	20.0	26,600	8.5
2013[h]	130,800	41.4	35,500	11.2	3,738	1.2	66,000	20.9	27,200	8.6
Changes										
2004 to 2013	17%	9%	-21%	-27%	-25%	-29%	58%	47%	20%	12%
2012 to 2013	2%	2%	-2%	-3%	-4%	0%	5%	4%	2%	1%

Source: Total and motor vehicle deaths, 1903-1932 based on National Center for Health Statistics (NCHS) death registration states; 1933-1948 (5th Rev.), 1949-1963, 1965-2012 are NCHS totals for the United States. Work deaths for 1992-2013 are from the Bureau of Labor Statistics Census of Fatal Occupational Injuries. All other figures are National Safety Council estimates.

[a]*Duplications between motor vehicle, work, and home are eliminated in the total column.*

[b]*Rates are deaths per 100,000 population.*

[c]*Data insufficient to estimate yearly totals.*

[d]*In 1948, a revision was made in the International Classification of Diseases. The first figures for 1948 are comparable with those for earlier years, the second with those for later years.*

[e]*Adoption of the Census of Fatal Occupational Injuries figures for the work class necessitated adjustments to the home and public classes. See the Technical Appendix for details.*

[f]*In 1999, a revision was made in the International Classification of Diseases. See the Technical Appendix for comparability with earlier years.*

[g]*Revised.*

[h]*Preliminary.*

Unintentional-Injury-Related Deaths by Age

Unintentional-injury-related deaths by age, United States, 1903-2013

Year	All ages	Younger than 5 years	5-14 years	15-24 years	25-44 years	45-64 years	65-74 years	75 years and older[a]
1903	70,600	9,400	8,200	10,300	20,100	12,600	10,000	
1904	71,500	9,700	9,000	10,500	19,900	12,500	9,900	
1905	70,900	9,800	8,400	10,600	19,600	12,600	9,900	
1906	80,000	10,000	8,400	13,000	24,000	13,600	11,000	
1907	81,900	10,500	8,300	13,400	24,900	14,700	10,100	
1908	72,300	10,100	7,600	11,300	20,500	13,100	9,700	
1909	72,700	9,900	7,400	10,700	21,000	13,300	10,400	
1910	77,900	9,900	7,400	11,900	23,600	14,100	11,000	
1911	79,300	11,000	7,500	11,400	22,400	15,100	11,900	
1912	78,400	10,600	7,900	11,500	22,200	14,700	11,500	
1913	82,500	9,800	7,400	12,200	24,500	16,500	12,100	
1914	77,000	10,600	7,900	11,000	21,400	14,300	11,800	
1915	76,200	10,300	8,200	10,800	20,500	14,300	12,100	
1916	84,800	11,600	9,100	7,700	24,900	17,800	13,700	
1917	90,100	11,600	9,700	11,700	24,400	18,500	14,200	
1918	85,100	10,600	10,100	10,600	21,900	17,700	14,200	
1919	75,500	10,100	10,000	10,200	18,600	13,800	12,800	
1920	75,900	10,200	9,900	10,400	18,100	13,900	13,400	
1921	74,000	9,600	9,500	9,800	18,000	13,900	13,200	
1922	76,300	9,700	9,500	10,000	18,700	14,500	13,900	
1923	84,400	9,900	9,800	11,000	21,500	16,900	15,300	
1924	85,600	10,200	9,900	11,900	20,900	16,800	15,900	
1925	90,000	9,700	10,000	12,400	22,200	18,700	17,000	
1926	91,700	9,500	9,900	12,600	22,700	19,200	17,800	
1927	92,700	9,200	9,900	12,900	22,900	19,700	18,100	
1928	95,000	8,900	9,800	13,100	23,300	20,600	19,300	
1929	98,200	8,600	9,800	14,000	24,300	21,500	20,000	
1930	99,100	8,200	9,100	14,000	24,300	22,200	21,300	
1931	97,300	7,800	8,700	13,500	23,100	22,500	21,700	
1932	89,000	7,100	8,100	12,000	20,500	20,100	21,200	
1933	90,932	6,948	8,195	12,225	21,005	20,819	21,740	
1934	100,977	7,034	8,272	13,274	23,288	24,197	24,912	
1935	99,773	6,971	7,808	13,168	23,411	23,457	24,958	
1936	110,052	7,471	7,866	13,701	24,990	26,535	29,489	
1937	105,205	6,969	7,704	14,302	23,955	24,743	27,532	
1938	93,805	6,646	6,593	12,129	20,464	21,689	26,284	
1939	92,628	6,668	6,378	12,066	20,164	20,842	26,505	
1940	96,885	6,851	6,466	12,763	21,166	21,840	27,799	
1941	101,513	7,052	6,702	14,346	22,983	22,509	27,921	
1942	95,889	7,220	6,340	13,732	21,141	20,764	26,692	
1943	99,038	8,039	6,636	15,278	20,212	20,109	28,764	
1944	95,237	7,912	6,704	14,750	19,115	19,097	27,659	
1945	95,918	7,741	6,836	12,446	19,393	20,097	29,405	
1946	98,033	7,949	6,545	13,366	20,705	20,249	29,219	
1947	99,579	8,219	6,069	13,166	21,155	20,513	30,457	
1948 (5th Rev.)[b]	98,001	8,387	5,859	12,595	20,274	19,809	31,077	
1948 (6th Rev.)[b]	93,000	8,350	5,850	12,600	20,300	19,300	9,800	16,800
1949	90,106	8,469	5,539	11,522	19,432	18,302	9,924	16,918
1950	91,249	8,389	5,519	12,119	20,663	18,665	9,750	16,144
1951	95,871	8,769	5,892	12,366	22,363	19,610	10,218	16,653
1952	96,172	8,871	5,980	12,787	21,950	19,892	10,026	16,667
1953	95,032	8,678	6,136	12,837	21,422	19,479	9,927	16,553
1954	90,032	8,380	5,939	11,801	20,023	18,299	9,652	15,938
1955	93,443	8,099	6,099	12,742	29,911	19,199	9,929	16,464
1956	94,780	8,173	6,319	13,545	20,986	19,207	10,160	16,393
1957	95,307	8,423	6,454	12,973	20,949	19,495	10,076	16,937
1958	90,604	8,789	6,514	12,744	19,658	18,095	9,431	15,373
1959	92,080	8,748	6,511	13,269	19,666	18,937	9,475	15,474
1960	93,806	8,950	6,836	13,457	19,600	19,385	9,689	15,829
1961	92,249	8,622	6,717	13,431	19,273	19,134	9,452	15,620
1962	97,139	8,705	6,751	14,557	19,955	20,335	10,149	16,687
1963	100,669	8,688	6,962	15,889	20,529	21,262	10,194	17,145
1964	100,500	8,670	7,400	17,420	22,080	22,100	10,400	16,930
1965	108,004	8,586	7,391	18,688	22,228	22,900	10,430	17,781
1966	113,563	8,507	7,958	21,030	23,134	24,022	10,706	18,206
1967	113,169	7,825	7,874	21,645	23,255	23,826	10,645	18,099
1968	114,864	7,263	8,369	23,012	23,684	23,896	10,961	17,679
1969	116,385	6,973	8,186	24,668	24,410	24,192	10,643	17,313
1970	114,638	6,594	8,203	24,336	23,979	24,164	10,644	16,718
1971	113,439	6,496	8,143	24,733	23,535	23,240	10,494	16,798
1972	115,448	6,142	8,242	25,762	23,852	23,658	10,446	17,346
1973	115,821	6,037	8,102	26,550	24,750	23,059	10,243	17,080

See source and footnotes on page 49.

Unintentional-injury-related deaths by age, United States, 1903-2013 (cont.)

Year	All ages	Younger than 5 years	5-14 years	15-24 years	25-44 years	45-64 years	65-74 years	75 years and older[a]
1974	104,622	5,335	7,037	24,200	22,547	20,334	9,323	15,846
1975	103,030	4,948	6,818	24,121	22,877	19,643	9,220	15,403
1976	100,761	4,692	6,308	24,316	22,399	19,000	8,823	15,223
1977	103,202	4,470	6,305	25,619	23,460	19,167	9,006	15,175
1978	105,561	4,766	6,118	26,622	25,024	18,774	9,072	15,185
1979	105,312	4,429	5,689	26,574	26,097	18,346	9,013	15,164
1980	105,718	4,479	5,224	26,206	26,722	18,140	8,997	15,950
1981	100,704	4,130	4,866	23,582	26,928	17,339	8,639	15,220
1982	94,082	4,108	4,504	21,306	25,135	15,907	8,224	14,898
1983	92,488	3,999	4,321	19,756	24,996	15,444	8,336	15,636
1984	92,911	3,652	4,198	19,801	25,498	15,273	8,424	16,065
1985	93,457	3,746	4,252	19,161	25,940	15,251	8,583	16,524
1986	95,277	3,843	4,226	19,975	27,201	14,733	8,499	16,800
1987	95,020	3,871	4,198	18,695	27,484	14,807	8,686	17,279
1988	97,100	3,794	4,215	18,507	28,279	15,177	8,971	18,157
1989	95,028	3,770	4,090	16,738	28,429	15,046	8,812	18,143
1990	91,983	3,496	3,650	16,241	27,663	14,607	8,405	17,921
1991	89,347	3,626	3,660	15,278	26,526	13,693	8,137	18,427
1992	86,777	3,286	3,388	13,662	25,808	13,882	8,165	18,586
1993	90,523	3,488	3,466	13,966	27,277	14,434	8,125	19,767
1994	91,437	3,406	3,508	13,898	27,012	15,200	8,279	20,134
1995	93,320	3,067	3,544	13,842	27,660	16,004	8,400	20,803
1996	94,948	2,951	3,433	13,809	27,092	16,717	8,780	22,166
1997	95,644	2,770	3,371	13,367	27,129	17,521	8,578	22,908
1998	97,835	2,689	3,254	13,349	27,172	18,286	8,892	24,193
1999[c]	97,860	2,743	3,091	13,656	27,121	18,924	8,208	24,117
2000	97,900	2,707	2,979	14,113	27,182	19,783	7,698	23,438
2001	101,537	2,690	2,836	14,411	27,784	21,002	7,835	24,979
2002	106,742	2,587	2,718	15,412	29,279	23,020	8,086	25,640
2003	109,277	2,662	2,618	15,272	29,307	25,007	8,081	26,330
2004	112,012	2,693	2,666	15,449	29,503	26,593	8,116	26,992
2005	117,809	2,747	2,415	15,753	30,916	29,192	8,632	28,154
2006	121,599	2,757	2,258	16,229	32,488	31,121	8,420	28,326
2007	123,706	2,873	2,194	15,897	31,908	32,508	8,753	29,573
2008	121,902	2,784	1,859	14,089	30,653	33,136	8,994	30,387
2009	118,046	2,674	1,680	12,454	29,159	32,945	8,976	30,158
2010	120,859	2,504	1,643	12,341	29,365	33,690	9,407	31,909
2011[d]	126,438	2,540	1,635	12,330	30,748	35,907	10,014	33,264
2012[d]	127,792	2,522	1,550	11,908	30,885	36,216	10,558	34,153
2013[e]	130,800	2,700	1,600	11,700	31,800	37,200	10,800	35,000
Changes								
2004 to 2013	17%	<1%	-40%	-24%	8%	40%	33%	30%
2012 to 2013	2%	7%	3%	-2%	3%	3%	2%	2%

Source: 1903-1932 based on National Center for Health Statistics (NCHS) data for registration states; 1933-1948 (5th Rev.), 1949-1963, 1965-2012 are NCHS totals. All other figures are National Safety Council estimates. See Technical Appendix for comparability.

[a]*Includes age unknown. In 2012, these deaths numbered 13.*

[b]*In 1948, a revision was made in the International Classification of Diseases. The first figures for 1948 are comparable with those for earlier years, the second with those for later years.*

[c]*In 1999, a revision was made in the International Classification of Diseases. See the Technical Appendix for comparability with earlier years.*

[d]*Revised.*

[e]*Preliminary.*

Unintentional-Injury-Related Death Rates by Age

Unintentional-injury-related death rates[a] by age, United States, 1903-2013

Year	Standardized rate[b]	All ages	Younger than 5 years	5-14 years	15-24 years	25-44 years	45-64 years	65-74 years	75 years and older[c]
1903	99.4	87.2	98.7	46.8	65.0	87.4	111.7		299.8
1904	103.4	86.6	99.1	50.9	64.9	84.6	108.1		290.0
1905	98.4	84.2	98.6	47.0	64.1	81.4	106.2		282.5
1906	114.2	93.2	99.1	46.5	77.1	97.3	111.7		306.0
1907	112.4	93.6	102.7	45.5	78.0	98.8	117.8		274.2
1908	99.7	81.2	97.5	41.2	64.4	79.5	102.2		256.7
1909	97.4	80.1	94.2	39.6	59.9	79.6	101.0		268.2
1910	103.0	84.4	92.8	39.1	65.3	87.3	104.0		276.0
1911	104.7	84.7	101.9	39.3	62.1	81.4	108.7		292.1
1912	100.4	82.5	97.1	40.5	62.3	79.2	103.2		275.8
1913	103.5	85.5	88.4	37.4	65.2	85.6	112.5		281.7
1914	95.9	78.6	94.3	38.9	58.5	73.2	94.6		268.1
1915	92.1	76.7	90.8	39.7	57.3	69.0	92.1		268.8
1916	101.4	84.1	101.4	43.3	40.8	82.5	112.1		297.6
1917	106.7	88.2	108.4	45.3	62.1	79.8	113.8		301.2
1918	101.2	82.1	91.0	46.5	58.7	72.2	106.3		294.2
1919	87.7	71.9	87.2	45.9	55.3	60.1	81.8		262.0
1920	87.8	71.2	87.4	44.9	55.5	56.9	85.6		289.5
1921	84.3	68.4	80.8	42.4	51.4	55.5	79.4		259.8
1922	86.9	69.4	80.6	41.5	51.4	57.1	81.4		265.1
1923	94.5	75.7	82.0	42.4	55.6	64.5	92.6		282.8
1924	93.3	75.6	82.9	42.4	58.6	61.7	90.2		283.5
1925	97.2	78.4	78.6	42.3	59.7	64.7	97.8		293.9
1926	97.7	78.7	77.9	41.4	59.9	65.4	98.2		298.7
1927	97.5	78.4	75.9	41.0	60.2	65.2	98.0		295.4
1928	99.6	79.3	74.4	40.4	59.9	65.6	99.9		306.2
1929	101.2	80.8	73.3	40.0	63.1	67.7	102.1		308.9
1930	101.8	80.5	71.8	36.9	62.3	67.0	102.9		317.9
1931	99.2	78.5	69.9	35.2	59.7	63.0	102.1		313.3
1932	90.5	71.3	65.1	32.8	52.7	55.6	89.3		296.9
1933	91.1	72.4	65.5	33.4	53.6	56.3	90.8		295.3
1934	100.5	79.9	68.1	33.9	57.8	61.8	103.3		328.5
1935	97.9	78.4	68.5	32.2	56.9	61.6	98.0		319.8
1936	108.1	85.9	74.4	32.9	58.8	65.3	108.6		367.4
1937	100.7	81.7	69.6	32.7	60.9	62.1	99.3		333.4
1938	89.4	72.3	65.3	28.5	51.3	52.5	85.4		308.9
1939	86.7	70.8	62.9	28.2	50.7	51.2	81.0		300.0
1940	89.1	73.4	64.8	28.8	53.5	53.2	83.4		305.7
1941	90.7	76.3	65.0	29.7	60.9	57.2	84.8		297.4
1942	84.3	71.6	63.9	27.9	59.8	52.4	77.1		275.5
1943	86.3	73.8	66.9	29.0	69.7	50.3	73.6		287.8
1944	82.5	71.7	63.2	29.1	72.9	48.9	68.9		268.6
1945	83.4	72.4	59.8	29.5	64.5	50.5	71.6		277.6
1946	81.0	70.0	60.2	28.1	61.7	48.8	70.9		267.9
1947	80.5	69.4	57.4	25.8	59.6	49.0	70.6		270.7
1948 (5th Rev.)[d]	79.5	67.1	56.3	24.6	56.8	46.2	66.8		267.4
1948 (6th Rev.)[d]	72.5	63.7	56.0	24.5	56.8	46.2	65.1	122.4	464.3
1949	69.0	60.6	54.4	23.0	52.2	43.5	60.6	120.4	450.7
1950	68.1	60.3	51.4	22.6	55.0	45.6	60.5	115.8	414.7
1951	70.1	62.5	50.8	23.6	57.7	49.0	62.7	117.1	413.6
1952	69.0	61.8	51.5	22.5	60.9	47.7	62.7	111.1	399.8
1953	67.0	60.1	49.5	22.1	61.4	46.4	60.5	106.7	383.6
1954	62.2	55.9	46.7	20.5	56.4	43.0	55.9	100.7	354.4
1955	63.4	56.9	43.9	20.7	60.1	44.7	57.7	100.8	350.2
1956	63.0	56.6	43.3	20.2	63.3	44.7	56.7	100.6	335.6
1957	62.2	55.9	43.5	19.9	59.5	44.6	56.6	97.5	333.3
1958	57.5	52.3	44.5	19.6	56.2	42.0	51.7	89.3	292.6
1959	57.4	52.2	43.6	18.9	56.5	42.1	53.2	87.7	284.7
1960	57.3	52.1	44.0	19.1	55.6	42.0	53.6	87.6	281.4
1961	55.4	50.4	42.0	18.1	54.0	41.2	52.1	83.8	267.9
1962	57.5	52.3	42.6	18.0	55.0	42.7	54.6	88.5	277.7
1963	58.6	53.4	42.8	18.2	57.2	44.0	56.3	87.9	277.0
1964	60.0	54.9	43.1	19.1	59.9	47.3	57.6	88.9	263.9
1965	61.9	55.8	43.4	18.7	61.6	47.7	58.8	88.5	268.7
1966	63.0	58.1	44.4	19.9	66.9	49.6	60.7	89.8	267.4
1967	62.1	57.3	42.2	19.4	66.9	49.7	59.2	88.5	257.4
1968	62.0	57.6	40.6	20.5	69.2	50.1	58.5	90.2	244.0
1969	61.8	57.8	40.2	20.0	71.8	51.2	58.4	86.6	232.0
1970	59.8	56.2	38.4	20.1	68.0	49.8	57.6	85.2	219.6
1971	58.1	54.8	37.7	20.1	66.1	48.4	54.7	82.7	213.2
1972	58.0	55.2	35.9	20.6	67.6	47.5	55.2	80.8	214.2
1973	57.1	54.8	35.8	20.6	68.2	48.0	53.3	77.3	206.3

See source and footnotes on page 51.

Unintentional-Injury-Related Death Rates by Age (cont.)

Unintentional-injury-related death rates[a] by age, United States, 1903-2013 (cont.)

Year	Standardized rate[b]	All ages	Younger than 5 years	5-14 years	15-24 years	25-44 years	45-64 years	65-74 years	75 years and older[c]
1974	50.9	49.0	32.4	18.2	60.9	42.7	46.7	68.7	186.7
1975	49.3	47.8	30.7	17.8	59.5	42.3	44.9	66.2	175.5
1976	47.3	46.3	30.0	16.7	58.9	40.3	43.2	62.0	168.4
1977	47.6	47.0	28.7	17.0	61.3	40.9	43.4	61.5	164.0
1978	47.8	47.5	30.3	16.9	63.1	42.3	42.4	60.5	159.7
1979	47.0	46.9	27.6	16.1	62.6	42.7	41.3	58.8	154.8
1980	46.5	46.5	27.2	15.0	61.7	42.3	40.8	57.5	158.6
1981	44.0	43.9	24.4	14.2	55.9	41.2	39.0	54.4	147.4
1982	40.6	40.6	23.8	13.2	51.2	37.3	35.8	50.9	140.0
1983	39.6	39.6	22.8	12.7	48.2	36.0	34.7	50.8	142.8
1984	39.4	39.4	20.6	12.4	48.9	35.7	34.3	50.7	142.8
1985	39.2	39.3	21.0	12.6	47.9	35.3	34.2	50.9	143.0
1986	39.4	39.7	21.4	12.6	50.5	36.1	33.0	49.6	141.5
1987	39.0	39.2	21.4	12.4	48.1	35.7	33.0	49.8	141.6
1988	39.5	39.7	20.9	12.3	48.5	36.1	33.4	50.9	145.3
1989	38.4	38.5	20.4	11.8	44.8	35.7	32.8	49.3	141.5
1990	36.8	36.9	18.5	10.4	44.0	34.2	31.6	46.4	136.5
1991	35.3	35.4	18.9	10.2	42.0	32.3	29.3	44.5	136.7
1992	34.0	34.0	16.8	9.3	37.8	31.3	28.7	44.2	134.5
1993	35.0	35.1	17.7	9.4	38.8	33.0	29.1	43.6	139.9
1994	35.0	35.1	17.3	9.4	38.4	32.5	29.9	44.3	139.2
1995	35.0	35.5	15.7	9.3	38.2	33.2	30.6	44.8	140.6
1996	35.3	35.8	15.3	8.9	38.1	32.3	31.1	47.0	145.9
1997	35.1	35.7	14.5	8.7	36.5	32.5	31.6	46.3	146.2
1998	35.5	36.2	14.2	8.3	35.9	32.6	31.9	48.3	151.1
1999[e]	35.2	35.9	14.5	7.8	36.1	32.7	32.0	45.0	147.7
2000	34.8	35.6	14.3	7.5	36.7	33.0	32.3	42.3	140.8
2001	35.7	35.6	13.9	6.9	36.1	32.7	32.6	42.8	146.8
2002	37.1	37.1	13.2	6.6	37.9	34.7	34.6	44.2	148.2
2003	37.6	37.6	13.5	6.4	37.0	34.8	36.4	44.0	149.6
2004	38.1	38.1	13.4	6.5	37.1	35.1	37.6	43.9	151.4
2005	39.5	39.7	13.5	6.0	37.4	36.8	40.1	46.3	155.2
2006	40.4	40.8	13.5	5.6	38.5	38.9	41.6	44.5	154.4
2007	40.5	41.1	13.9	5.5	37.5	38.2	42.4	45.2	159.2
2008	39.4	40.0	13.2	4.6	32.8	36.8	42.6	44.7	162.8
2009	37.7	38.5	12.6	4.1	28.9	35.1	41.5	43.2	160.6
2010	38.1	39.0	11.7	4.0	28.6	35.3	41.7	44.1	168.2
2011[f]	39.3	40.6	12.6	4.0	28.2	37.3	43.4	44.5	175.9
2012[f]	39.1	40.7	12.6	3.8	27.1	37.3	43.7	47.0	178.3
2013[g]	39.5	41.4	13.6	3.9	26.6	38.2	44.8	42.9	179.3

Changes

2003 to 2012		9%	1%	-40%	-28%	9%	19%	-2%	18%
2011 to 2012		2%	8%	3%	-2%	2%	3%	-9%	1%

2013 population (thousands)

Total[h]		316,160	19,881	41,228	43,960	83,288	83,084	25,198	19,520
Male		155,648	10,158	21,066	22,525	41,777	40,529	11,786	7,806
Female		160,512	9,723	20,162	21,434	41,511	42,555	13,413	11,714

Source: All figures are National Safety Council estimates. See Technical Appendix for comparability.
[a]*Rates are deaths per 100,000 resident population in each age group.*
[b]*Adjusted to the year 2000 standard population to remove the influence of changes in age distribution between 1903 and 2013.*
[c]*Includes age unknown.*
[d]*In 1948, a revision was made in the International Classification of Diseases. The first figures for 1948 are comparable with those for earlier years, the second with those for later years.*
[e]*In 1999, a revision was made in the International Classification of Diseases. See the Technical Appendix for comparability.*
[f]*Revised.*
[g]*Preliminary.*
[h]*Sum of parts may not equal total due to rounding.*

Principal Types of Unintentional-Injury-Related Deaths

Principal types of unintentional-injury-related deaths, United States, 1903-1998

Year	Total	Motor vehicle	Falls	Drowning[a]	Fire, flames, or smoke[b]	Choking[b]	Firearms	Poison (solid or liquid)	Poison (gas or vapor)	All other
1903	70,600	(c)	(c)	9,200	(c)	(c)	2,500	(c)	(c)	58,900
1904	71,500	(c)	(c)	9,300	(c)	(c)	2,800	(c)	(c)	59,400
1905	70,900	(c)	(c)	9,300	(c)	(c)	2,000	(c)	(c)	59,600
1906	80,000	400	(c)	9,400	(c)	(c)	2,100	(c)	(c)	68,100
1907	81,900	700	(c)	9,000	(c)	(c)	1,700	(c)	(c)	70,500
1908	72,300	800	(c)	9,300	(c)	(c)	1,900	(c)	(c)	60,300
1909	72,700	1,300	(c)	8,500	(c)	(c)	1,600	(c)	(c)	61,300
1910	77,900	1,900	(c)	8,700	(c)	(c)	1,900	(c)	(c)	65,400
1911	79,300	2,300	(c)	9,000	(c)	(c)	2,100	(c)	(c)	65,900
1912	78,400	3,100	(c)	8,600	(c)	(c)	2,100	(c)	(c)	64,600
1913	82,500	4,200	15,100	10,300	8,900	(c)	2,400	3,200	(c)	38,400
1914	77,000	4,700	15,000	8,700	9,100	(c)	2,300	3,300	(c)	33,900
1915	76,200	6,600	15,000	8,600	8,400	(c)	2,100	2,800	(c)	32,700
1916	84,800	8,200	15,200	8,900	9,500	(c)	2,200	2,900	(c)	37,900
1917	90,100	10,200	15,200	7,600	10,800	(c)	2,300	2,800	(c)	41,200
1918	85,100	10,700	13,200	7,000	10,200	(c)	2,500	2,700	(c)	38,800
1919	75,500	11,200	11,900	9,100	9,100	(c)	2,800	3,100	(c)	28,300
1920	75,900	12,500	12,600	6,100	9,300	(c)	2,700	3,300	(c)	29,400
1921	74,000	13,900	12,300	7,800	7,500	(c)	2,800	2,900	(c)	26,800
1922	76,300	15,300	13,200	7,000	8,300	(c)	2,900	2,800	(c)	26,800
1923	84,400	18,400	14,100	6,800	9,100	(c)	2,900	2,800	2,700	27,600
1924	85,600	19,400	14,700	7,400	7,400	(c)	2,900	2,700	2,900	28,200
1925	90,000	21,900	15,500	7,300	8,600	(c)	2,800	2,700	2,800	28,400
1926	91,700	23,400	16,300	7,500	8,800	(c)	2,800	2,600	3,200	27,100
1927	92,700	25,800	16,500	8,100	8,200	(c)	3,000	2,600	2,700	25,800
1928	95,000	28,000	17,000	8,600	8,400	(c)	2,900	2,800	2,800	24,500
1929	98,200	31,200	17,700	7,600	8,200	(c)	3,200	2,600	2,800	24,900
1930	99,100	32,900	18,100	7,500	8,100	(c)	3,200	2,600	2,500	24,200
1931	97,300	33,700	18,100	7,600	7,100	(c)	3,100	2,600	2,100	23,000
1932	89,000	29,500	18,600	7,500	7,100	(c)	3,000	2,200	2,100	19,000
1933	90,932	31,363	18,962	7,158	6,781	(c)	3,014	2,135	1,633	19,886
1934	100,977	36,101	20,725	7,077	7,456	(c)	3,033	2,148	1,643	22,794
1935	99,773	36,369	21,378	6,744	7,253	(c)	2,799	2,163	1,654	21,413
1936	110,052	38,089	23,562	6,659	7,939	(c)	2,817	2,177	1,665	27,144
1937	105,205	39,643	22,544	7,085	7,214	(c)	2,576	2,190	1,675	22,278
1938	93,805	32,582	23,239	6,881	6,491	(c)	2,726	2,077	1,428	18,381
1939	92,623	32,386	23,427	6,413	6,675	(c)	2,618	1,963	1,440	17,701
1940	96,885	34,501	23,356	6,202	7,521	(c)	2,375	1,847	1,583	19,500
1941	101,513	39,969	22,764	6,389	6,922	(c)	2,396	1,731	1,464	19,878
1942	95,889	28,309	22,632	6,696	7,901	(c)	2,678	1,607	1,741	24,325
1943	99,038	23,823	24,701	7,115	8,726	921	2,282	1,745	2,014	27,711
1944	95,237	24,282	22,989	6,511	8,372	896	2,392	1,993	1,860	25,942
1945	95,918	28,076	23,847	6,624	7,949	897	2,385	1,987	2,120	22,033
1946	98,033	33,411	23,109	6,442	7,843	1,076	2,801	1,961	1,821	19,569
1947	99,579	32,697	24,529	6,885	8,033	1,206	2,439	1,865	1,865	14,060
1948 (5th Rev.)[d]	98,001	32,259	24,836	6,428	7,743	1,315	2,191	1,753	2,045	19,611
1948 (6th Rev.)[d]	93,000	32,259	22,000	6,500	6,800	1,299	2,330	1,600	2,020	17,192
1949	90,106	31,701	22,308	6,684	5,982	1,341	2,326	1,634	1,617	16,513
1950	91,249	34,763	20,783	6,131	6,405	1,350	2,174	1,584	1,769	16,290
1951	95,871	36,996	21,376	6,489	6,788	1,456	2,247	1,497	1,627	17,395
1952	96,172	37,794	20,945	6,601	6,922	1,434	2,210	1,440	1,397	17,429
1953	95,032	37,955	20,631	6,770	6,579	1,603	2,277	1,391	1,223	16,603
1954	90,032	35,586	19,771	6,334	6,083	1,627	2,271	1,339	1,223	15,798
1955	93,443	38,426	20,192	6,344	6,352	1,608	2,120	1,431	1,163	15,807
1956	94,780	39,628	20,282	6,263	6,405	1,760	2,202	1,422	1,213	15,605
1957	95,307	38,702	20,545	6,613	6,269	2,043	2,369	1,390	1,143	16,233
1958	90,604	36,981	18,248	6,582[e]	7,291[e]	2,191[e]	2,172	1,429	1,187	14,523
1959	92,080	37,910	18,774	6,434	6,898	2,189	2,258	1,661	1,141	14,815
1960	93,806	38,137	19,023	6,529	7,645	2,397	2,334	1,679	1,253	14,809
1961	92,249	38,091	18,691	6,525	7,102	2,499	2,204	1,804	1,192	14,141
1962	97,139	40,804	19,589	6,439	7,534	1,813	2,092	1,833	1,376	15,659
1963	100,669	43,564	19,335	6,347	8,172	1,949	2,263	2,061	1,489	15,489
1964	105,000	47,700	18,941	6,709	7,379	1,865	2,275	2,100	1,360	16,571
1965	108,004	49,163	19,984	6,799	7,347	1,836	2,344	2,110	1,526	16,895
1966	113,563	53,041	20,066	7,084	8,084	1,831	2,558	2,283	1,648	16,968
1967	113,169	52,924	20,120	7,076	7,423	1,980	2,896	2,506	1,574	16,670
1968	114,864	54,862	18,651	7,372[e]	7,335	3,100[e]	2,394[e]	2,583	1,526	17,041
1969	116,385	55,791	17,827	7,699	7,163	3,712	2,309	2,967	1,549	16,368
1970	114,638	54,633	16,926	7,860	6,718	2,753	2,406	3,679	1,620	18,043
1971	113,439	54,381	16,755	7,396	6,776	2,877	2,360	3,710	1,646	17,538
1972	115,448	56,278	16,744	7,586	6,714	2,830	2,442	3,728	1,690	17,436
1973	115,821	55,511	16,506	8,725	6,503	3,013	2,618	3,683	1,652	17,610

See source and footnotes on page 53.

Principal types of unintentional-injury-related deaths, United States, 1903-1998 (cont.)

Year	Total	Motor vehicle	Falls	Drowning[a]	Fire, flames, or smoke[b]	Choking[b]	Firearms	Poison (solid or liquid)	Poison (gas or vapor)	All other
1974	104,622	46,402	16,339	7,876	6,236	2,991	2,513	4,016	1,518	16,731
1975	103,030	45,853	14,896	8,000	6,071	3,106	2,380	4,694	1,577	16,453
1976	100,761	47,038	14,136	6,827	6,338	3,033	2,059	4,161	1,569	15,600
1977	103,202	49,510	13,773	7,126	6,357	3,037	1,982	3,374	1,596	16,447
1978	105,561	52,411	13,690	7,026	6,163	3,063	1,806	3,035	1,737	16,630
1979	105,312	53,524	13,216	6,872	5,991	3,243	2,004	3,165	1,472	15,825
1980	105,718	53,172	13,294	7,257	5,822	3,249	1,955	3,089	1,242	16,638
1981	100,704	51,385	12,628	6,277	5,697	3,331	1,871	3,243	1,280	14,992
1982	94,082	45,779	12,077	6,351	5,210	3,254	1,756	3,474	1,259	14,922
1983	92,488	44,452	12,024	6,353	5,028	3,387	1,695	3,382	1,251	14,916
1984	92,911	46,263	11,937	5,388	5,010	3,541	1,668	3,808	1,103	14,193
1985	93,457	45,901	12,001	5,316	4,938	3,551	1,649	4,091	1,079	14,931
1986	95,277	47,865	11,444	5,700	4,835	3,692	1,452	4,731	1,009	14,549
1987	95,020	48,290	11,733	5,100	4,710	3,688	1,440	4,415	900	14,744
1988	97,100	49,078	12,096	4,966	4,965	3,805	1,501	5,353	873	14,463
1989	95,028	47,575	12,151	4,015	4,716	3,578	1,489	5,603	921	14,980
1990	91,983	46,814	12,313	4,685	4,175	3,303	1,416	5,055	748	13,474
1991	89,347	43,536	12,662	4,818	4,120	3,240	1,441	5,698	736	13,096
1992	86,777	40,982	12,646	3,542	3,958	3,182	1,409	6,449	633	13,976
1993	90,523	41,893	13,141	3,807	3,900	3,160	1,521	7,877	660	14,564
1994	91,437	42,524	13,450	3,942	3,986	3,065	1,356	8,309	685	14,120
1995	93,320	43,363	13,986	4,350	3,761	3,185	1,225	8,461	611	14,378
1996	94,948	43,649	14,986	3,959	3,741	3,206	1,134	8,872	638	14,763
1997	95,644	43,458	15,447	4,051	3,490	3,275	981	9,587	576	14,779
1998	97,835	43,501	16,274	4,406	3,255	3,515	866	10,255	546	15,217

Principal types of unintentional-injury-related deaths, United States, 1999-2013

Year	Total	Motor vehicle	Falls	Poisoning	Choking[b]	Drowning[f]	Fire, flames, or smoke[b]	Mechanical suffocation	Firearms	All other
1999[g]	97,860	42,401	13,162	12,186	3,885	3,529	3,348	1,618	824	16,907
2000	97,900	43,354	13,322	12,757	4,313	3,482	3,377	1,335	776	15,184
2001	101,537	43,788	15,019	14,078	4,185	3,281	3,309	1,370	802	15,705
2002	106,742	45,380	16,257	17,550	4,128	3,447	3,159	1,389	762	13,670
2003	109,277	44,757	17,229	19,457	4,272	3,306	3,369	1,309	730	14,850
2004	112,012	44,933	18,807	20,950	4,470	3,308	3,229	1,421	649	14,245
2005	117,809	45,343	19,656	23,617	4,386	3,582	3,197	1,514	789	15,725
2006	121,599	45,316	20,823	27,531	4,332	3,579	3,109	1,580	642	14,687
2007	123,706	43,945	22,631	29,846	4,344	3,443	3,286	1,653	613	14,558
2008	121,902	39,790	24,013	31,116	4,366	3,548	2,912	1,759	592	14,398
2009	118,046	36,216	24,792	31,758	4,370	3,517	2,756	1,569	554	13,068
2010	120,859	35,332	26,009	33,041	4,570	3,782	2,782	1,595	606	13,748
2011[h]	126,438	35,303	27,483	36,280	4,708	3,556	2,746	1,534	591	14,237
2012[h]	127,792	36,415	28,753	36,332	4,634	3,551	2,464	1,604	548	13,491
2013[i]	130,800	35,500	30,300	38,800	4,800	3,700	2,400	1,800	530	12,970
Changes										
2004 to 2013	17%	-21%	61%	85%	7%	12%	-26%	27%	-18%	-9%
2012 to 2013	2%	-2%	5%	7%	4%	4%	-3%	12%	-3%	-4%

Source: National Center for Health Statistics and National Safety Council. See *Technical Appendix* for comparability.
[a]Includes drowning in water transport incidents.
[b]Fire, flames, or smoke includes burns by fire and deaths resulting from conflagration regardless of nature of injury. Choking is the inhalation of food or other object obstructing breathing.
[c]Comparable data not available.
[d]In 1948, a revision was made in the International Classification of Diseases. The first figures for 1948 are comparable with those for earlier years, the second with those for later years.
[e]Data are not comparable to previous years shown due to classification changes in 1958 and 1968.
[f]Excludes water transport drownings.
[g]In 1999, a revision was made in the International Classification of Diseases. See the Technical Appendix for comparability.
[h]Revised.
[i]Preliminary.

Unintentional-Injury-Related Death Rates for Principal Types

Unintentional-injury-related death rates[a] for principal types, United States, 1903-1998

Year	Total	Motor vehicle	Falls	Drowning[b]	Fire, flames, or smoke[c]	Choking[c]	Firearms	Poison (solid or liquid)	Poison (gas or vapor)	All other
1903	87.2	(d)	(d)	11.4	(d)	(d)	3.1	(d)	(d)	72.7
1904	86.6	(d)	(d)	11.3	(d)	(d)	3.4	(d)	(d)	71.9
1905	84.2	(d)	(d)	11.1	(d)	(d)	2.4	(d)	(d)	70.7
1906	93.2	0.5	(d)	11.0	(d)	(d)	2.4	(d)	(d)	79.3
1907	93.6	0.8	(d)	10.4	(d)	(d)	2.0	(d)	(d)	80.4
1908	81.2	0.9	(d)	10.5	(d)	(d)	2.1	(d)	(d)	67.7
1909	80.1	1.4	(d)	9.4	(d)	(d)	1.8	(d)	(d)	67.5
1910	84.4	2.0	(d)	9.4	(d)	(d)	2.1	(d)	(d)	70.9
1911	84.7	2.5	(d)	9.6	(d)	(d)	2.2	(d)	(d)	70.4
1912	82.5	3.3	(d)	9.0	(d)	(d)	2.2	(d)	(d)	68.0
1913	85.5	4.4	15.5	10.6	9.1	(d)	2.5	3.3	(d)	40.1
1914	78.6	4.8	15.1	8.8	9.1	(d)	2.3	3.3	(d)	35.2
1915	76.7	6.6	14.9	8.6	8.4	(d)	2.1	2.8	(d)	33.3
1916	84.1	8.1	14.9	8.7	9.3	(d)	2.2	2.8	(d)	38.1
1917	88.2	10.0	14.7	7.4	10.5	(d)	2.2	2.7	(d)	40.7
1918	82.1	10.3	12.8	6.8	9.9	(d)	2.4	2.6	(d)	37.3
1919	71.9	10.7	11.4	6.9	8.7	(d)	2.7	3.0	(d)	28.5
1920	71.2	11.7	11.8	5.7	8.7	(d)	2.5	3.1	(d)	27.7
1921	68.4	12.9	11.3	7.2	6.9	(d)	2.6	2.7	(d)	24.8
1922	69.4	13.9	12.0	6.4	7.5	(d)	2.6	2.5	(d)	24.5
1923	75.7	16.5	12.6	6.1	8.1	(d)	2.6	2.5	2.4	24.9
1924	75.6	17.1	12.9	6.5	8.4	(d)	2.5	2.4	2.5	23.3
1925	78.4	19.1	13.4	6.3	7.4	(d)	2.4	2.3	2.4	25.1
1926	78.7	20.1	13.9	6.4	7.5	(d)	2.4	2.2	2.7	23.5
1927	78.4	21.8	13.9	6.8	6.9	(d)	2.5	2.2	2.3	22.0
1928	79.3	23.4	14.1	7.1	7.0	(d)	2.4	2.3	2.3	20.7
1929	80.8	25.7	14.5	6.2	6.7	(d)	2.6	2.1	2.3	20.7
1930	80.5	26.7	14.7	6.1	6.6	(d)	2.6	2.1	2.0	19.7
1931	78.5	27.2	14.6	6.1	5.7	(d)	2.5	2.1	1.7	18.6
1932	71.3	23.6	14.9	6.0	5.7	(d)	2.4	1.8	1.7	15.2
1933	72.4	25.0	15.1	5.7	5.4	(d)	2.4	1.7	1.3	15.8
1934	79.9	28.6	16.4	5.6	5.9	(d)	2.4	1.7	1.3	18.0
1935	78.4	28.6	16.8	5.3	5.7	(d)	2.2	1.7	1.3	16.8
1936	85.9	29.7	18.4	5.2	6.2	(d)	2.2	1.7	1.3	21.2
1937	81.7	30.8	17.5	5.5	5.6	(d)	2.0	1.7	1.3	17.3
1938	72.3	25.1	17.9	5.3	5.0	(d)	2.1	1.6	1.1	14.2
1939	70.8	24.7	17.9	4.9	5.1	(d)	2.0	1.5	1.1	13.6
1940	73.4	26.1	17.7	4.7	5.7	(d)	1.8	1.4	1.2	14.8
1941	76.3	30.0	17.1	4.8	5.2	(d)	1.8	1.3	1.1	15.0
1942	71.6	21.1	16.9	5.0	5.9	(d)	2.0	1.2	1.3	18.2
1943	73.8	17.8	18.4	5.3	6.5	0.7	1.7	1.3	1.5	20.6
1944	71.7	18.3	17.3	4.9	6.3	0.7	1.8	1.5	1.4	19.5
1945	72.4	21.2	18.0	5.0	6.0	0.7	1.8	1.5	1.6	16.6
1946	70.0	23.9	16.5	4.6	5.6	0.8	2.0	1.4	1.3	13.9
1947	69.4	22.8	17.1	4.8	5.6	0.8	1.7	1.3	1.3	14.0
1948 (5th Rev.)[e]	67.1	22.1	17.0	4.4	5.3	0.9	1.5	1.2	1.4	13.3
1948 (6th Rev.)[e]	63.7	22.1	15.1	4.5	4.7	0.9	1.6	1.1	1.4	12.3
1949	60.6	21.3	15.0	4.5	4.0	0.9	1.6	1.1	1.1	11.1
1950	60.3	23.0	13.7	4.1	4.2	0.9	1.4	1.1	1.2	10.7
1951	62.5	24.1	13.9	4.2	4.4	1.0	1.5	1.0	1.1	11.3
1952	61.8	24.3	13.5	4.2	4.5	0.9	1.4	0.9	0.9	11.2
1953	60.1	24.0	13.0	4.3	4.2	1.0	1.4	0.9	0.8	10.2
1954	55.9	22.1	12.3	3.9	3.8	1.0	1.4	0.8	0.8	9.8
1955	56.9	23.4	12.3	3.9	3.9	1.0	1.3	0.9	0.7	9.5
1956	56.6	23.7	12.1	3.7	3.8	1.1	1.3	0.8	0.7	9.4
1957	55.9	22.7	12.1	3.9	3.7	1.2	1.4	0.8	0.7	9.4
1958	52.3	21.3	10.5	3.8[f]	4.2[f]	1.3[f]	1.3	0.8	0.7	8.4
1959	52.2	21.5	10.6	3.7	3.9	1.2	1.3	0.9	0.7	8.4
1960	52.1	21.2	10.6	3.6	4.3	1.3	1.3	0.9	0.7	8.2
1961	50.4	20.8	10.2	3.6	3.9	1.4	1.2	1.0	0.7	7.6
1962	52.3	22.0	10.5	3.5	4.1	1.0	1.1	1.0	0.7	8.4
1963	53.4	23.1	10.3	3.4	4.3	1.0	1.2	1.1	0.8	8.2
1964	54.9	25.0	9.9	3.5	3.9	1.0	1.2	1.1	0.7	8.4
1965	55.8	25.4	10.3	3.5	3.8	1.0	1.2	1.1	0.8	8.7
1966	58.1	27.1	10.3	3.6	4.8	0.9	1.3	1.2	0.8	8.1
1967	57.3	26.8	10.2	3.6	3.8	1.0	1.5	1.3	0.8	8.3
1968	57.6	27.5	9.4	3.7[f]	3.7[f]	1.6[f]	1.2[f]	1.3	0.8	8.4
1969	57.8	27.7	8.9	3.8	3.6	1.8	1.2	1.5	0.8	8.5
1970	56.2	26.8	8.3	3.9	3.3	1.4	1.2	1.8	0.8	8.7
1971	54.8	26.3	8.1	3.6	3.3	1.4	1.1	1.8	0.8	8.4
1972	55.2	26.9	8.0	3.6	3.2	1.4	1.2	1.8	0.8	8.3
1973	54.8	26.3	7.8	4.1	3.1	1.4	1.2	1.7	0.8	8.4

See source and footnotes on page 55.

Unintentional-injury-related death rates[a] for principal types, United States, 1903-1998 (cont.)

Year	Total	Motor vehicle	Falls	Drowning[b]	Fire, flames, or smoke[c]	Choking[c]	Firearms	Poison (solid or liquid)	Poison (gas or vapor)	All other
1974	49.0	21.8	7.7	3.7	2.9	1.4	1.2	1.8	0.7	7.8
1975	47.8	21.3	6.9	3.7	2.8	1.4	1.1	2.2	0.7	7.7
1976	46.3	21.6	6.5	3.1	2.9	1.4	0.9	1.9	0.7	7.3
1977	47.0	22.5	6.3	3.2	2.9	1.4	0.9	1.5	0.7	7.6
1978	47.5	23.6	6.2	3.2	2.8	1.4	0.8	1.4	0.8	7.3
1979	46.9	23.8	5.9	3.1	2.7	1.4	0.9	1.4	0.7	7.0
1980	46.5	23.4	5.9	3.2	2.6	1.4	0.9	1.4	0.5	7.2
1981	43.9	22.4	5.5	2.7	2.5	1.5	0.8	1.4	0.6	6.5
1982	40.6	19.8	5.2	2.7	2.2	1.4	0.8	1.5	0.5	6.5
1983	39.6	19.0	5.1	2.7	2.2	1.4	0.7	1.4	0.5	6.6
1984	39.4	19.6	5.1	2.3	2.1	1.5	0.7	1.6	0.5	6.0
1985	39.3	19.3	5.0	2.2	2.1	1.5	0.7	1.7	0.5	6.3
1986	39.7	19.9	4.8	2.4	2.0	1.5	0.6	2.0	0.4	6.1
1987	39.2	19.9	4.8	2.1	1.9	1.5	0.6	1.8	0.4	6.2
1988	39.7	20.1	4.9	2.0	2.0	1.6	0.6	2.2	0.4	5.9
1989	38.5	19.3	4.9	1.9	1.9	1.4	0.6	2.3	0.4	5.8
1990	36.9	18.8	4.9	1.9	1.7	1.3	0.6	2.0	0.3	5.4
1991	35.4	17.3	5.0	1.8	1.6	1.3	0.6	2.3	0.3	5.2
1992	34.0	16.1	5.0	1.4	1.6	1.2	0.6	2.5	0.2	5.4
1993	35.1	16.3	5.1	1.5	1.5	1.2	0.6	3.1	0.3	5.5
1994	35.1	16.3	5.2	1.5	1.5	1.2	0.5	3.2	0.3	5.4
1995	35.5	16.5	5.3	1.7	1.4	1.2	0.5	3.2	0.2	5.5
1996	35.8	16.5	5.6	1.5	1.4	1.2	0.4	3.3	0.2	5.7
1997	35.7	16.2	5.8	1.5	1.3	1.2	0.4	3.6	0.2	5.5
1998	36.2	16.1	6.0	1.6	1.2	1.3	0.3	3.8	0.2	5.7

Unintentional-injury-related death rates[a] for principal types, United States, 1999-2013

Year	Total	Motor vehicle	Falls	Poisoning	Choking[c]	Drowning[g]	Fire, flames, or smoke[c]	Mechanical suffocation	Firearms	All other
1999[h]	35.9	15.5	4.8	4.5	1.4	1.3	1.2	0.6	0.3	6.3
2000	35.6	15.7	4.8	4.6	1.6	1.3	1.2	0.5	0.3	5.5
2001	35.6	15.4	5.3	4.9	1.5	1.2	1.2	0.5	0.3	5.5
2002	37.1	15.8	5.6	6.4	1.4	1.2	1.1	0.5	0.3	4.7
2003	37.6	15.4	5.9	6.7	1.5	1.1	1.2	0.4	0.3	5.1
2004	38.1	15.3	6.4	7.1	1.5	1.1	1.1	0.5	0.2	4.9
2005	39.7	15.3	6.6	8.0	1.5	1.2	1.1	0.5	0.3	5.3
2006	40.8	15.2	7.0	9.2	1.5	1.2	1.0	0.5	0.2	4.9
2007	41.1	14.6	7.5	9.9	1.4	1.1	1.1	0.5	0.2	4.8
2008	40.0	13.1	7.9	10.2	1.4	1.2	1.0	0.6	0.2	4.7
2009	38.5	11.8	8.1	10.3	1.4	1.1	0.9	0.5	0.2	4.1
2010	39.0	11.4	8.4	10.7	1.5	1.2	0.9	0.5	0.9	4.4
2011[i]	40.6	11.3	8.8	11.6	1.5	1.1	0.9	0.5	0.2	4.6
2012[i]	40.7	11.6	9.2	11.6	1.5	1.1	0.8	0.5	0.2	4.3
2013[j]	41.4	11.2	9.6	12.3	1.5	1.2	0.8	0.6	0.2	4.2
Changes										
2004 to 2013	9%	-27%	50%	73%	0%	9%	-27%	20%	0%	-14%
2012 to 2013	2%	-3%	4%	6%	0%	9%	0%	20%	0%	-2%

Source: National Safety Council estimates. See Technical Appendix for comparability.
[a]*Deaths per 100,000 population.*
[b]*Includes drowning in water transport incidents.*
[c]*Fire, flames, or smoke includes burns by fire and deaths resulting from conflagration regardless of nature of injury. Choking is the inhalation of food or other object obstructing breathing.*
[d]*Comparable data not available.*
[e]*In 1948, a revision was made in the International Classification of Diseases. The first figures for 1948 are comparable with those for earlier years, the second with those for later years.*
[f]*Data are not comparable to previous years shown due to classification changes in 1958 and 1968.*
[g]*Excludes water transport drownings.*
[h]*In 1999, a revision was made in the International Classification of Diseases. See the Technical Appendix for comparability.*
[i]*Revised.*
[j]*Preliminary.*

Occupational

Occupational Injuries and Illnesses With Days Away From Work, United States, 2012

1,153,980 Injuries

905,690 (78%)
Private industry

181,340 (16%)
Local governments

66,950 (6%)
State governments

219,630 (24%)
Slips, trips, or falls

127,290
Othe

...imately 9,060 injured people
...imately 9,060 injured service workers
...imately 9,060 injured goods-producing w...

NATIONAL SAFETY CO...

Occupational Non-Fatal Injury and Illness Undercount — pg. 72

Over the last several years, there has been increasing concern that occupational injuries and illnesses are being underestimated.

A study in Washington State conducted interviews with organizations to determine the factors that may be contributing to the undercount. The study found that most organizations (90%) did not comply with OSHA recordkeeping regulations. Undercounting appears to be worse in organizations that use injury data to evaluate the performance of those responsible for maintaining the injury data.

**Workplace
Safety**

National Safety Council

The 2013 fatality data presented in this section are preliminary. All Census of Fatal Occupational Injuries fatal injury rates published by the Bureau of Labor Statistics (BLS) for the years 1992-2007 were employment-based, and measured the risk of fatal injury for those employed during a given period of time, regardless of hours worked.

Starting in 2008, BLS moved to hours-based rates to measure fatal injury risk per standardized length of exposure, which are generally considered more accurate than employment-based rates. Caution should be used when comparing fatality rates prior to 2008.

In addition to unintentional fatal work injuries, 667 homicides and suicides occurred in the workplace in 2013. These intentional injuries are not included in the unintentional-injury data shown here.

The State Data section, which begins on page 171, shows fatal occupational injuries and nonfatal injury and illness incidence rates by state.

Unintentional-injury-related deaths 3,738
Unintentional-injury-related deaths per 100,000 full-time equivalent workers[a] 2.8
Medically consulted injuries 4,800,000
Workers 145,171,000
Costs .... $206.1 billion

Unintentional injuries at work by industry (preliminary), United States, 2013

Industry division	Hours worked[a] (millions)	Deaths[a]		Deaths per 100,000 full-time equivalent workers[a]		Medically consulted injuries[c]
		2013	Change from 2012	2013	Change from 2012	
All industries	268,127	3,738	-4%	2.8	-7%	4,800,000
Agriculture[b]	4,238	459	-8%	21.7	-6%	120,000
Mining[b]	2,508	153	-14%	12.2	-22%	30,000
Construction	16,972	770	-1%	9.1	-5%	320,000
Manufacturing	30,211	272	-4%	1.8	-5%	600,000
Wholesale trade	7,484	169	-9%	4.5	-8%	120,000
Retail trade	27,936	134	-10%	1.0	-9%	530,000
Transportation and warehousing	10,477	625	-7%	11.9	-10%	250,000
Utilities	1,802	22	0%	2.4	-4%	20,000
Information	5,489	33	6%	1.2	9%	40,000
Financial activities	18,889	49	-13%	0.5	-17%	120,000
Professional and business services	31,046	349	-3%	2.2	-8%	250,000
Educational and health services	39,936	102	-4%	0.5	0%	880,000
Leisure and hospitality	21,514	104	-24%	1.0	-23%	410,000
Other services[b]	12,429	132	8%	2.1	5%	160,000
Government	37,095	365	12%	2.0	11%	960,000

Source: Deaths are preliminary data from the Bureau of Labor Statistics (BLS) Census of Fatal Occupational Injuries. All other figures are National Safety Council estimates based on data from BLS.
[a]Deaths include persons of all ages. Workers and death rates include persons 16 or older. The rate is calculated as: (number of fatal work injuries x 200,000,000/ total hours worked). The base for 100,000 full-time equivalent workers is 200,000,000 hours. Prior to 2008, rates were based on estimated employment – not hours worked.
[b]Agriculture includes forestry, fishing, and hunting. Mining includes oil and gas extraction. "Other services" excludes public administration.
[c]See Technical Appendix for the definition of medically consulted injury.

Occupational unintentional-injury-related deaths and death rates by industry, United States, 2013

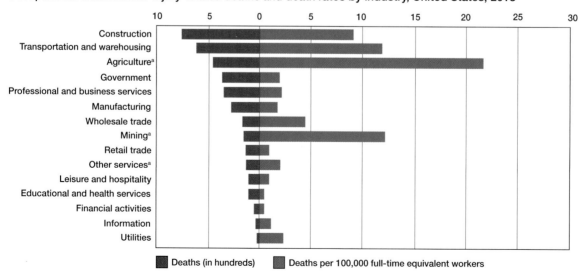

Deaths (in hundreds)   Deaths per 100,000 full-time equivalent workers

[a] Agriculture includes forestry, fishing, and hunting. Mining includes oil and gas extraction. "Other services" excludes public administration.

Occupational Injuries and Illnesses With Days Away From Work, United States, 2012

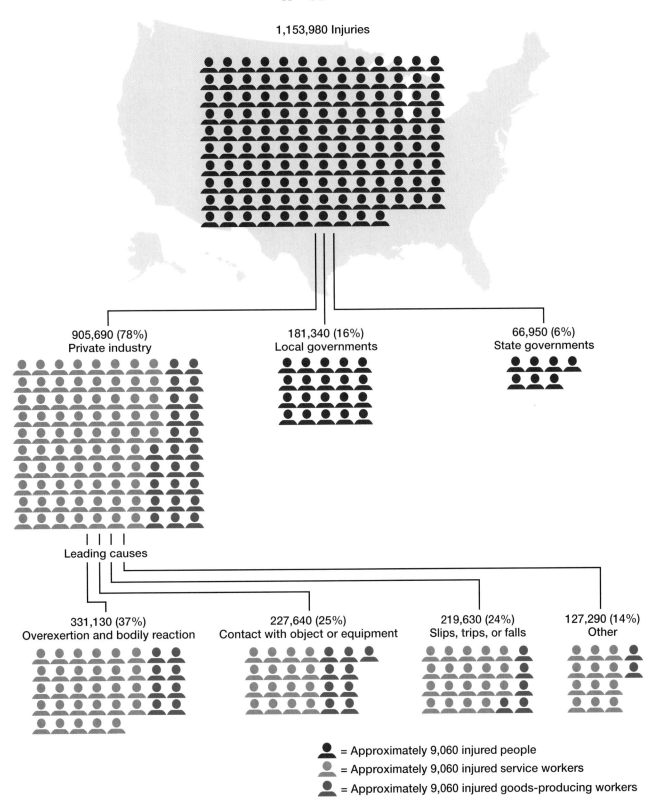

1,153,980 Injuries

905,690 (78%)
Private industry

181,340 (16%)
Local governments

66,950 (6%)
State governments

Leading causes

331,130 (37%)
Overexertion and bodily reaction

227,640 (25%)
Contact with object or equipment

219,630 (24%)
Slips, trips, or falls

127,290 (14%)
Other

● = Approximately 9,060 injured people
● = Approximately 9,060 injured service workers
● = Approximately 9,060 injured goods-producing workers

Unintentional-work-related-injury deaths and death rates, United States, 1992-2013

Year	Deaths	Workers (in thousands)	Hours worked[a] (in millions)	Deaths per 100,000 workers[a]
1992	4,965	119,168		4.2
1993	5,034	120,778		4.2
1994	5,338	124,470		4.3
1995	5,015	126,248		4.0
1996	5,069	127,997		4.0
1997	5,160	130,810		3.9
1998	5,117	132,772		3.9
1999	5,184	134,688		3.8
2000	5,022	136,402		3.7
2001	5,042	136,246		3.7
2002	4,726	137,731		3.4
2003	4,725	138,988		3.4
2004	4,995	140,504		3.6
2005	4,984	142,946		3.5
2006	5,088	145,607		3.5
2007	4,829	147,203		3.3
2008[a]	4,423	146,535	271,958	3.3[a]
2009	3,744	141,102	254,771	2.9
2010	3,896	140,298	255,948	3.0
2011	3,901	140,298	258,293	3.0
2012[b]	3,903	143,709	264,374	3.0
2013[c]	3,738	145,171	268,127	2.8

Source: Deaths are from the Bureau of Labor Statistics (BLS) Census of Fatal Occupational Injuries (CFOI). Employment is from BLS and is based on the Current Population Survey. All other data are National Safety Council estimates.
Note: Deaths include persons of all ages. Workers and death rates include persons 16 and older. Workers are persons 16 years and older who are gainfully employed, including owners, managers, other paid employees, the self-employed, unpaid family workers, and active-duty resident military personnel. Because of adoption of CFOI, deaths and rates from 1992 to present are not comparable to prior years. See the Technical Appendix for additional information.
[a]Starting in 2008, BLS moved from employment-based rates to hours-based rates to measure fatal injury risk per standardized length of exposure, which are generally considered more accurate than employment-based rates. Caution should be used when comparing with rates prior to 2008.
[b]Revised.
[c]Preliminary. BLS urges caution when using preliminary estimates.

Workers, unintentional-work-related-injury deaths, and death rates, United States, 1992-2013

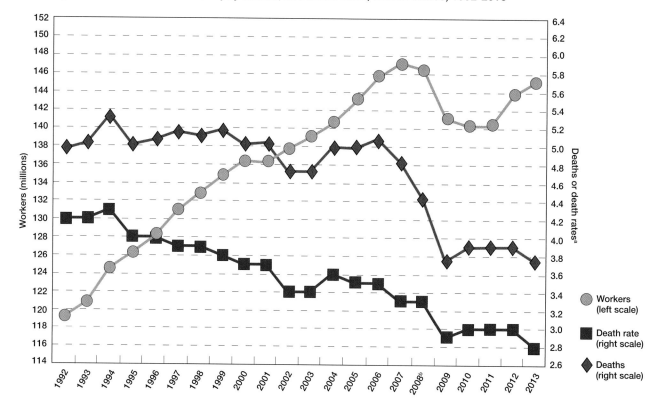

[a]Deaths in thousands; rate per 100,000 workers.
[b]Starting in 2008, the Bureau of Labor Statistics changed from an employment-based rate to an hours-based rate.

OCCUPATIONAL

Work, 2013 (cont.)

Occupational injury-related deaths and death rates, United States, 1993-2002

Year	Total	Homicide and suicide	Unintentional								
			All industries[a]	Agriculture[b]	Mining, quarrying[c]	Construction	Manufacturing	Transportation and public utilities	Trade[d]	Services[e]	Government
Deaths											
1993	6,331	1,297	5,034	842	169	895	698	753	450	631	527
1994	6,632	1,294	5,338	814	177	1,000	734	819	492	676	534
1995	6,275	1,260	5,015	769	155	1,021	640	784	461	608	528
1996	6,202	1,133	5,069	762	151	1,025	660	883	451	615	321
1997	6,238	1,078	5,160	799	156	1,075	678	882	451	593	504
1998	6,055	938	5,117	808	143	1,136	631	830	443	634	465
1999	6,054	870	5,184	776	122	1,168	671	918	425	623	451
2000	5,920	898	5,022	693	153	1,114	624	872	447	643	460
2001	5,915	873[f]	5,042	714	169	1,183	546	844	431	636	507
2002	5,534	808	4,726	758	120	1,092	523	843	381	569	437
Deaths per 100,000 workers											
1993	5.2	1.0	4.2	26.0	25.3	13.3	3.6	11.0	1.8	1.6	2.6
1994	5.3	1.0	4.3	22.8	26.5	14.4	3.7	11.6	1.9	1.7	2.7
1995	4.9	1.0	4.0	21.4	24.8	14.3	3.1	11.0	1.8	1.5	2.7
1996	4.8	0.9	4.0	21.2	26.6	13.7	3.2	12.2	1.7	1.4	1.6
1997	4.8	0.8	3.9	22.5	24.7	13.7	3.3	11.6	1.7	1.3	2.6
1998	4.5	0.7	3.9	22.7	23.1	14.1	3.1	10.8	1.6	1.4	2.4
1999	4.5	0.6	3.8	22.6	21.7	13.8	3.4	11.5	1.5	1.3	2.2
2000	4.3	0.7	3.7	20.1	29.4	12.4	3.1	10.8	1.6	1.4	2.3
2001	4.3	0.6[f]	3.7	22.0	29.9	13.0	2.9	10.4	1.6	1.3	2.5
2002	4.0	0.6	3.4	21.8	23.3	11.9	2.9	10.5	1.4	1.1	2.1

Source: Deaths are from the Bureau of Labor Statistics (BLS) Census of Fatal Occupational Injuries. Rates are National Safety Council estimates based on BLS employment data. Deaths include persons of all ages. Death rates include persons 16 or older. Industry divisions are based on the Standard Industrial Classification Manual.
[a]Includes deaths with industry unknown.
[b]Agriculture includes forestry, fishing, and agricultural services.
[c]Mining includes oil and gas extraction.
[d]Trade includes wholesale and retail trade.
[e]Services includes finance, insurance, and real estate.
[f]Excludes 2,886 homicides of workers on Sept. 11, 2001.

Occupational injury-related deaths and death rates, United States, 2003-2013

Year	Total	Homicide and suicide	Unintentional															
			All industries[a]	Agriculture, forestry, fishing, and hunting	Mining	Construction	Manufacturing	Wholesale trade	Retail trade	Transportation and warehousing	Utilities	Information	Financial activities	Professional and business services	Educational and health services	Leisure and hospitality	Other services	Government
Deaths																		
2003	5,575	850	4,725	676	141	1,094	379	169	148	735	29	57	82	396	116	142	123	434
2004	5,764	769	4,995	651	151	1,203	421	187	189	779	49	49	68	401	123	144	144	432
2005	5,734	750	4,984	697	154	1,161	357	197	198	831	28	56	66	442	122	114	149	404
2006	5,840	752	5,088	635	190	1,199	423	210	190	803	52	61	82	407	142	136	142	409
2007	5,657	828	4,829	564	180	1,163	364	193	160	819	33	70	69	415	121	138	116	421
2008	5,214	791	4,423	640	173	937	364	157	158	724	37	36	65	351	110	118	130	414
2009	4,551	807	3,744	545	96	793	290	168	137	576	13	28	58	363	101	119	110	347
2010	4,690	794	3,896	603	170	744	284	157	148	595	26	32	65	316	133	142	131	350
2011	4,692	791	3,901	532	148	706	293	173	133	692	34	47	49	374	109	137	122	352
2012[b]	4,628	725	3,903	500	177	775	284	185	149	670	22	31	56	360	106	136	122	327
2013[c]	4,405	667	3,738	459	153	770	272	169	134	625	22	33	49	349	102	104	132	365
Deaths per 100,000 workers[d]																		
2003	4.0	0.6	3.4	30.0	26.9	11.4	2.3	3.8	0.9	16.0	3.3	1.6	0.9	2.9	0.6	1.3	1.8	2.1
2004	4.1	0.5	3.6	29.7	28.1	11.7	2.6	4.1	1.2	16.7	5.9	1.5	0.7	2.9	0.7	1.3	2.1	2.0
2005	4.0	0.5	3.5	31.7	24.8	10.8	2.2	4.3	1.2	16.7	3.4	1.7	0.7	3.2	0.6	1.0	2.1	1.9
2006	4.0	0.5	3.5	29.1	27.8	10.6	2.6	4.6	1.1	15.7	6.2	1.8	0.8	2.8	0.7	1.2	2.0	1.9
2007	3.8	0.5	3.3	26.9	24.7	10.2	2.2	4.4	1.0	15.6	3.9	2.1	0.7	2.7	0.6	1.2	1.7	1.9
2008[d]	3.8	0.6	3.3	29.4	17.8	9.4	2.3	3.8	1.1	13.6	4.0	1.1	0.7	2.4	0.6	1.1	2.1	2.1
2009	3.6	0.6	2.9	26.3	12.2	9.5	2.1	4.4	1.0	12.1	1.4	1.0	0.6	2.7	0.5	1.2	1.8	1.8
2010	3.7	0.6	3.0	27.9	19.6	9.4	2.0	4.1	1.0	12.4	2.8	1.1	0.7	2.3	0.7	1.4	2.2	1.8
2011	3.6	0.6	3.0	24.1	15.2	8.8	2.0	4.5	1.0	14.2	3.7	1.6	0.6	2.6	0.6	1.4	2.1	1.9
2012[b]	3.5	0.5	3.0	23.1	15.6	9.6	1.9	4.9	1.1	13.2	2.5	1.1	0.6	2.4	0.5	1.3	2.0	1.8
2013[c]	3.3	0.5	2.8	21.7	12.2	9.1	1.8	4.5	1.0	11.9	2.4	1.2	0.5	2.2	0.5	1.0	2.1	2.0

Source: Deaths are from the Bureau of Labor Statistics (BLS) Census of Fatal Occupational Injuries. Rates are National Safety Council estimates based on BLS employment data. Deaths include persons of all ages. Death rates include persons 16 or older. Industry sectors are based on the North American Industry Classification System.
[a]Includes deaths with industry unknown.
[b]Revised.
[c]Preliminary. BLS urges caution when using preliminary estimates.
[d]Starting in 2008, BLS moved from employment-based rates to hours-based rates to measure fatal injury risk per standardized length of exposure. Caution should be used when comparing with rates prior to 2008.

Work Injury Costs

The true cost to the nation, employers, and individuals of work-related deaths and injuries is much greater than the cost of workers' compensation insurance alone. The figures presented below show National Safety Council estimates of the total economic costs of occupational deaths and injuries. Cost-estimating procedures were revised for the 1993 edition of Accident Facts and additional revisions were made for the 2005-2006 edition of *Injury Facts*®. For this reason, *costs should not be compared to prior years.*

TOTAL COST IN 2013 ....$206.1 BILLION

Includes wage and productivity losses of $91.0 billion, medical costs of $57.9 billion, and administrative expenses of $40.6 billion. Includes employers' uninsured costs of $11.5 billion, such as the money value of time lost by workers other than those with disabling injuries; who are directly or indirectly involved in injuries; and the cost of time required to investigate injuries, write up injury reports, etc. Also includes damage to motor vehicles in work-related injuries of $2.3 billion and fire losses of $2.8 billion.

COST PER WORKER $1,400

Includes the value of goods or services each worker must produce to offset the cost of work injuries. It is *not* the average cost of a work-related injury.

COST PER DEATH $1,450,000

COST PER MEDICALLY CONSULTED INJURY $42,000

Includes estimates of wage losses, medical expenses, administrative expenses, and employer costs; excludes property damage costs except to motor vehicles.

Time Lost Due to Work-Related Injuries

	Days lost
TOTAL TIME LOST IN 2013	95,000,000
Due to injuries in 2013	60,000,000

Includes primarily the actual time lost during the year from disabling injuries, except it does not include time lost on the day of the injury or time required for further medical treatment or check-up following the injured person's return to work.

Fatalities are included at an average loss of 150 days per case, and permanent impairments are included at actual days lost plus an allowance for lost efficiency resulting from the impairment.

Not included is time lost by people with nondisabling injuries or other people directly or indirectly involved in the incidents.

	Days lost
Due to injuries in prior years	35,000,000

Represents productive time lost in 2013 due to permanently disabling injuries that occurred in prior years.

	Days lost
TIME LOST IN FUTURE YEARS FROM 2013 INJURIES	45,000,000

Includes time lost in future years due to on-the-job deaths and permanently disabling injuries that occurred in 2013.

Worker Deaths and Injuries On and Off the Job

Nine out of 10 deaths and about 74% of the medically consulted injuries[a] suffered by workers in 2013 occurred off the job. While over 14 times the number of deaths occur off the job compared to on the job (14.3 to 1), nearly three times as many medically consulted injuries occur off the job (2.9 to 1).

Production time lost due to off-the-job injuries totaled about 240,000,000 days in 2013, compared with 60,000,000 days lost by workers injured on the job.

Production time lost in future years due to off-the-job injuries in 2013 will total an estimated 525,000,000 days, nearly 12 times the 45,000,000 days lost in future years from 2013's on-the-job injuries.

Off-the-job injuries to workers cost the nation at least $280.7 billion in 2013 compared with $206.1 billion for on-the-job injuries.

Workers' on- and off-the-job deaths and injuries, United States, 2013

Place	Deaths		Medically consulted injuries[a]	
	Number	Rate[b]	Number	Rate[b]
On and off the job	57,338	0.013	18,600,000	4.4
On the job	3,738	0.002	4,800,000	3.1
Off the job	53,600	0.019	13,800,000	5.0
Motor vehicle	17,900	0.062	2,200,000	7.6
Public non-motor vehicle	8,900	0.020	3,500,000	7.8
Home	26,800	0.013	8,100,000	4.0

Source: National Safety Council estimates. Procedures for allocating time spent on and off the job were revised for the 1990 edition. Rate basis changed to 200,000 hours for the 1998 edition. Death and injury rates are not comparable to rate estimates prior to the 1998 edition.
[a]Medically consulted injuries are not comparable to estimates provided in earlier editions that used the definition of disabling injury. Please see the Technical Appendix for more information on medically consulted injuries.
[b]Per 200,000 hours exposure by place.

Workers' on- and off-the-job injuries, United States, 2013

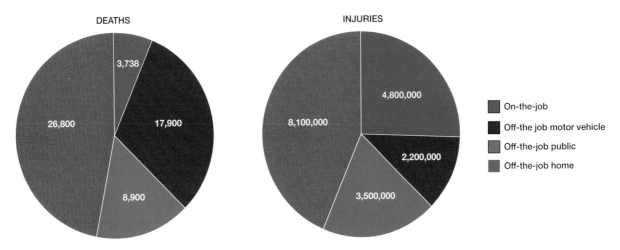

Workers' off-the-job fatalities by event, 2013

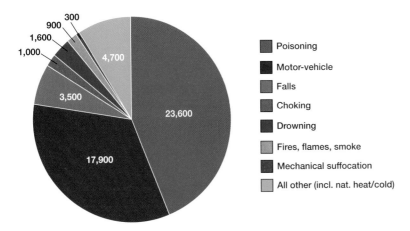

Workers' Compensation Cases

According to the National Academy of Social Insurance, an estimated $61.9 billion, including benefits under deductible provisions, was paid out under workers' compensation in 2012 (the latest year for which data were available) – an increase of 1.3% from 2011. Of this total, $31.0 billion was for income benefits and $30.8 billion was for medical and hospitalization costs. Private carriers paid about $33.4 billion of the total workers' compensation benefits in 2012. In 2012, approximately 127.9 million workers were covered by workers' compensation – an increase of 1.6% from the 125.8 million in 2011.

The table below shows the trend in the number of compensated or reported cases in each reporting state. Due to the differences in population, industries, and coverage of compensation laws, comparisons among states should not be made.

Workers' compensation cases, 2011-2013

State	Deaths[a]			Cases[a]			2012 compensation paid ($000)
	2013	2012	2011	2013	2012	2011	
Alabama	16	32	45	13,471	14,809	15,043	649,682
Alaska	17	27	37	19,140	19,726	21,213	248,038
Arkansas[b]	73	86	98	6,624	7,525	8,048	213,971
California	441	504	581	561,702	570,425	567,227	11,503,654
Colorado[c]	–	88	72	–	26,757	24,372	845,136
Delaware	–	14	10	–	13,478	15,814	215,518
Florida[d]	101	111	127	51,696	56,339	57,828	2,835,750
Illinois	–	139	149	42,701	44,600	49,236	2,702,471
Iowa[c]	48	49	68	15,645	16,782	17,576	642,147
Kansas	51	33	54	55,269	57,542	57,181	424,122
Kentucky[c]	–	28	45	–	38,742	33,850	659,192
Michigan[c]	410	435	451	47,860	50,319	51,743	1,189,483
Minnesota[e]	–	49	35	–	96,000	95,700	1,043,694
Mississippi[b]	62	67	84	10,834	11,313	11,845	336,208
Missouri	92	78	117	101,720	105,650	109,648	838,913
Montana	29	31	54	25,121	25,351	25,905	250,542
Nebraska	35	50	41	40,411	42,552	43,659	312,448
New Hampshire	18	16	20	38,998	39,502	39,954	229,024
New Mexico	–	34	34	–	20,726	21,672	306,304
North Carolina	88	98	12	64,515	55,268	59,182	1,425,596
Oregon[b]	29	30	28	18,634	18,463	18,693	660,553
Pennsylvania	–	101	110	110,319	85,117	83,144	2,910,262
Rhode Island	4	2	3	19,184	18,935	19,539	177,664
South Carolina[b]	62	82	72	62,213	61,788	67,354	905,405
Tennessee[f]	94	96	95	98,892	101,950	102,258	803,103
Virginia	49	71	72	133,193	143,271	144,581	913,755
West Virginia	18	17	13	31,018	34,381	40,058	470,251
Wyoming	15	5	6	12,955	13,239	13,451	162,304

Source: Deaths and Cases–State workers' compensation authorities for calendar or fiscal year. States not listed did not respond to the survey. Compensation paid–Sengupta, I., Baldwin, M. L., & Reno, V. (2014 August). Workers' compensation: benefits, coverage, and costs, 2012. Washington, DC: National Academy of Social Insurance.

Note: Dash (–) indicates data not available.

Definitions

Reported case: A reported case may or may not be work-related and may not receive compensation.

Compensated case: A case determined to be work-related and for which compensation was paid.

[a]Reported cases involving medical and indemnity benefits, unless otherwise noted.

[b]Closed or compensated cases only.

[c]Reported cases involving indemnity benefits only.

[d]Lost-time only cases involving medical and indemnity benefits.

[e]Number of paid cases by year, projected to full maturity.

[f]Includes reported and closed or compensated cases.

Disabling Workplace Injuries and Illnesses

The most disabling workplace injuries and illnesses in 2011 amounted to $55.4 billion in direct workers' compensation costs, according to the 2013 Liberty Mutual Workplace Safety Index (WSI). The WSI combines information from Liberty Mutual, the Bureau of Labor Statistics, and the National Academy of Social Insurance to identify the top causes of serious workplace injuries—those that cause an employee to miss six or more days of work. The 2013 WSI begins a new series reflecting a significant change in the Bureau of Labor Statistics' injury event coding and its results are not directly comparable to those of the prior series.

The top 10 causes of serious workplace injuries produced about 85% of the direct workers' compensation costs of disabling work-place injuries in 2011. Overexertion injuries involving an outside source were the largest contributor to the overall burden, accounting for $14.2 billion, or nearly 26%, of the total cost. "Fall on the same level" ($8.6 billion) and "struck by object or equipment" ($5.6 billion) were the next most costly injury causes. The cost of the combined fall categories was slightly less than the cost for the "overexertion" category, indicating that total falls were comparable to "overexertion" in terms of impact on the overall cost burden.

Source: 2013 Liberty Mutual Workplace Safety Index, accessed July 29, 2014 from www.libertymutualgroup.com/researchinstitute.

Worker' compensation costs for the top 10 causes of disabling workplace injuries, United States, 2011

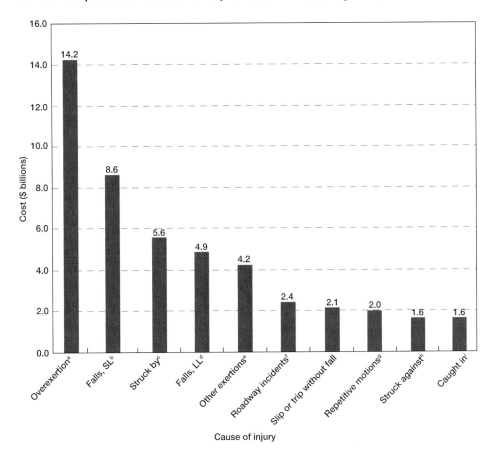

^aOverexertion involving an outside source; includes injuries from excessive lifting, pushing, pulling, holding, carrying, or throwing.
^bFalls on same level.
^cStruck by object–such as a tool falling on a worker from above.
^dFalls to lower level.
^eOther exertions or bodily reactions; includes injuries from bending, crawling, reaching, twisting, climbing, stepping, kneeling, sitting, standing, or walking (and no longer includes slipping or tripping without falling).
^fRoadway incidents involving motorized land vehicle.
^gRepetitive motions involving micro-tasks.
^hStruck against object or equipment--such as a worker walking into a door.
ⁱCaught in or compressed by equipment or objects.

Workers' Compensation Claims Costs, 2011-2012

■ *Head injuries are the most costly workers' compensation claims.*

The data in the graphs on this and the next page are from the National Council on Compensation Insurance's (NCCI) Workers Compensation Statistical Plan (WCSP) database.[a] WCSP reflects claims experience on workers' compensation insurance policies issued in states in which NCCI collects such data. The aggregate unit statistical data were valued 30 months after the inception date of the policy (as of the second report). The average cost for all claims combined in 2011-2012 was $36,894.

NCCI data that appeared in *Injury Facts* prior to the 2011 edition were sourced to NCCI's Detailed Claim Information file, which was a stratified random sample of lost-time claims in 42 states. Workers' compensation estimates provided in this edition are not comparable to estimates provided in editions prior to 2011.

Cause of injury. The most costly lost-time workers' compensation claims by cause of injury, according to NCCI data, are for those resulting from motor vehicle crashes. These injuries averaged $72,540 per workers' compensation claim filed in 2011 and 2012. The only other causes with above-average costs were falls or slips ($43,035) and burns ($39,402).

Nature of injury. The most costly lost-time workers' compensation claims by nature of injury are for those resulting from amputation. These injuries averaged $72,019 per workers' compensation claim filed in 2011 and 2012. The next highest costs were for injuries resulting in fracture, crush, or dislocation ($52,712); other trauma ($44,621); and burns ($39,326).

Part of body. The most costly lost-time workers' compensation claims are for those involving the head or central nervous system. These injuries averaged $80,882 per claim filed in 2011 and 2012. The next highest costs were for injuries involving multiple body parts ($58,667) and the neck ($58,055). Injuries to the hip, thigh, and pelvis; leg; arm or shoulders; and lower back also had above-average costs.

Average total incurred costs per claim by cause of injury, 2011-2012

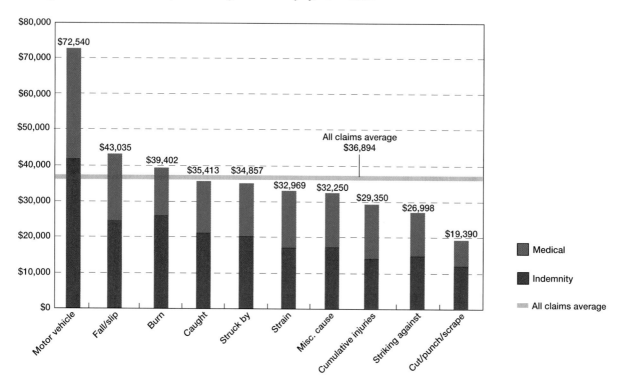

[a] *The National Council on Compensation Insurance makes no representations or warranties of any kind nor assumes any responsibility for the accuracy of the underlying data or any third-party use of the data on this and the following page.*

Average total incurred costs per claim by nature of injury, 2011-2012

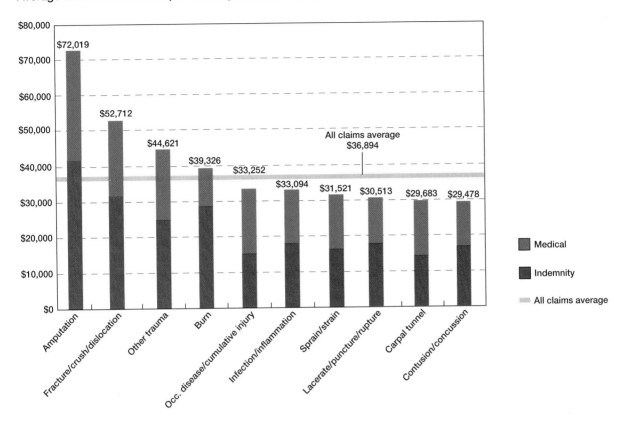

Amputation — $72,019
Fracture/crush/dislocation — $52,712
Other trauma — $44,621
Burn — $39,326
Occ. disease/cumulative injury — $33,252
Infection/inflammation — $33,094
Sprain/strain — $31,521
Lacerate/puncture/rupture — $30,513
Carpal tunnel — $29,683
Contusion/concussion — $29,478

All claims average $36,894

Legend: Medical, Indemnity, All claims average

Average total incurred costs per claim by part of body, 2011-2012

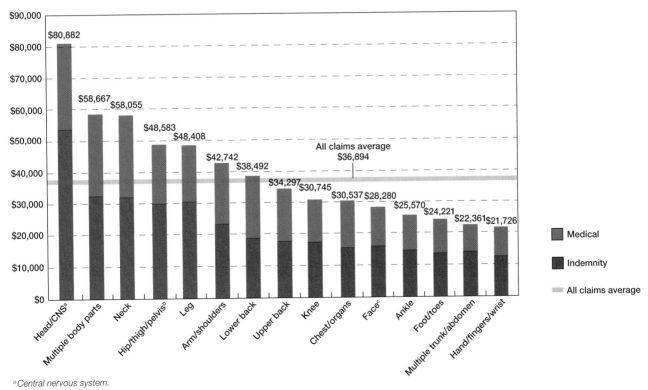

Head/CNS[a] — $80,882
Multiple body parts — $58,667
Neck — $58,055
Hip/thigh/pelvis[b] — $48,583
Leg — $48,408
Arm/shoulders — $42,742
Lower back — $38,492
Upper back — $34,297
Knee — $30,745
Chest/organs — $30,537
Face[c] — $28,280
Ankle — $25,570
Foot/toes — $24,221
Multiple trunk/abdomen — $22,361
Hand/fingers/wrist — $21,726

All claims average $36,894

Legend: Medical, Indemnity, All claims average

[a] Central nervous system.
[b] Includes sacrum and coccyx.
[c] Includes teeth, mouth, and eyes.

Forklifts

Beginning with 2011, occupational injury data from the Bureau of Labor Statistics are based on the revised Occupational Injury and Illness Classification System (OIICS) 2.01 and are not comparable to the data for prior years in the tables below. Fatal occupational injuries in private industry with a forklift as the primary source of injury numbered 67 in 2012, a 1% increase from 2011. There were an additional 27 fatal occupational injuries with a forklift as the secondary source of injury in 2012, up 12% from 2011. Forklift fatalities are most prevalent in the trade, transportation, and utilities; manufacturing; and construction industries.

The rate of nonfatal forklift injuries involving days away from work was 0.8 per 10,000 full-time workers in 2012, up from 0.7 in 2011. Natural resources and mining had the highest rate of nonfatal forklift injuries, followed by trade, transportation, and utilities and manufacturing.

Number of fatal occupational injuries with a forklift as the source of injury, private industry, United States, 2009-2012

Industry division	Year							
	2009		2010		2011[a]		2012[a]	
	Forklift as primary[b] source	Forklift as secondary[c] source	Forklift as primary[b] source	Forklift as secondary[c] source	Forklift as primary[b] source	Forklift as secondary[c] source	Forklift as primary[b] source	Forklift as secondary[c] source
All industries	58	33	54	31	66	24	67	27
Natural resources and mining[d]	6	–	5	–	8	–	6	4
Construction	11	8	8	4	11	4	9	5
Manufacturing	15	7	9	11	16	3	18	8
Trade, transportation, and utilities	22	13	21	13	24	9	28	10
Information	–	–	–	–	–	–	–	–
Financial activities	–	–	–	–	–	3	–	–
Professional and business services	–	–	7	–	6	3	–	–
Education and health services	–	–	–	–	–	–	–	–
Leisure and hospitality	–	–	–	–	–	–	–	–
Other services[d]	–	–	3	–	–	–	3	–

Source: Bureau of Labor Statistics (BLS) Census of Fatal Occupational Injuries and Illnesses, accessed August 29, 2014. Available at www.bls.gov/iif/oshcfoi1.htm. Data may not add to totals because of rounding or exclusion of data that do not meet publication guidelines. Dashes (–) indicate no data reported or data that do not meet publication guidelines.
[a]Data for 2011 and 2012 are based on the revised BLS Occupational Injury and Illness Classification System (OIICS) 2.01 and not comparable to data for prior years.
[b]The primary source of a fatal occupational injury is the object, substance, person, bodily motion, or exposure that most directly led to, produced, or inflicted the injury or illness.
[c]The secondary source of a fatal occupational injury is the object, substance, person, or exposure other than the source (if any) that most actively generated the source or contributed to the injury or illness.
[d]"Natural resources" includes agriculture, forestry, fishing, and hunting and excludes farms with fewer than 11 employees. "Mining" includes oil and gas extraction. "Other services" excludes public administration.

Incidence rates[a] of nonfatal occupational injuries and illnesses involving days away from work[b] with a forklift as the source of injury or illness, private industry, United States, 2006-2012

Industry division	All sources rate[a]	Forklift injury rate[a]						
	2012	2006	2007	2008	2009	2010	2011[c]	2012[c]
All industries	102.3	1.3	1.2	1.1	0.9	0.8	0.7	0.8
Natural resources and mining[d]	142.8	1.9	1.5	1.2	0.6	1.1	0.9	2.5
Construction	143.4	1.5	0.8	0.9	0.8	0.7	0.7	0.9
Manufacturing	106.2	2.4	2.3	2.0	1.5	1.9	1.5	1.6
Trade, transportation, and utilities	132.1	2.9	2.7	2.6	2.3	2.0	1.7	1.9
Information	63.2	0.4	0.3	0.5	0.2	0.2	0.1	0.1
Financial activities	38.2	0.1	0.0[e]	0.0[e]	0.2	0.0[e]	0.0[e]	0.0[e]
Professional and business services	52.0	0.5	0.4	0.3	0.4	0.3	0.2	0.2
Education and health services	121.8	0.1	0.0[e]	0.1	0.1	0.0[e]	0.0[e]	0.0[e]
Leisure and hospitality	103.1	0.1	0.1	0.1	0.0	0.0[e]	0.0[e]	0.0[e]
Other services[d]	92.2	0.3	0.1	0.2	0.1	0.3	0.2	0.2

Source: Bureau of Labor Statistics (BLS) Occupational Injuries and Illnesses and Fatal Injuries Profiles, accessed August 29, 2014. Available at http://data.bls.gov/gqt/InitialPage.
Dashes (–) indicate no data reported or data that do not meet publication guidelines.
[a]Incidence rates represent the number of injuries and illnesses per 10,000 full-time workers and were calculated as: (N/EH) x 20,000,000, where N = number of injuries and illnesses, EH = total hours worked by all employees during the calendar year, and 20,000,000 = base for 10,000 full-time equivalent workers (working 40 hours per week, 50 weeks per year).
[b]Days away from work include those that result in days away from work with or without restricted work activity.
[c]Data for 2011 and 2012 are based on the revised BLS Occupational Injury and Illness Classification System (OIICS) 2.01 and not comparable to data for prior years.
[d]"Natural resources" includes agriculture, forestry, fishing, and hunting and excludes farms with fewer than 11 employees. "Mining" includes oil and gas extraction. "Other services" excludes public administration.
[e]Rounded to zero.

Following highway crashes, falls to a lower level is the second leading unintentional fatal workplace event and the fifth leading event resulting in cases with days away from work. In 2012, 570 workers died while an additional 46,160 were injured. The 2012 fatality count represents about a 3% increase from 2011, while the nonfatal injuries represent a 1% decrease. From 2003, fall-to-a-lower-level fatalities have decreased more than 5%, while nonfatal cases with days away from work have decreased by 44%.

Fatal falls to a lower level typically involve injuries to the head or multiple body parts while nonfatal injuries most often involve the lower extremities, multiple body parts, upper extremities, or trunk. The most common nonfatal injuries include sprains, strains, or tears, followed by fractures. Falls to a lower level result in dramatically more days away from work than typical injury events. Fall-to-a-lower-level cases result in a median of 18 days away from work compared with eight days across all injury events. In fact, more than 42% of the fall-to-a-lower-level cases involving days away from work result in 31 or more lost workdays. Falls to a lower level resulting in days away from work most often occur on floors, walkways, or ground surfaces (34%) closely followed by ladders (33%). New employees are disproportionably represented, with 31% of nonfatal injuries involving workers with less than one year of service.

By far, construction is the industry most at risk from falls to a lower level. In 2012, 279 workers in the construction industry died as a result of falls to a lower level, representing 49% of all fall-to-a-lower-level fatalities. The fall-to-a-lower-level fatality rate in the construction industry is 3.4 per 100,000 workers, eight times the general industry rate of 0.4. Falls to a lower level also represent the single most dangerous injury event within the construction industry, representing 35% of all construction fatalities. The construction industry also experiences the most nonfatal cases involving days away from work, representing 19% of all nonfatal fall-to-a-lower-level cases with 8,860.

Compared to falls to a lower level, falls on the same level tend to result in less severe but more frequent injuries. In 2012, there were 131,280 fall-on-the-same-level cases involving days away from work and 120 fatalities. The rate for cases involving days away from work was 14.8 per 10,000 workers compared with 5.2 for falls to a lower level. Agriculture, forestry, fishing and hunting has the highest fall-on-the-same-level rate with 26.8 per 10,000 workers, followed by education and health services (23.3) and leisure and hospitality (21.8).

The following two pages provide injury profiles for both falls to a lower level and falls on the same level.

Source: This research was conducted with restricted access to Bureau of Labor Statistics (BLS) data. The views expressed here do not necessarily reflect the views of BLS

Workplace falls to a lower level, United States, 2003-2012

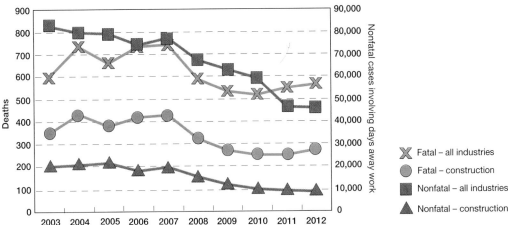

Source: National Safety Council analysis of Bureau of Labor Statistics data.

"Fall to lower level" applies to instances in which the injury was produced by impact between the injured person and another surface of lower elevation – the motion producing the contact being that of the person – under the following circumstances:

- The motion of the person and the force of impact were generated by gravity.

- The point of contact with the source of injury was lower than the surface supporting the person at the inception of the fall.

Fall to lower level ranks second behind highway crashes in number of workplace fatalities, and is the sixth leading event resulting in cases involving days away from work.

Fall-to-lower-level nonfatal occupational injuries and illnesses involving days away from work[a] and fatal occupational injuries by selected worker and case characteristics, United States, 2012

Characteristic	Private industry[b,c] nonfatal cases	All industries fatalities
Total	**46,160**	**570**
Sex		
Men	35,150	554
Women	10,970	16
Age		
Younger than 16	–	–
16 to 19	650	8
20 to 24	4,000	19
25 to 34	8,270	70
35 to 44	9,870	91
45 to 54	12,770	167
55 to 64	8,010	130
65 and older	1,900	85
Occupation		
Management, business, and financial	1,910	34
Professional and related	2,100	–
Service	6,300	83
Sales and related	3,470	11
Office and administrative support	2,340	5
Farming, fishing, and forestry	990	11
Construction and extractive	8,260	297
Installation, maintenance, and repair	6,320	44
Production	3,290	23
Transportation and material moving	11,160	58
Military occupations	–	–
Race or ethnic origin[d]		
White, non-Hispanic	20,220	365
Black, non-Hispanic	3,310	32
Hispanic	6,520	144
Other, multiple, and not reported	16,110	29
Nature of injury or illness		
Fractures	10,530	5
Sprains or strains tears	12,070	–
Amputations	–	–
Cuts, lacerations, or punctures	940	–
Bruises or contusions	6,140	–
Chemical burns and corrosions	–	–
Heat (thermal) burns	–	–
Multiple injuries	3,920	213
Soreness or pain	7,710	–
Carpal tunnel syndrome	–	–
Tendonitis	20	–
All other	4,820	346

Characteristic	Private industry[b,c] nonfatal cases	All industries fatalities
Part of body affected		
Head	2,270	237
Eye	*20*	*–*
Neck	530	27
Trunk	8,200	56
Back	*4,650*	*10*
Upper extremities	9,370	–
Shoulder	*3,120*	*–*
Arm	*2,180*	*–*
Wrist	*2,450*	*–*
Hand	*1,080*	*–*
Lower extremities	15,310	6
Knee	*3,970*	*–*
Ankle	*4,850*	*–*
Foot or toe	*2,370*	*–*
Body systems	40	28
Multiple	10,210	215
All other	220	–
Industry		
Agriculture, Forestry, Fishing, and Hunting	1,250	26
Mining	360	22
Construction	8,860	279
Manufacturing	5,190	29
Wholesale Trade	3,450	24
Retail Trade	5,880	19
Transportation and Warehousing	5,360	28
Utilities	240	–
Information	900	–
Financial Activities	1,460	16
Professional and Business Services	4,710	73
Education and Health Services	3,920	7
Leisure and Hospitality	3,320	12
Other Services	1,250	10
Government	N/A	22

Source: This research was conducted with restricted access to Bureau of Labor Statistics (BLS) data. The views expressed here do not necessarily reflect the views of BLS.

Note: Because of rounding and data exclusion of nonclassifiable responses, data may not sum to the totals. Dashes (–) indicate data that do not meet publication guidelines. "N/A" means not applicable.

[a]*Days away from work include those that result in days away from work with or without restricted work activity or job transfer.*

[b]*Excludes farms with fewer than 11 employees.*

[c]*Data for mining operators in coal, metal, and nonmetal mining and for employees in railroad transportation are provided to BLS by the Mine Safety and Health Administration, U.S. Department of Labor; and the Federal Railroad Administration, U.S. Department of Transportation. Independent mining contractors are excluded from the coal, metal, and nonmetal mining industries. MSHA and FRA data do not reflect the changes in OSHA recordkeeping requirements in 2002.*

[d]*In the fatalities column, non-Hispanic categories include cases with Hispanic origin not reported.*

Fall on Same Level

"Fall on same level" applies to instances in which the injury was produced by impact between the injured person and another surface without elevation – the motion producing the contact being that of the person – under the following circumstances:

- The motion of the person was generated by gravity following the employee's loss of equilibrium (the person was unable to maintain an upright position).

- The point of contact with the source of injury was at the same level or above the surface supporting the person at the inception of the fall.

Fall on same level ranks second behind overexertion in the number of nonfatal injuries involving days away from work, but generally is not one of the top 10 events resulting in fatalities.

Fall-on-same-level nonfatal occupational injuries and illnesses involving days away from work[a] and fatal occupational injuries by selected worker and case characteristics, United States, 2012

Characteristic	Private industry[b,c] nonfatal cases	All industries fatalities
Total	**131,280**	**120**
Sex		
Men	53,730	84
Women	77,520	36
Age		
Younger than 16	–	–
16 to 19	2,500	–
20 to 24	8,420	–
25 to 34	21,190	6
35 to 44	22,800	14
45 to 54	34,110	23
55 to 64	31,570	26
65 and older	9,290	50
Occupation		
Management, business, and financial	7,630	16
Professional and related	15,110	–
Service	40,650	37
Sales and related	11,840	15
Office and administrative support	12,300	8
Farming, fishing, and forestry	1,820	–
Construction and extractive	5,580	8
Installation, maintenance, and repair	6,960	–
Production	10,830	6
Transportation and material moving	18,280	20
Military occupations	–	–
Race or ethnic origin[d]		
White, non-Hispanic	54,090	85
Black, non-Hispanic	11,480	12
Hispanic	15,110	15
Other, multiple, and not reported	50,600	8
Nature of injury or illness		
Fractures	21,360	15
Sprains or strains tears	37,540	–
Amputations	–	–
Cuts, lacerations, or punctures	4,120	–
Bruises or contusions	21,840	–
Chemical burns and corrosions	–	–
Heat (thermal) burns	100	–
Multiple traumatic injuries	9,550	8
Soreness or pain	23,290	–
Carpal tunnel syndrome	–	–
Tendonitis	30	–
All other	13,440	90

Characteristic	Private industry[b,c] nonfatal cases	All industries fatalities
Part of body affected		
Head	8,580	71
Eye	*180*	–
Neck	850	7
Trunk	24,610	18
Back	*15,750*	–
Upper extremities	31,620	–
Shoulder	*9,430*	–
Arm	*7,210*	–
Wrist	*7,540*	–
Hand	*3,980*	–
Lower extremities	39,200	13
Knee	*20,330*	5
Ankle	*9,280*	–
Foot or toe	*3,080*	–
Body systems	410	–
Multiple	25,160	7
All other	850	–
Industry		
Agriculture, Forestry, Fishing, and Hunting	2,420	8
Mining	700	–
Construction	6,140	9
Manufacturing	12,240	7
Wholesale Trade	5,590	9
Retail Trade	19,250	21
Transportation and Warehousing	9,210	6
Utilities	420	–
Information	2,550	–
Financial Activities	4,070	–
Professional and Business Services	11,500	6
Education and Health Services	34,050	13
Leisure and Hospitality	18,900	13
Other Services	4,230	–
Government	N/A	18

Source: This research was conducted with restricted access to Bureau of Labor Statistics (BLS) data. The views expressed here do not necessarily reflect the views of BLS.

Note: Because of rounding and data exclusion of nonclassifiable responses, data may not sum to the totals. Dashes (–) indicate data that do not meet publication guidelines. "N/A" means not applicable.

[a]Days away from work include those that result in days away from work with or without restricted work activity or job transfer.

[b]Excludes farms with fewer than 11 employees.

[c]Data for mining operators in coal, metal, and nonmetal mining and for employees in railroad transportation are provided to BLS by the Mine Safety and Health Administration, U.S. Department of Labor; and the Federal Railroad Administration, U.S. Department of Transportation. Independent mining contractors are excluded from the coal, metal, and nonmetal mining industries. MSHA and FRA data do not reflect the changes in OSHA record eeping requirements in 2002.

[d]In the fatalities column, non-Hispanic categories include cases with Hispanic origin not reported.

Occupational Non-Fatal Injury and Illness Undercount

Occupational Injuries and Illnesses are being dramatically undercounted!

The Bureau of Labor Statistics (BLS) conducts two annual occupation injury surveillance programs, the Survey of Occupational Injury and Illnesses (SOII) and the Census of Fatal Occupational Injuries (CFOI). The SOII is an employer survey that provides non-fatal injury and illness estimates. While the CFOI is a surveillance program that uses multiple data sources in an attempt to provide a comprehensive count of every occupational fatality occurring in the United States. Over the last several years, there has been increasing concern that occupational injuries and illnesses are being underestimated. Provided below is a summary of recent research exploring the potential extent of the undercount as well as the factors that may be contributing to the issue.

Injuries

There is currently little concern that the number of fatal occupational injuries is being significantly undercounted. CFOI uses multiple data sources (including death certificates, state workers' compensation records, news media, and OSHA reports) to achieve a comprehensive estimate. The SOII estimates, however, may undercount non-fatal injuries and illnesses to a large degree.

A study in California linked SOII and workers' compensation records to estimate the proportion of injuries and illnesses involving at least four days away from work that are captured by SOII. Results found that SOII missed between 40% to 50% of claims (Boden, 2014). Another California study used three data sets (workers' compensation claims, health care facility data, and physician reports) to compile a comprehensive count of amputations and carpal tunnel syndrome (CTS) cases. The study identified a total of 6,862 amputation cases and 39,589 CTS cases in California in 2007 and 2008. In contrast, SOII estimated only 1,390 amputations and 3,720 CTS cases or 20% and 9% of the total, respectively (Joe et al. 2014). A Massachusetts study also investigated three data sets (workers' compensation records, hospital administrative records, and SOII) to calculate a comprehensive estimate of work-related amputations in 2007 and 2008. The study found a total of 787 amputations compared to the SOII estimate of 210. The estimated SOII undercount was 48%, although some of the missing SOII cases were reported as other injury types (Davis et al., 2014).

A study in Washington State conducted interviews with organizations to determine the factors that may be contributing to the undercount. The study found that most organizations (90%) did not comply with OSHA recordkeeping regulations. Undercounting appears to be worse in organizations that use injury data to evaluate the performance of those responsible for maintaining the injury data (Wuellner & Bonauto, 2014).

Illness

Currently no surveillance system adequately tracks workplace illnesses in the United States. BLS' occupational fatality surveillance system, CFOI, does not include illnesses in its scope:

"Because of the latency period of many occupational illnesses and the resulting difficulty associated with linking illnesses to work, it is difficult to compile a complete count of all fatal illnesses in a given year. Thus, information on illness-related deaths is excluded from the basic CFOI count" (BLS, 2010).

Although non-fatal illnesses are tracked by SOII, it is acknowledged by BLS that many non-fatal occupational illnesses are likely going uncounted. The BLS Handbook of Methods indicates:

"Each year, the SOII measures the number of new work-related illness cases which are recognized, diagnosed, and reported. But some conditions, such as long-term latent illnesses caused by exposure to carcinogens, often are difficult to relate to the workplace and are not adequately recognized and reported and are believed to be understated in the SOII. In contrast, the overwhelming majority of the reported new illnesses are those which are easier to directly relate to workplace activity" (BLS, 2010).

As noted by Russer (2010), former Associate Director for Occupational Safety and Health Statistics with BLS:

"A central problem is that many work-related illnesses take years to develop and may be difficult to attribute to the workplace. Thus, a recording mechanism based on employer records, as is SOII, will generally fail to capture these illnesses."

Potential Solutions

There is no easy fix for the undercounting issue. To more accurately count non-fatal injuries, BLS will likely need to adopt the use of additional data sources such as workers' compensation data. However, this solution is likely to be expensive and difficult to implement given the lack of standardization among state based workers' compensation programs. To address the illness undercount, the National Institute for Occupational Safety and Health has proposed capturing work relatedness data through electronic medical records. This approach may allow the linking of illnesses with long latency periods back to original occupational exposures.

Sources: Boden, L.I. (2014). Capture-recapture estimates of the undercount of workplace injuries and illnesses: sensitivity analysis. American Journal of Industrial Medicine, 57, 1090-1099.
Bureau of Labor Statistics [BLS]. Handbook of Methods 2010. Downloaded on Oct. 14, 2014 from: http://www.bls.gov/opub/hom/
Davis, L.K., Grattan, K.M., Sangwoo, T., Bullock, L.F., Ozonoff, A., & Boden, L.I. (2014). Use of multiple data sources for surveillance of work-related amputations in Massachusetts, comparison with official estimates and implications for national surveillance. American Journal of Industrial Medicine, 57, 1120-1132.
Joe, L., Roisman, R., Beckman, S., Jones, M., Beckman, J., Frederick, M., & Harrison, R. (2014). Using multiple data sets for public health tracking of work-related injuries and illnesses in California. American Journal of Industrial Medicine, 57, 1110-1119.
Russer, J.W. (2010). Allegations of undercounting in the BLS Survey of Occupational Injuries and Illnesses. Downloaded on Oct. 20, 2014 from: http://www.bls.gov/osmr/pdf/st100170.pdf
Wuellner, S.E., & Bonauto, D.K. (2014). Injury classification agreement in linked bureau of labor statistics and workers' compensation data. American Journal of Industrial Medicine, 57, 1100-1109.

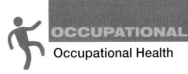

■ *More than 33,000 new cases of skin diseases or disorders were diagnosed in 2013.*

Approximately 199,400 occupational illnesses were recognized or diagnosed by employers in 2013, according to the Bureau of Labor Statistics (BLS). The all-industry illness data published by BLS now includes data for state and local governments in addition to the private sector. The overall incidence rate of occupational illness for all industries was 18.8 per 10,000 full-time workers. The highest overall incidence rate for all illnesses was for agriculture, forestry, fishing and hunting at 36.7 cases per 10,000 full-time workers – nearly double the all industries rate.

Workers in agriculture, forestry, fishing, and hunting had the highest incidence rates for skin diseases or disorders, respiratory conditions, poisoning, and "all other occupational illnesses." Workers in manufacturing had the highest rate for hearing loss.

State and local government, manufacturing, and education and health services accounted for 66% of all new illness cases in 2013. Skin diseases or disorders were the most common illness with 33,600 new cases, followed by hearing loss with 21,200, respiratory conditions with 19,600, and poisonings with 3,200.

The table below shows the number of occupational illnesses and the incidence rate per 10,000 full-time workers as measured by the 2013 BLS survey. To convert these to incidence rates per 100 full-time workers, which are comparable to other published BLS rates, divide the rates in the table by 100. The BLS survey records illnesses only for the year in which they are recognized or diagnosed as work-related. Because only recognized cases are included, the figures underestimate the incidence of occupational illness.

Nonfatal occupational illness incidence rates and number of illnesses by type of illness and industry sector, 2013

Industry sector	All illnesses	Skin diseases or disorders	Respiratory conditions	Poisoning	Hearing loss	All other occupational illnesses
Incidence rate per 10,000 full-time workers						
All industries, including state and local government[a]	**18.8**	**3.2**	**1.8**	**0.3**	**2.0**	**11.5**
Private industry[a]	**16.6**	**2.8**	**1.4**	**0.2**	**2.0**	**10.2**
Goods producing[a]	27.6	3.5	1.4	0.3	7.4	15.0
Agriculture, forestry, fishing, and hunting[a]	36.7	8.8	5.9	1.2	0.8	20.0
Mining[b,c]	11.6	0.8	2.8	[(d)]	2.1	6.0
Construction	9.8	2.0	0.7	0.3	0.6	6.2
Manufacturing	35.9	4.0	1.3	0.2	11.3	19.2
Service providing	13.7	2.7	1.4	0.2	0.6	8.9
Wholesale trade	8.8	1.6	1.0	0.1	0.8	5.2
Retail trade	10.2	1.3	1.0	[(d)]	0.1	7.5
Transportation and warehousing	18.8	1.5	1.0	0.2	[(d)]	10.1
Utilities	24.6	5.2	1.1	0.3	7.4	10.5
Information	11.0	1.1	[(d)]	[(d)]	0.9	8.0
Financial activities	6.9	0.9	0.7	[(d)]	[(d)]	5.3
Professional and business services	8.3	[(d)]	0.9	[(d)]	0.2	4.5
Education and health services	27.4	4.9	3.2	0.2	0.1	19.0
Leisure and hospitality	11.2	3.4	1.0	0.2	0.1	6.4
Other services	10.4	2.7	1.0	[(d)]	0.2	6.5
State and local government[a]	**32.7**	**5.2**	**4.6**	**1.1**	**2.1**	**19.7**
Number of Illnesses (in thousands)						
All industries, including state and local government[a]	**199.4**	**33.6**	**19.6**	**3.2**	**21.2**	**121.9**
Private industry[a]	**152.3**	**26.0**	**13.0**	**1.6**	**18.1**	**93.5**
Goods producing[a]	52.5	6.7	2.7	0.5	14.0	28.6
Agriculture, forestry, fishing, and hunting[a]	3.5	0.9	0.6	0.1	0.1	1.9
Mining[b,c]	1.0	0.1	0.2	[(d)]	0.2	0.5
Construction	5.2	1.1	0.4	0.2	0.3	3.3
Manufacturing	42.7	4.7	1.5	0.3	13.4	22.8
Service providing	99.9	19.3	10.3	1.1	4.1	65.0
Wholesale trade	5.0	0.9	0.6	0.1	0.4	2.9
Retail trade	11.6	1.5	1.1	[(d)]	0.1	8.6
Transportation and warehousing	7.6	0.6	0.4	0.1	[(d)]	4.1
Utilities	1.3	0.3	0.1	[(d)]	0.4	0.6
Information	2.7	0.3	[(d)]	[(d)]	0.2	2.0
Financial activities	4.9	0.6	0.5	[(d)]	[(d)]	3.8
Professional and business services	11.8	[(d)]	1.3	0.1	0.3	6.4
Education and health services	41.7	7.5	4.9	0.3	0.1	28.8
Leisure and hospitality	10.1	3.1	0.9	0.2	0.1	5.8
Other services	3.1	0.8	0.3	[(d)]	0.1	2.0
State and local government[a]	**47.1**	**7.5**	**6.6**	**1.5**	**3.1**	**28.4**

Source: Bureau of Labor Statistics. Components may not add to totals due to rounding.
[a]*Excludes farms with fewer than 11 employees.*
[b]*Data for mining do not reflect the changes OSHA made to its recordkeeping requirements effective Jan. 1, 2002; therefore, estimates for this industry are not comparable with estimates for other industries.*
[c]*Mining includes quarrying and oil and gas extraction.*
[d]*Data do not meet publication guidelines/too small to be displayed.*

Nature of Injury

According to the Bureau of Labor Statistics, sprains, strains, or tears were the most common type of injury involving days away from work in 2012, accounting for 38% of the total 905,690 injuries in private industry. Soreness or pain was the second most common type of injury, followed by cuts, lacerations, or punctures. Overall, the education and health services, retail trade, and manufacturing industry sectors had the greatest number of injuries, combining to make up 47% of the total.

Number of nonfatal occupational injuries and illnesses involving days away from work[a] by nature of injury and industry sector, private industry, United States, 2012

Nature of injury	Private sector[b,c,d]	Industry sector								
		Education and health services	Retail trade	Manufacturing	Leisure and hospitality	Transportation and warehousing[d]	Construction	Professional and business services	Wholesale trade	All other sectors[b,d,e]
Total[c]	905,690	178,330	125,650	125,280	89,480	89,260	71,730	70,330	58,330	97,300
Fractures	71,830	9,560	8,180	12,450	5,870	6,210	8,500	7,430	4,940	8,690
Sprains, strains, or tears	340,900	84,330	48,960	38,840	26,140	39,140	21,800	21,990	24,200	35,500
Amputations	5,100	100	360	2,100	430	230	590	330	350	610
Cuts, lacerations, or punctures	85,030	6,590	12,350	16,610	14,380	3,980	9,870	8,510	4,270	8,470
Cuts or lacerations	*71,880*	*4,660*	*11,200*	*13,820*	*13,850*	*3,450*	*8,520*	*5,730*	*3,740*	*6,910*
Punctures (except gunshot wounds)	*13,150*	*1,930*	*1,150*	*2,790*	*530*	*530*	*1,350*	*2,790*	*530*	*1,550*
Bruises or contusions	74,150	16,050	13,060	8,990	7,120	8,070	4,540	4,740	4,410	7,170
Chemical burns and corrosions	3,250	370	270	870	380	230	200	510	120	300
Heat (thermal) burns	13,700	1,480	1,280	2,250	5,920	230	770	350	710	710
Multiple traumatic injuries	27,640	6,060	3,760	3,610	2,020	2,690	1,820	2,310	2,120	3,250
With sprains and other injuries	*11,760*	*3,320*	*1,920*	*1,160*	*850*	*1,100*	*590*	*850*	*760*	*1,210*
With fractures and other injuries	*6,280*	*770*	*590*	*1,050*	*660*	*500*	*520*	*750*	*600*	*840*
Soreness or pain	130,900	29,270	17,130	13,410	13,970	14,170	10,760	11,630	8,160	12,400
Carpal tunnel syndrome	7,540	1,120	970	2,590	480	260	190	400	410	1,120
Tendonitus	2,680	510	280	650	150	460	50	200	120	260
All other	142,980	22,900	19,050	22,910	12,610	13,600	12,640	11,930	8,510	18,830

Source: Bureau of Labor Statistics Occupational Injuries/Illnesses and Fatal Injuries Profiles, accessed August 21, 2014 from http://data.bls.gov/gqt/InitialPage.
[a]*Days-away-from-work cases include those that result in days away from work with or without job transfer or restriction.*
[b]*Excludes farms with fewer than 11 employees.*
[c]*Data may not sum to row and column totals because of rounding and exclusion of nonclassifiable responses.*
[d]*Data for transportation and mining do not reflect the changes OSHA made to its recordkeeping requirements effective Jan. 1, 2002; therefore, estimates for these industries are not comparable with estimates for other industries.*
[e]*Includes agriculture, forestry, fishing, and hunting; financial activities; information; mining (including oil and gas extraction); other services (except public administration); and utilities.*

Percent of injuries involving days away from work by nature of injury, private industry, United States, 2012

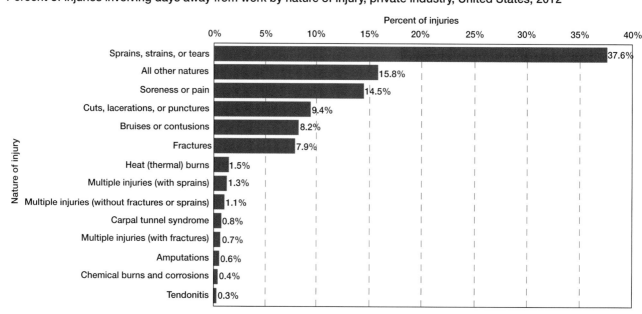

According to the Bureau of Labor Statistics, the back was the body part most frequently affected in injuries involving days away from work in 2012, accounting for 20% of the total 905,690 injuries in private industry. Hand injuries were the second most common, followed by injuries to multiple body parts. Overall, the education and health services, retail trade, and manufacturing industry sectors had the highest number of injuries, combining to make up 47% of the total.

Number of nonfatal occupational injuries and illnesses involving days away from work[a] by part of body affected and industry sector, private industry, United States, 2012

Part of body affected	Private sector[b,c,d]	Industry sector								
		Education and health services	Retail trade	Manufacturing	Leisure and hospitality	Transportation and warehousing[d]	Construction	Professional and business services	Wholesale trade	All other sectors[b,d,e]
Total[c]	905,690	178,330	125,650	125,280	89,480	89,260	71,730	70,330	58,330	97,300
Head	65,320	10,340	10,370	9,830	6,380	4,950	5,720	6,380	3,210	8,140
Eye	*20,300*	*1,820*	*2,560*	*4,880*	*1,250*	*1,290*	*3,080*	*1,680*	*1,080*	*2,660*
Neck	12,490	3,850	1,710	1,220	680	1,900	770	610	710	1,040
Trunk	233,340	55,490	33,400	27,020	18,330	24,750	17,280	17,270	16,550	23,250
Back	*177,580*	*46,630*	*25,710*	*18,740*	*13,910*	*17,320*	*11,690*	*13,670*	*13,150*	*16,760*
Upper extremities	285,680	44,850	36,750	54,430	34,460	24,930	22,800	20,100	17,310	30,050
Shoulder	*68,090*	*13,540*	*8,350*	*9,770*	*5,190*	*9,180*	*5,900*	*4,120*	*5,400*	*6,640*
Arm	*41,230*	*6,840*	*5,440*	*6,700*	*4,720*	*4,700*	*3,270*	*2,940*	*2,840*	*3,780*
Wrist	*38,230*	*7,810*	*5,140*	*6,930*	*3,440*	*3,480*	*1,820*	*3,400*	*1,950*	*4,260*
Hand	*121,580*	*12,600*	*15,740*	*28,430*	*19,410*	*6,300*	*11,280*	*8,620*	*6,020*	*13,180*
Lower extremities	200,110	35,370	29,250	23,590	19,770	22,130	17,760	15,470	14,090	22,680
Knee	*76,960*	*15,400*	*11,570*	*8,310*	*7,920*	*8,150*	*6,460*	*5,090*	*5,360*	*8,700*
Ankle	*43,870*	*8,530*	*5,800*	*4,130*	*4,650*	*5,190*	*4,050*	*3,510*	*2,490*	*5,520*
Foot	*41,620*	*5,690*	*7,310*	*6,300*	*3,860*	*4,300*	*3,730*	*3,230*	*3,100*	*4,100*
Body systems	17,590	3,610	2,490	1,520	1,770	1,350	1,100	1,870	880	3,000
Multiple parts	82,900	23,440	10,270	6,980	7,290	8,490	5,740	7,520	4,900	8,270
All other	8,270	1,400	1,410	700	800	750	550	1,100	690	870

Source: Bureau of Labor Statistics Occupational Injuries/Illnesses and Fatal Injuries Profiles, accessed August 21, 2014, from http://data.bls.gov/gqt/InitialPage.
[a]*Days-away-from-work cases include those that result in days away from work with or without job transfer or restriction.*
[b]*Excludes farms with fewer than 11 employees.*
[c]*Data may not sum to row and column totals because of rounding and exclusion of nonclassifiable responses.*
[d]*Data for transportation and mining do not reflect the changes OSHA made to its recordkeeping requirements effective Jan. 1, 2002; therefore, estimates for these industries are not comparable with estimates for other industries.*
[e]*Includes agriculture, forestry, fishing, and hunting; financial activities; information; mining (including oil and gas extraction); other services (except public administration); and utilities.*

Percent of injuries involving days away from work by part of body affected, private industry, United States, 2012

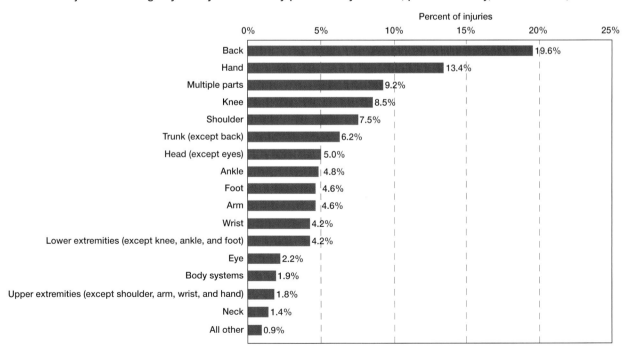

Safety professionals in business and industry often want to compare, or benchmark, the occupational injury and illness incidence rates of their establishments with the national average rates compiled by the Bureau of Labor Statistics (BLS) through its annual Survey of Occupational Injuries and Illnesses.[a] The incidence rates published on the following pages are for 2013 and were compiled under the revised Occupational Safety and Health Administration (OSHA) recordkeeping requirements that went into effect in 2002.

Step 1

The first step in benchmarking is to calculate the incidence rates for the establishment. The basic formula for computing incidence rates is *(N x 200,000)/EH*, or the number of cases *(N)* multiplied by 200,000 then divided by the number of hours worked *(EH)* by all employees during the time period, where *200,000* is the base for 100 full-time workers (working 40 hours per week, 50 weeks per year). Because BLS rates are based on reports from entire establishments, both the OSHA 300 log and the number of hours worked should cover the whole establishment being benchmarked. The hours worked and the log also should cover the same time period (e.g., a month, quarter, or full year). The following rates may be calculated.

Total cases – The incidence rate of total OSHA recordable cases per 200,000 hours worked. For this rate, *N* is the total number of cases on the OSHA 300 log.

Cases with days away from work or job transfer or restriction – The incidence rate of cases with days away from work, job transfer, or restriction. *N* is the count of cases with a check in column H or column I of the OSHA 300 log.

Cases with days away from work – The incidence rate of cases with days away from work. *N* is the count of cases with a check in column H of the OSHA 300 log.

Cases with job transfer or restriction – The incidence rate of cases with job transfer or restriction, but no days away from work. *N* is the count of cases with a check in column I of the OSHA 300 log.

Other recordable cases – The incidence rate of recordable cases without days away from work or job transfer or restriction. *N* is the count of cases with a check in column J of the OSHA 300 log.

In the flow chart on the opposite page, post the number of cases to each box in the top row and the number of employee hours worked in its box. Then use the formula to calculate the rates and write them in the last row of boxes in Step 1.

An alternative approach is to use the Incidence Rate Calculator and Comparison Tool available on BLS's website at *http://data.bls.gov/iirc*. This tool will calculate your rate and provide a report comparing your rate to your industry.

Step 2

After computing one or more of the rates, the next step is to determine the North American Industry Classification System (NAICS) code for the establishment.[b] (NAICS replaced the Standard Industrial Classification [SIC] code beginning in 2003.) This code is used to find the appropriate BLS rate for comparison. NAICS codes can be found at *www.census.gov/eos/www/naics*. The website also contains a crosswalk between NAICS and SIC codes. Otherwise, call a regional BLS office for assistance.

Write the establishment's NAICS code in the box in Step 2 of the flow chart.

Step 3

Once the NAICS code is known, the national average incidence rates may be found by (a) consulting the table of rates on pages 80-82, (b) visiting BLS's website, or (c) by calling a regional BLS office. Note that some tables on the website provide incidence rates by size of establishment and rate quartiles within each NAICS code. These rates may be useful for a more precise comparison. Note that the incidence rates for 2001 and earlier years were compiled under the old OSHA recordkeeping requirements in effect at that time. Caution must be used in comparing rates computed for 2002 and later years with earlier years – keeping in mind the differences in recordkeeping requirements.

In the flow chart on the opposite page, post the rates from the BLS survey to the boxes in Step 3. Now compare these with the rates calculated in Step 1.

An alternative way of benchmarking is to compare the current incidence rates for an establishment to its own prior historical rates to determine if the rates are improving and if progress is satisfactory (using criteria set by the organization).

[a]*Bureau of Labor Statistics. (1997).* BLS Handbook of Methods. *Washington, DC: U.S. Government Printing Office (Or at www.bls.gov/opub/hom/home.htm).*
[b]*Executive Office of the President, Office of Management and Budget. (2002).* North American Industry Classification System, United States, 2002. *Springfield, VA: National Technical Information Service.*

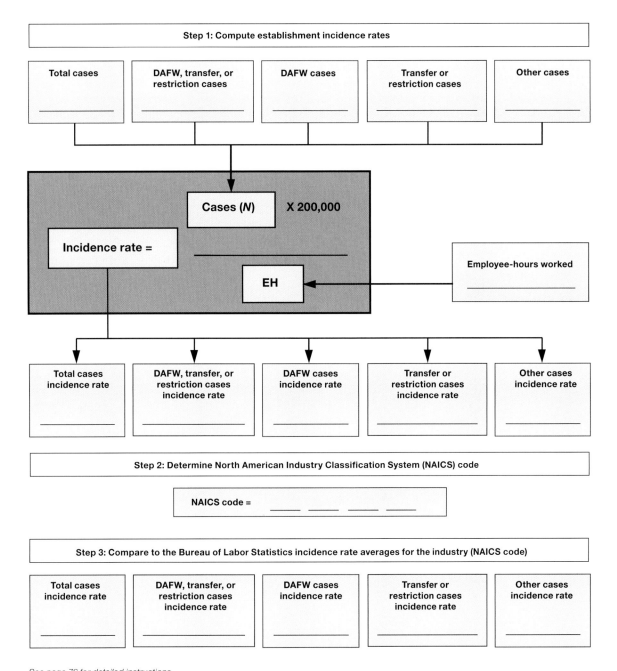

Step 1: Compute establishment incidence rates

| Total cases | DAFW, transfer, or restriction cases | DAFW cases | Transfer or restriction cases | Other cases |

Cases (*N*) X 200,000

Incidence rate = _____
                        EH

Employee-hours worked

| Total cases incidence rate | DAFW, transfer, or restriction cases incidence rate | DAFW cases incidence rate | Transfer or restriction cases incidence rate | Other cases incidence rate |

Step 2: Determine North American Industry Classification System (NAICS) code

NAICS code = ____ ____ ____ ____

Step 3: Compare to the Bureau of Labor Statistics incidence rate averages for the industry (NAICS code)

| Total cases incidence rate | DAFW, transfer, or restriction cases incidence rate | DAFW cases incidence rate | Transfer or restriction cases incidence rate | Other cases incidence rate |

See page 76 for detailed instructions.
DAFW = Days away from work.

Trends in Occupational Incidence Rates

■ *Total recordable incidence rate continues steady decrease in 2013.*

Two of the five private-sector occupational injury and illness incidence rates published by the Bureau of Labor Statistics (BLS) for 2013 decreased from 2012, while the remaining three incidence rates were unchanged. The incidence rate for total recordable cases was 3.3 per 100 full-time workers in 2013, down nearly 3% from the 2012 rate of 3.4. The incidence rate for cases with days away from work, job transfer, or restriction was 1.7 in 2013, down about 6% from 2012. The incidence rates for cases with days away from work, cases with job transfer or restriction, and other recordable cases were all unchanged from 2012.

There have been several changes that affect comparability of incidence rates from year to year. The North American Industry Classification System replaced the Standard Industrial Classification system beginning with the 2003 survey of occupational injuries and illnesses. Revisions to the Occupational Safety and Health Administration's occupational injury and illness recordkeeping requirements went into effect in 2002. Beginning with 1992, BLS revised its annual survey to include only nonfatal cases and stopped publishing the incidence rate of lost workdays.

Occupational injury and illness incidence rates, private industry, United States, 1990-2013

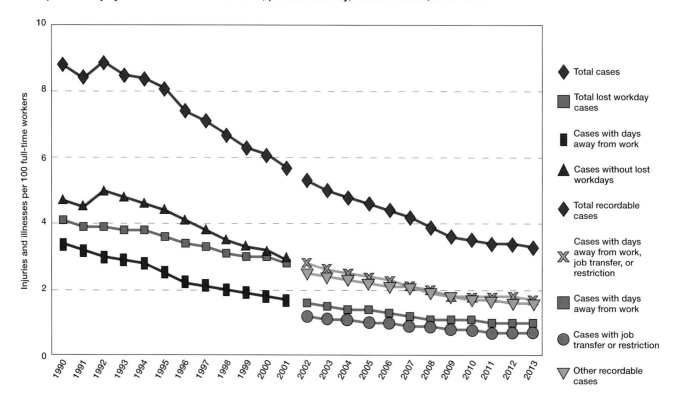

Source: Bureau of Labor Statistics.
Note: Beginning in 1992, all rates are for nonfatal cases only. Changes in OSHA recordkeeping requirements in 2002 affect comparison with earlier years.

The tables below and on pages 80-82 present the results of the 2013 Survey of Occupational Injuries and Illnesses conducted by the Bureau of Labor Statistics (BLS). The survey collects data on injuries and illnesses (from the OSHA 300 log) and employee-hours worked from a nationwide sample of about 230,000 private-industry establishments, as well as state and local governments. The survey excludes private households, the self-employed, and farms with fewer than 11 employees. The incidence rates give the number of cases per 100 full-time workers per year using 200,000 employee-hours as the equivalent. Definitions of the terms are given in the Glossary on page 207.

Beginning with 1992 data, BLS revised its annual survey to include only nonfatal cases and stopped publishing incidence rates of lost workdays. Beginning with 2003 data, BLS adopted the North American Industry Classification System for publication of the incidence rates by industry.

Bureau of Labor Statistics estimates of nonfatal occupational injury and illness incidence rates and number of injuries and illnesses by industry sector, 2013

Industry sector	Total recordable cases	Cases with days away from work, job transfer, or restriction			
		Total	Cases with days away from work	Cases with job transfer or restriction	Other recordable cases
Incidence rate per 100 full-time workers[c]					
All industries, including state and local government[d]	**3.5**	**1.8**	**1.1**	**0.7**	**1.7**
Private sector[d]	**3.3**	**1.7**	**1.0**	**0.7**	**1.6**
Goods producing[d]	3.9	2.2	1.2	1.0	1.7
Agriculture, forestry, fishing, and hunting[d]	5.7	3.4	2.0	1.3	2.3
Mining[e]	2.0	1.3	0.9	0.3	0.7
Construction	3.8	2.2	1.5	0.7	1.6
Manufacturing	4.0	2.2	1.0	1.2	1.8
Service providing	3.1	1.6	0.9	0.6	1.5
Wholesale trade	3.1	1.9	1.0	0.9	1.2
Retail trade	3.8	2.1	1.1	1.0	1.7
Transportation and warehousing	4.7	3.3	2.2	1.1	1.5
Utilities	2.1	1.1	0.6	0.5	1.0
Information	1.5	0.9	0.6	0.2	0.7
Financial activities	1.3	0.6	0.4	0.2	0.7
Professional and business services	1.6	0.8	0.5	0.3	0.8
Education and health services	4.4	2.0	1.2	0.8	2.4
Leisure and hospitality	3.8	1.6	1.0	0.6	2.2
Other services	2.5	1.2	0.8	0.4	1.3
State and local government[d]	**5.2**	**2.3**	**1.7**	**0.6**	**2.8**
Number of injuries and illnesses (in thousands)					
All industries, including state and local government[d]	**3,753.3**	**1,908.2**	**1,162.2**	**746.0**	**1,845.1**
Private sector[d]	**3,007.3**	**1,572.7**	**917.1**	**655.6**	**1,434.6**
Goods producing[d]	751.5	426.8	229.5	197.3	324.7
Agriculture, forestry, fishing, and hunting[d]	54.9	32.5	19.6	13.0	22.4
Mining[e]	16.9	10.8	7.8	3.0	6.1
Construction	203.0	118.1	82.0	36.1	84.9
Manufacturing	476.7	265.3	120.1	145.2	211.4
Service providing	2,255.8	1,145.9	687.6	458.3	1,109.9
Wholesale trade	173.8	105.2	57.2	48.0	68.6
Retail trade	438.3	240.7	128.8	111.9	197.7
Transportation and warehousing	192.0	132.0	87.2	44.8	60.0
Utilities	11.4	5.9	3.3	2.5	5.5
Information	38.0	21.8	16.1	5.7	16.2
Financial activities	91.0	43.5	29.0	14.5	47.5
Professional and business services	223.6	107.1	69.7	37.4	116.4
Education and health services	666.3	305.3	177.6	127.7	361.0
Leisure and hospitality	346.3	148.5	94.7	53.8	197.8
Other services	75.0	35.9	23.9	12.0	39.1
State and local government[d]	**746.0**	**335.5**	**245.1**	**90.4**	**410.6**

Source: Bureau of Labor Statistics.

[a]*Industry sector and two- and three-digit NAICS code totals on pages 80-82 include data for industries not shown separately.*

[b]*North American Industry Classification System–United States, 2007, for industries shown on pages 80-82.*

[c]*Incidence rate =* $\dfrac{\text{Number of injuries and illnesses} \times 200{,}000}{\text{Total hours worked by all employees during period covered}}$

where 200,000 is the base for 100 full-time workers (working 40 hours per week, 50 weeks per year). The "Total recordable cases" rate is based on the number of cases with check marks in columns (G), (H), (I), and (J) of the OSHA 300 log. The "Cases with days away from work, job transfer, or restriction – total" rate is based on columns (H) and (I). The "Cases with days away from work" rate is based on column (H). The "Cases with job transfer or restriction" rate is based on column (I). The "Other recordable cases" rate is based on column (J).

[d]*Excludes farms with fewer than 11 employees.*

[e]*These data do not reflect the changes the Occupational Safety and Health Administration made to its recordkeeping requirements effective Jan. 1, 2002; therefore, estimates for these industries are not comparable to estimates in other industries.*

[f]*Industry scope changed in 2009.*

[g]*Data do not meet publication guidelines/too small to be displayed.*

Occupational Injuries and Illnesses (cont.)

Bureau of Labor Statistics estimates of nonfatal occupational injury and illness incidence rates for selected industries, 2013

Industry[a]	NAICS code[b]	Total recordable cases	Cases with days away from work, job transfer, or restriction			Other recordable cases
			Total	Cases with days away from work	Cases with job transfer or restriction	
All industries, including state and local government[d]		**3.5**	**1.8**	**1.1**	**0.7**	**1.7**
Private sector[d]		**3.3**	**1.7**	**1.0**	**0.7**	**1.6**
Goods producing[d]		**3.9**	**2.2**	**1.2**	**1.0**	**1.7**
Natural resources and mining[d, e]		**3.9**	**2.4**	**1.5**	**0.9**	**1.6**
Agriculture, forestry, fishing, and hunting[d]	11	5.7	3.4	2.0	1.3	2.3
Crop production[f]	111	5.5	3.2	1.8	1.4	2.4
Animal production[f]	112	6.2	3.6	2.2	1.5	2.6
Forestry and logging	113	3.3	2.6	2.1	0.5	0.8
Support activities for agriculture and forestry	115	6.0	3.7	2.3	1.4	2.4
Mining[e]	21	2.0	1.3	0.9	0.3	0.7
Oil and gas extraction	211	1.3	0.7	0.5	0.2	0.6
Mining (except oil and gas)[e]	212	2.6	1.7	1.3	0.4	0.9
Coal mining[e]	2121	3.6	2.4	2.2	0.2	1.3
Metal ore mining[e]	2122	2.4	1.6	0.9	0.8	0.7
Nonmetallic mineral mining and quarrying[e]	2123	1.8	1.2	0.7	0.5	0.6
Support activities for mining	213	1.9	1.2	0.9	0.4	0.7
Construction		**3.8**	**2.2**	**1.5**	**0.7**	**1.6**
Construction of buildings	236	3.3	1.9	1.3	0.6	1.4
Residential building construction	2361	4.0	2.5	1.7	(g)	1.5
Nonresidential building construction	2362	2.7	1.5	0.9	0.5	1.3
Heavy and civil engineering construction	237	3.2	1.8	1.1	0.7	1.4
Utility system construction	2371	2.9	1.7	1.0	0.7	1.2
Land subdivision	2372	1.8	0.8	0.5	0.3	1.0
Highway, street, and bridge construction	2373	4.3	2.3	1.5	0.8	2.0
Other heavy and civil engineering construction	2379	2.5	1.3	0.7	0.6	1.2
Specialty trade contractors	238	4.2	2.4	1.7	0.7	1.7
Foundation, structure, and building exterior contractors	2381	5.5	3.3	2.2	1.2	2.2
Building equipment contractors	2382	4.2	2.4	1.7	0.7	1.8
Building finishing contractors	2383	3.9	2.4	1.8	0.6	1.5
Other specialty trade contractors	2389	2.9	1.7	1.3	0.4	1.2
Manufacturing		**4.0**	**2.2**	**1.0**	**1.2**	**1.8**
Food manufacturing	311	5.0	3.3	1.3	2.0	1.7
Animal food manufacturing	3111	4.8	3.5	2.1	1.4	1.4
Grain and oilseed milling	3112	3.9	2.3	1.1	1.3	1.6
Sugar and confectionery product manufacturing	3113	4.9	3.1	1.2	1.9	1.7
Fruit and vegetable preserving and specialty food manufacturing	3114	4.5	2.7	1.2	1.5	1.8
Dairy product manufacturing	3115	5.7	3.5	1.8	1.8	2.2
Animal slaughtering and processing	3116	5.7	3.9	1.0	2.9	1.9
Seafood product preparation and packaging	3117	6.6	3.7	2.5	1.3	2.9
Bakeries and tortilla manufacturing	3118	4.1	2.8	1.4	1.4	1.3
Other food manufacturing	3119	4.2	2.8	1.4	1.5	1.4
Beverage and tobacco product manufacturing	312	5.5	3.8	1.5	2.3	1.6
Beverage manufacturing	3121	5.6	4.0	1.6	2.4	1.6
Tobacco manufacturing	3122	3.3	1.7	1.1	0.5	1.7
Textile mills	313	3.3	2.0	0.8	1.2	1.3
Fiber, yarn, and thread mills	3131	2.5	1.5	0.3	1.2	1.0
Fabric mills	3132	3.9	2.4	1.1	1.3	1.6
Textile and fabric finishing and fabric coating mills	3133	2.8	1.9	0.9	1.0	1.0
Textile product mills[f]	314	3.8	2.3	0.9	1.4	1.5
Textile furnishings mills	3141	3.4	2.0	0.9	1.0	1.4
Other textile product mills[f]	3149	4.2	2.6	0.9	1.7	1.6
Apparel manufacturing[f]	315	1.9	1.0	0.5	0.5	0.9
Apparel knitting mills	3151	2.3	1.3	0.5	0.8	1.0
Cut and sew apparel manufacturing[f]	3152	1.6	0.9	0.5	0.4	0.7
Apparel accessories and other apparel manufacturing	3159	3.2	1.2	0.7	0.5	2.0
Leather and allied product manufacturing	316	5.4	3.3	1.5	1.8	2.1
Footwear manufacturing	3162	6.2	3.3	1.7	1.6	2.9
Other leather and allied product manufacturing	3169	3.7	2.8	1.3	1.5	1.0
Wood product manufacturing	321	6.4	3.6	1.9	1.7	2.8
Sawmills and wood preservation	3211	6.0	3.5	2.0	1.6	2.5
Veneer, plywood, and engineered wood product manufacturing	3212	6.8	3.6	2.1	1.4	3.2
Other wood product manufacturing	3219	6.5	3.7	1.8	1.9	2.8
Paper manufacturing	322	2.8	1.5	0.8	0.8	1.2
Pulp, paper, and paperboard mills	3221	2.2	1.2	0.7	0.5	1.0
Converted paper product manufacturing	3222	3.0	1.7	0.8	0.9	1.3
Printing and related support activities	323	2.8	1.5	0.8	0.8	1.2
Petroleum and coal products manufacturing	324	1.6	0.9	0.5	0.4	0.7
Chemical manufacturing	325	2.0	1.1	0.5	0.6	0.8
Basic chemical manufacturing	3251	1.5	0.9	0.5	0.5	0.6
Resin, synthetic rubber, and artificial and synthetic fibers and filaments manufacturing	3252	1.6	0.9	0.4	0.6	0.7
Pesticide, fertilizer, and other agricultural chemical manufacturing	3253	1.9	1.1	0.3	0.8	0.8
Pharmaceutical and medicine manufacturing	3254	1.8	1.1	0.5	0.6	0.8
Paint, coating, and adhesive manufacturing	3255	2.4	1.4	0.6	0.8	1.0
Soap, cleaning compound, and toilet preparation manufacturing	3256	2.7	1.5	0.7	0.8	1.2
Other chemical product and preparation manufacturing	3259	2.5	1.4	0.7	0.7	1.1

See source and footnotes on page 79.

Bureau of Labor Statistics estimates of nonfatal occupational injury and illness incidence rates for selected industries, 2013 (cont.)

Industry[a]	NAICS code[b]	Total recordable cases	Cases with days away from work, job transfer, or restriction			Other recordable cases
			Total	Cases with days away from work	Cases with job transfer or restriction	
Plastics and rubber products manufacturing[f]	326	4.4	2.7	1.1	1.6	1.8
Plastics product manufacturing[f]	3261	4.3	2.6	1.1	1.5	1.7
Rubber product manufacturing[f]	3262	5.0	3.2	1.3	1.9	1.8
Nonmetallic mineral product manufacturing	327	5.0	2.8	1.4	1.4	2.1
Clay product and refractory manufacturing	3271	4.5	2.5	1.1	1.4	1.9
Glass and glass product manufacturing	3272	4.4	2.6	1.2	1.5	1.8
Cement and concrete product manufacturing	3273	5.8	3.3	1.8	1.6	2.5
Lime and gypsum product manufacturing	3274	2.6	1.3	0.8	0.5	1.3
Other nonmetallic mineral product manufacturing	3279	4.2	2.3	1.2	1.0	1.9
Primary metal manufacturing	331	5.2	2.8	1.3	1.5	2.4
Iron and steel mills and ferroalloy manufacturing	3311	3.1	1.6	0.8	0.8	1.5
Steel product manufacturing from purchased steel	3312	5.4	3.2	1.5	1.7	2.2
Alumina and aluminum production and processing	3313	4.1	2.5	1.0	1.4	1.6
Nonferrous metal (except aluminum) production and processing	3314	4.2	2.6	1.2	1.3	1.6
Foundries	3315	7.7	3.8	1.7	2.1	3.9
Fabricated metal product manufacturing	332	5.2	2.6	1.3	1.3	2.6
Forging and stamping	3321	6.5	3.3	1.7	1.6	3.2
Cutlery and hand tool manufacturing	3322	3.7	1.9	1.0	0.9	1.8
Architectural and structural metals manufacturing	3323	5.8	3.0	1.5	1.5	2.8
Boiler, tank, and shipping container manufacturing	3324	5.8	2.8	1.5	1.4	2.9
Hardware manufacturing	3325	4.3	2.2	1.1	1.1	2.2
Spring and wire product manufacturing	3326	5.4	3.0	1.2	1.8	2.4
Machine shops; turned product; and screw, nut, and bolt manufacturing	3327	4.8	2.0	1.2	0.8	2.8
Coating, engraving, heat treating, and allied activities	3328	4.9	2.8	1.2	1.6	2.0
Other fabricated metal product manufacturing	3329	4.7	2.7	1.2	1.5	2.0
Machinery manufacturing[f]	333	4.0	1.8	0.9	0.9	2.2
Agriculture, construction, and mining machinery manufacturing	3331	4.4	2.2	1.1	1.0	2.2
Industrial machinery manufacturing[f]	3332	4.0	1.3	0.7	0.6	2.7
Commercial and service machinery manufacturing	3333	2.7	1.2	0.6	0.6	1.5
Ventilation, heating, air conditioning, and commercial refrigeration equipment manufacturing[f]	3334	4.3	2.1	0.8	1.3	2.2
Metalworking machinery manufacturing	3335	4.7	2.0	1.2	0.8	2.7
Engine, turbine, and power transmission equipment manufacturing	3336	3.4	1.5	0.7	0.8	1.8
Other general purpose machinery manufacturing[f]	3339	3.9	1.9	0.9	1.0	2.0
Computer and electronic product manufacturing	334	1.3	0.7	0.3	0.4	0.6
Computer and peripheral equipment manufacturing	3341	0.6	0.3	0.2	0.1	0.2
Communications equipment manufacturing[f]	3342	0.9	0.5	0.2	0.2	0.4
Audio and video equipment manufacturing	3343	1.8	0.9	0.5	0.4	0.9
Semiconductor and other electronic component manufacturing	3344	1.6	0.9	0.4	0.4	0.8
Navigational, measuring, electromedical, and control instruments manufacturing[f]	3345	1.4	0.8	0.4	0.4	0.7
Manufacturing and reproducing magnetic and optical media	3346	1.4	1.0	0.5	0.5	0.4
Electrical equipment, appliance, and component manufacturing	335	2.8	1.6	0.6	1.0	1.3
Electric lighting equipment manufacturing	3351	3.7	2.7	1.1	1.7	1.0
Household appliance manufacturing	3352	3.7	1.9	0.7	1.2	1.7
Electrical equipment manufacturing	3353	2.4	1.2	0.5	0.7	1.2
Other electrical equipment and component manufacturing	3359	2.7	1.5	0.5	1.0	1.2
Transportation equipment manufacturing[f]	336	4.9	2.7	1.1	1.6	2.2
Motor vehicle manufacturing	3361	7.1	3.5	1.4	2.2	3.6
Motor vehicle body and trailer manufacturing	3362	7.7	3.9	1.8	2.2	3.8
Motor vehicle parts manufacturing	3363	4.9	2.6	1.0	1.6	2.4
Aerospace product and parts manufacturing	3364	3.1	1.8	0.6	1.2	1.2
Ship and boat building[f]	3366	7.0	4.2	2.1	2.1	2.8
Other transportation equipment manufacturing	3369	3.9	1.8	0.8	1.0	2.1
Furniture and related product manufacturing[f]	337	4.9	2.6	1.2	1.3	2.3
Household and institutional furniture and kitchen cabinet manufacturing[f]	3371	5.1	2.7	1.3	1.4	2.4
Office furniture (including fixtures) manufacturing	3372	4.5	2.1	1.1	1.0	2.4
Other furniture-related product manufacturing	3379	4.6	3.2	1.2	1.9	1.4
Miscellaneous manufacturing	339	3.1	1.6	0.9	0.7	1.5
Medical equipment and supplies manufacturing	3391	2.1	1.1	0.5	0.6	1.0
Other miscellaneous manufacturing	3399	4.3	2.2	1.3	0.9	(g)
Service providing		**3.1**	**1.6**	**0.9**	**0.6**	**1.5**
Trade, transportation, and utilities		**3.8**	**2.2**	**1.3**	**1.0**	**1.5**
Wholesale trade	42	3.1	1.9	1.0	0.9	1.2
Merchant wholesalers, durable goods	423	2.9	1.6	0.9	0.7	1.3
Merchant wholesalers, nondurable goods	424	3.9	2.6	1.4	1.2	1.3
Retail trade	44-45	3.8	2.1	1.1	1.0	1.7
Motor vehicle and parts dealers	441	3.6	1.8	1.1	0.7	1.8
Furniture and home furnishings stores	442	3.9	2.2	1.4	0.7	1.7
Electronics and appliance stores	443	1.7	1.0	0.7	0.3	0.7

See source and footnotes on page 79.

Occupational Injuries and Illnesses (cont.)

Bureau of Labor Statistics estimates of nonfatal occupational injury and illness incidence rates for selected industries, 2013 (cont.)

Industry[a]	NAICS code[b]	Total recordable cases	Incidence rates[c]			Other recordable cases
			Cases with days away from work, job transfer, or restriction			
			Total	Cases with days away from work	Cases with job transfer or restriction	
Building material and garden equipment and supplies dealers	444	4.8	3.1	1.6	1.5	1.7
Food and beverage stores	445	4.7	2.8	1.5	1.3	1.9
Health and personal care stores	446	2.4	1.2	0.9	(g)	1.2
Gasoline stations	447	2.4	1.2	0.7	0.5	1.2
Clothing and clothing accessories stores	448	2.6	1.1	0.8	(g)	1.5
Sporting goods, hobby, book, and music stores	451	2.7	1.1	0.6	0.5	1.6
General merchandise stores	452	4.8	2.7	1.1	1.6	2.1
Miscellaneous store retailers	453	4.0	1.8	1.0	0.8	2.2
Nonstore retailers	454	3.2	2.0	1.2	0.8	(g)
Transportation and warehousing	48-49	4.7	3.3	2.2	1.1	1.5
Air transportation	481	7.5	5.5	4.2	1.4	1.9
Rail transportation	482	2.0	1.4	1.3	0.1	0.6
Water transportation	483	2.5	1.6	1.4	0.2	1.0
Truck transportation	484	4.6	3.2	2.3	0.9	1.4
Transit and ground passenger transportation	485	4.4	2.7	2.0	0.8	1.6
Pipeline transportation	486	1.2	0.5	0.5	(g)	0.8
Scenic and sightseeing transportation	487	3.5	1.5	1.0	0.5	2.0
Support activities for transportation	488	3.7	2.4	1.5	0.9	1.3
Couriers and messengers	492	6.5	4.4	2.7	1.7	2.1
Warehousing and storage	493	5.2	3.7	1.8	2.0	1.5
Utilities	22	2.1	1.1	0.6	0.5	1.0
Electric power generation, transmission, and distribution	2211	1.8	0.9	0.5	0.3	0.9
Natural gas distribution	2212	3.0	1.7	0.9	0.8	1.3
Water, sewage, and other systems	2213	2.6	1.4	0.6	0.8	1.2
Information		**1.5**	**0.9**	**0.6**	**0.2**	**0.7**
Publishing industries (except Internet)	511	1.0	0.5	0.4	0.1	0.5
Motion picture and sound recording industries	512	1.8	0.5	0.3	0.1	1.3
Broadcasting (except Internet)	515	1.8	1.1	0.6	0.5	0.7
Telecommunications[f]	517	2.1	1.4	1.1	0.3	0.6
Other information services[f]	519	0.4	0.2	0.2	0.1	0.2
Finance activities		**1.3**	**0.6**	**0.4**	**0.2**	**0.7**
Finance and insurance	52	0.7	0.3	0.2	(g)	0.5
Monetary authorities	521	0.8	0.5	0.5	0.1	0.3
Credit intermediation and related activities	522	0.8	0.3	0.2	(g)	0.6
Securities, commodity contracts, and other financial investments and related activities	523	(g)	0.1	0.1	(g)	(g)
Insurance carries and related activities	524	0.8	0.3	0.2	(g)	(g)
Funds, trusts, and other financial activities	525	1.0	0.5	0.1	0.4	0.5
Real estate and rental and leasing	53	2.9	1.7	1.1	0.6	1.3
Real estate[f]	531	2.6	1.5	1.0	0.5	1.1
Rental and leasing services	532	3.8	2.1	1.2	0.8	1.8
Lessors of nonfinancial intangible assets (except copyrighted works)	533	0.5	0.2	0.2	(g)	0.3
Professional and business services		**1.6**	**0.8**	**0.5**	**0.3**	**0.8**
Professional, scientific, and technical services	54	1.0	0.3	0.2	0.1	0.7
Management of companies and enterprises	55	1.2	0.6	0.4	0.2	0.6
Administrative and support and waste management and remediation services	56	2.7	1.5	1.0	0.5	1.2
Administrative and support services[f]	561	2.5	1.3	0.9	0.4	1.2
Waste management and remediation services	562	4.7	3.4	2.2	1.3	1.3
Educational and health services		**4.4**	**2.0**	**1.2**	**0.8**	**2.4**
Educational services	61	2.0	0.8	0.6	0.2	1.2
Health care and social assistance	62	4.7	2.2	1.3	0.9	2.5
Ambulatory health care services	621	2.7	0.9	0.6	0.3	1.8
Hospitals	622	6.4	2.6	1.5	1.1	3.8
Nursing and residential care facilities	623	7.3	4.5	2.2	2.3	2.9
Social assistance	624	3.8	1.8	1.2	0.6	1.6
Leisure and hospitality		**3.8**	**1.6**	**1.0**	**0.6**	**2.2**
Arts, entertainment, and recreation	71	4.8	2.2	1.4	0.8	2.6
Accommodation and food services	72	3.7	1.5	1.0	0.6	2.1
Accommodation	721	5.3	2.9	1.5	1.4	2.4
Food services and drinking places	722	3.3	1.2	0.9	0.4	2.1
Other services, except public administration		**2.5**	**1.2**	**0.8**	**0.4**	**1.3**
Repair and maintenance	811	2.8	1.4	1.0	0.4	1.4
Personal and laundry services	812	2.3	1.3	0.7	0.6	1.0
Religious, grantmaking, civic, professional, and similar organizations	813	2.2	0.8	0.6	0.2	1.4
State and local government[d]		**5.2**	**2.3**	**1.7**	**0.6**	**2.8**
State government[d]		**3.9**	**2.1**	**1.6**	**0.5**	**1.9**
Local government[d]		**5.7**	**2.4**	**1.7**	**0.7**	**3.2**

See source and footnotes on page 79.

Bureau of Labor Statistics estimates of nonfatal occupational injury and illness incidence rates[a]
for selected industries, 2013

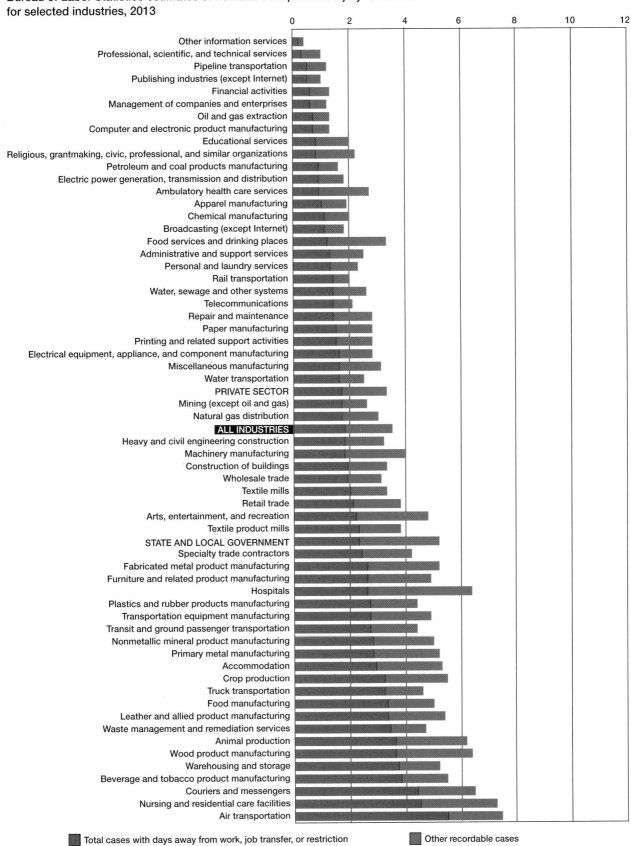

Total cases with days away from work, job transfer, or restriction ■ Other recordable cases

Note: Industries are shown at the two-, three-, or four-digit NAICS level.
[a]*Total cases with days away from work, job transfer, or restriction plus other recordable cases equals total recordable cases per 200,000 hours worked.*

Causes of Work-Related Deaths and Injuries

Roadway incidents involving motorized land vehicles are the leading cause of work-related deaths, followed by intentional injuries by persons, and contact with objects and equipment.

For nonfatal cases with days away from work, events involving overexertion and bodily reaction are the leading cause, followed by contact with objects and equipment and falls, slips, or trips.

Work-related deaths and injuries by event or exposure, United States, 2012

Event or exposure	Deaths[a]	Cases with days away from work[b]
Total, all events or exposures	**4,628**	**905,690**
Violence and other injuries by persons or animals	803	35,370
Intentional injury by person	725	12,560
Intentional injury by other person	475	12,410
Self-inflicted injury – intentional	249	–
Injury by person – unintentional or intent unknown	40	12,050
Injury by other person – unintentional or intent unknown	23	10,780
Self-inflicted injury – unintentional or intent unknown	17	30
Animal- and insect-related incidents	38	10,560
Transportation incidents	1,923	41,300
Aircraft incidents	127	570
Rail vehicle incidents	38	430
Animal and other nonmotorized vehicle transportation incidents	15	490
Pedestrian vehicular incidents	293	4,590
Water vehicle incidents	63	310
Roadway incidents involving motorized land vehicle	1,153	27,840
Nonroadway incident involving motorized land vehicles	233	6,470
Fires and explosions	122	1,750
Fires	34	910
Explosions	88	840
Slips, trips, or falls	704	219,630
Fall to lower level	570	46,160
Fall on same level	120	131,280
Exposure to harmful substances or environments	340	39,510
Exposure to electricity	156	1,730
Exposure to temperature extremes	41	17,090
Exposure to other harmful substances	110	15,710
Exposure to oxygen deficiency, n.e.c.[c]	33	570
Contact with objects and equipment	723	227,640
Struck by object or equipment	519	127,880
Struck against object or equipment	4	53,010
Caught in or compressed by equipment or objects	124	35,090
Struck, caught, or crushed in collapsing structure, equipment, or material	73	450
Overexertion and bodily reaction	6	331,130
Overexertion involving outside sources	4	220,650
Overexertion involving lifting, lowering	–	106,210
Overexertion in lifting–single episode	–	80,000
Repetitive motions involving microtasks	–	25,500
Nonclassifiable	–	9,370

Deaths[a] by event or exposure, United States, 2012

Cases with days away from work[b] by event or exposure, United States, 2012

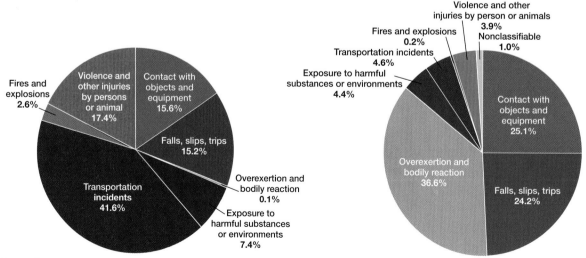

Source: Bureau of Labor Statistics.
[a]*Includes deaths among all workers.*
[b]*Includes cases with days away from work among private-sector wage and salary workers. Excludes government employees, the self-employed, and unpaid family workers.*
[c]*"n.e.c." means "not elsewhere classified."*

The tables on pages 86-101 present data on the characteristics of injured and ill workers and the injuries and illnesses that affected them. These data indicate how many workers died from on-the-job injuries and how many were affected by nonfatal injuries and illnesses. The data may be used to help set priorities for occupational safety and health programs and for benchmarking.

The fatality information covers only deaths due to injuries and comes from the Bureau of Labor Statistics (BLS) Census of Fatal Occupational Injuries. The data are for calendar year 2012 and include wage and salary workers, the self-employed, and unpaid family workers in all types of businesses and industries.

The data on nonfatal cases cover both occupational injuries and illnesses and come from the BLS Survey of Occupational Injuries and Illnesses for 2012. The survey also is used to produce the incidence rates shown on the preceding pages.

The estimates on the following pages are the number of cases involving days away from work (with or without days of restricted work activity). The nonfatal cases presented on pages 86-100 do not cover the self-employed; unpaid family workers; or federal, state, or local government employees. Nonfatal cases involving state and local government employees are presented on page 101.

Data are presented for the sex, age, occupation, and race or ethnic origin of the worker and for the nature of the injury or illness, the part of body affected, the source of the injury or illness, and the event or exposure that produced the injury or illness.

The text at the top of each page describes the kind of establishments that are included in the industry sector and gives the total number of workers in the industry in 2012 and the number working in the private sector.

How to benchmark

Incidence rates, percent distributions, or ranks may be used for benchmarking purposes. The results of the calculations described here may be compared to similar rates, percent distributions, and rankings based on data for a company.

For nonfatal incidence rates, multiply the number of cases by 1,000 and then divide by the private-sector employment given in the text at the top of the page. This will give the number of cases with days away from work per 1,000 employees per year. For fatality rates, multiply the number of fatalities by 100,000 then divide by the total employment given at the top of the page. This will give the number of deaths per 100,000 employees per year.

To compute percent distributions, divide the number of cases for each characteristic by the total number of cases found on the first line of the table. Multiply the quotient by 100 and round to one decimal place. Percent distributions may not add to 100% because of unclassifiable cases not shown.

Ranks are determined by arranging the characteristics from largest to smallest within each group and then numbering consecutively starting with one for the largest.

Industry sectors

Page 86 shows nonfatal injury and illness data for the private sector of the economy (excluding government entities) and fatal injury data for all industries (including government). Pages 87-100 present the data for industry sectors based on the North American Industry Classification System. Page 101 presents the fatal injury data for all government and nonfatal cases for state and local government (the BLS survey does not cover federal government entities).

The nonfatal occupational injury and illness data cover only private sector employees and exclude employees in federal, state, and local government entities and the self-employed. The fatal injury data cover all workers in both the private sector and government.

There were 143,706,000 people employed in 2012, of which 122,049,000 worked in the private sector.

Number of nonfatal occupational injuries and illnesses involving days away from work[a] and fatal occupational injuries by selected worker and case characteristics, private industry, United States, 2012

Characteristic	Private industry[b,c] nonfatal cases	All industries fatalities
Total	**905,690**	**4,628**
Sex		
Men	559,830	4,277
Women	342,640	351
Age		
Younger than 16	120	19
16 to 19	21,170	69
20 to 24	89,590	287
25 to 34	202,200	736
35 to 44	195,270	829
45 to 54	219,150	1,161
55 to 64	136,880	936
65 and older	27,260	588
Occupation		
Management, business, and financial	28,270	467
Professional and related	78,660	66
Service	220,150	783
Sales and related	57,530	225
Office and administrative support	64,280	89
Farming, fishing, and forestry	14,480	260
Construction and extractive	67,940	871
Installation, maintenance, and repair	83,860	352
Production	109,880	221
Transportation and material moving	177,760	1,259
Military occupations	–	31
Race or ethnic origin[d]		
White, non-Hispanic	362,480	3,176
Black, non-Hispanic	70,710	486
Hispanic	118,940	748
Other, multiple, and not reported	353,560	218
Nature of injury or illness		
Fractures	71,830	28
Sprains, strains, or tears	340,900	10
Amputations	5,100	13
Cuts, lacerations, or punctures	85,030	68
Bruises or contusions	74,150	–
Chemical burns and corrosions	3,250	–
Heat (thermal) burns	13,700	94
Multiple traumatic injuries	27,640	1,692
Soreness or pain	130,900	–
Carpal tunnel syndrome	7,540	–
Tendonitis	2,680	–
All other	142,980	2,719
Part of body affected		
Head	65,320	1,020
Eye	20,300	–
Neck	12,490	208
Trunk	233,340	768
Back	177,580	62
Upper extremities	285,680	19
Shoulder	68,090	–
Arm	41,230	7
Wrist	38,230	–
Hand	121,580	–
Lower extremities	200,110	59
Knee	76,960	13
Ankle	43,870	8
Foot or toe	41,620	–
Body systems	17,590	610
Multiple	82,900	1,944
All other	8,270	–

Characteristic	Private industry[b,c] nonfatal cases	All industries fatalities
Source of injury or illness		
Chemicals or chemical products	11,560	129
Containers	106,010	65
Furniture or fixtures	37,460	14
Machinery	53,000	368
Parts and materials	82,760	205
Worker motion or position	129,470	5
Health care patient	49,600	–
Floors, walkways, or ground surfaces	141,560	155
Handtools	40,760	21
Ladders	20,510	133
Vehicles	87,430	2,083
All other	145,570	1,446
Event or exposure		
Violence and other injuries by persons or animals	35,370	803
Intentional injury by other person	12,410	475
Injury by person unintentional or intent unknown	12,050	40
Transportation incidents	41,300	1,923
Roadway incidents involving motorized land vehicles	27,840	1,153
Fires or explosions	1,750	122
Falls, slips, or trips	219,630	704
Slips or trips without fall	36,140	6
Fall on same level	131,280	120
Fall to lower level	46,160	570
Exposed to harmful substances or environments	39,510	340
Contact with object or equipment	227,640	723
Struck by object	127,880	519
Struck against object	53,010	–
Caught in object, equipment, or material	35,090	124
Overexertion and bodily reaction	331,130	6
Overexertion in lifting or lowering	106,210	–
Repetitive motion involving microtasks	25,500	–
All other	9,370	7

Source: This research was conducted with restricted access to Bureau of Labor Statistics (BLS) data. The views expressed here do not necessarily reflect the views of BLS.

Note: Because of rounding and data exclusion of nonclassifiable responses, data may not sum to the totals. Dashes (–) indicate data that do not meet publication guidelines.

[a]*Days away from work include those that result in days away from work with or without restricted work activity or job transfer.*

[b]*Excludes farms with fewer than 11 employees.*

[c]*Data for mining operators in coal, metal, and nonmetal mining and for employees in railroad transportation are provided to BLS by the Mine Safety and Health Administration (MSHA), U.S. Department of Labor; and the Federal Railroad Administration (FRA), U.S. Department of Transportation. Independent mining contractors are excluded from the coal, metal, and nonmetal mining industries. MSHA and FRA data do not reflect the changes in OSHA recordkeeping requirements in 2002.*

[d]*In the fatalities column, non-Hispanic categories include cases with Hispanic origin not reported.*

Agriculture, Forestry, Fishing, and Hunting

The Agriculture, Forestry, Fishing and Hunting industry sector includes growing crops; raising animals; harvesting timber; harvesting fish and other animals from a farm, ranch, or their natural habitats; and agricultural support services.

Employment in Agriculture, Forestry, Fishing, and Hunting totaled 2,186,000 in 2012, of which 2,128,000 were private sector employees.

Number of nonfatal occupational injuries and illnesses involving days away from work[a] and fatal occupational injuries by selected worker and case characteristics, private industry, United States, Agriculture, Forestry, Fishing, and Hunting, 2012

Characteristic	Nonfatal cases[b]	Fatalities
Total	**17,620**	**509**
Sex		
Men	13,950	484
Women	3,640	25
Age		
Younger than 16	–	14
16 to 19	540	17
20 to 24	2,000	25
25 to 34	4,550	52
35 to 44	3,710	56
45 to 54	3,630	90
55 to 64	2,160	96
65 and older	380	156
Occupation		
Management, business, and financial	450	231
Professional and related	330	–
Service	570	–
Sales and related	50	–
Office and administrative support	230	–
Farming, fishing, and forestry	12,960	243
Construction and extractive	30	–
Installation, maintenance, and repair	680	7
Production	470	–
Transportation and material moving	1,840	18
Military occupations	–	–
Race or ethnic origin[c]		
White, non-Hispanic	4,170	423
Black, non-Hispanic	460	12
Hispanic	9,510	61
Other, multiple, and not reported	3,480	13
Nature of injury or illness		
Fractures	2,020	–
Sprains, strains, or tears	4,910	–
Amputations	80	–
Cuts, lacerations, or punctures	1,990	–
Bruises or contusions	1,740	–
Chemical burns and corrosions	80	–
Heat (thermal) burns	60	6
Multiple traumatic injuries	940	161
Soreness or pain	2,180	–
Carpal tunnel syndrome	60	–
Tendonitis	80	–
All other	3,470	335
Part of body affected		
Head	1,960	95
Eye	990	–
Neck	290	11
Trunk	3,550	120
Back	2,270	–
Upper extremities	5,140	–
Shoulder	1,040	–
Arm	680	–
Wrist	450	–
Hand	2,800	–
Lower extremities	4,890	7
Knee	1,680	–
Ankle	940	–
Foot or toe	1,200	–
Body systems	320	109
Multiple	1,270	166
All other	180	–

Characteristic	Nonfatal cases[b]	Fatalities
Source of injury or illness		
Chemicals or chemical products	250	7
Containers	1,310	12
Furniture or fixtures	170	–
Machinery	1,240	70
Parts and materials	1,490	14
Worker motion or position	1,980	–
Health care patient	–	–
Floors, walkways, or ground surfaces	2,390	10
Handtools	1,110	–
Ladders	730	–
Vehicles	2,150	265
All other	4,800	127
Event or exposure		
Violence and other injuries by persons or animals	1,560	27
Intentional injury by other person	50	–
Injury by person unintentional or intent unknown	50	–
Transportation incidents	1,170	244
Roadway incidents involving motorized land vehicles	420	73
Fires or explosions	–	9
Falls, slips, or trips	4,580	35
Slips or trips without fall	810	–
Fall on same level	2,420	8
Fall to lower level	1,250	26
Exposed to harmful substances or environments	850	27
Contact with object or equipment	5,660	166
Struck by object	2,900	125
Struck against object	1,160	–
Caught in object, equipment, or material	1,300	33
Overexertion and bodily reaction	3,570	–
Overexertion in lifting or lowering	990	–
Repetitive motion involving microtasks	260	–
All other	210	–

Source: This research was conducted with restricted access to Bureau of Labor Statistics (BLS) data. The views expressed here do not necessarily reflect the views of BLS.

Note: Because of rounding and data exclusion of nonclassifiable responses, data may not sum to the totals. Dashes (–) indicate data that do not meet publication guidelines.

[a]Days away from work include those that result in days away from work with or without restricted work activity or job transfer.

[b]Excludes farms with less than 11 employees.

[c]In the fatalities column, non-Hispanic categories include cases with Hispanic origin not reported.

Mining

The Mining industry sector includes extraction of naturally occurring mineral solids, such as coal and ores; liquid minerals, such as crude petroleum; and gases, such as natural gas. It also includes quarrying, well operations, beneficiating, other preparation customarily performed at the site, and mining support activities.

Mining employment in 2012 totaled 957,000 workers of which 952,000 were private sector employees.

Number of nonfatal occupational injuries and illnesses involving days away from work[a] and fatal occupational injuries by selected worker and case characteristics, private industry, United States, Mining, 2012

Characteristic	Nonfatal cases[b]	Fatalities
Total	**7,420**	**181**
Sex		
Men	7,260	177
Women	160	–
Age		
Younger than 16	–	–
16 to 19	110	5
20 to 24	730	17
25 to 34	2,530	48
35 to 44	1,610	39
45 to 54	1,410	38
55 to 64	880	27
65 and older	110	7
Occupation		
Management, business, and financial	60	7
Professional and related	110	7
Service	–	–
Sales and related	–	–
Office and administrative support	20	–
Farming, fishing, and forestry	–	–
Construction and extractive	3,780	101
Installation, maintenance, and repair	660	10
Production	460	8
Transportation and material moving	1,320	44
Military occupations	–	–
Race or ethnic origin[c]		
White, non-Hispanic	1,360	128
Black, non-Hispanic	60	11
Hispanic	1,060	36
Other, multiple, and not reported	4,940	6
Nature of injury or illness		
Fractures	1,090	–
Sprains, strains, or tears	2,970	–
Amputations	170	–
Cuts, lacerations, or punctures	240	–
Bruises or contusions	570	–
Chemical burns and corrosions	30	–
Heat (thermal) burns	120	14
Multiple traumatic injuries	210	81
Soreness or pain	370	–
Carpal tunnel syndrome	–	–
Tendonitis	–	–
All other	1,650	84
Part of body affected		
Head	530	26
Eye	*120*	–
Neck	30	–
Trunk	1,770	31
Back	*1,200*	–
Upper extremities	2,230	–
Shoulder	*590*	–
Arm	*330*	–
Wrist	*190*	–
Hand	*1,060*	–
Lower extremities	2,140	–
Knee	*770*	–
Ankle	*560*	–
Foot or toe	*310*	–
Body systems	170	22
Multiple	550	96
All other	–	–

Characteristic	Nonfatal cases[b]	Fatalities
Source of injury or illness		
Chemicals or chemical products	120	10
Containers	320	12
Furniture or fixtures	20	–
Machinery	970	38
Parts and materials	1,490	20
Worker motion or position	660	–
Health care patient	–	–
Floors, walkways, or ground surfaces	990	–
Handtools	410	–
Ladders	120	–
Vehicles	580	79
All other	1,740	16
Event or exposure		
Violence and other injuries by persons or animals	20	–
Intentional injury by other person	–	–
Injury by person unintentional or intent unknown	–	–
Transportation incidents	250	78
Roadway incidents involving motorized land vehicles	*130*	*55*
Fires or explosions	40	25
Falls, slips, or trips	1,360	23
Slips or trips without fall	*260*	–
Fall on same level	*700*	–
Fall to lower level	*360*	*22*
Exposed to harmful substances or environments	360	12
Contact with object or equipment	2,860	39
Struck by object	*1,540*	*31*
Struck against object	*480*	–
Caught in object, equipment, or material	*780*	–
Overexertion and bodily reaction	2,470	–
Overexertion in lifting or lowering	*750*	–
Repetitive motion involving microtasks	–	–
All other	60	–

Source: This research was conducted with restricted access to Bureau of Labor Statistics (BLS) data. The views expressed here do not necessarily reflect the views of BLS.

Note: Because of rounding and data exclusion of nonclassifiable responses, data may not sum to the totals. Dashes (–) indicate data that do not meet publication guidelines.

[a]*Days away from work include those that result in days away from work with or without restricted work activity or job transfer.*

[b]*Data for mining operators in coal, metal, and nonmetal mining are provided to BLS by the Mine Safety and Health Administration (MSHA), Department of Labor. Independent mining contractors are excluded from the coal, metal, and nonmetal mining industries. MSHA data do not reflect the changes in OSHA recordkeeping requirements in 2002.*

[c]*In the fatalities column, non-Hispanic categories include cases with Hispanic origin not reported.*

Construction

The Construction industry sector includes establishments engaged in construction of buildings, heavy construction other than buildings, and specialty trade contractors such as plumbing, electrical, carpentry, etc.

In 2012, employment in the Construction industry totaled 8,965,000 workers, of which 8,551,000 were private sector employees.

Number of nonfatal occupational injuries and illnesses involving days away from work[a] and fatal occupational injuries by selected worker and case characteristics, private industry, United States, Construction, 2012

Characteristic	Nonfatal cases	Fatalities
Total	**71,730**	**806**
Sex		
Men	70,270	800
Women	1,400	6
Age		
Younger than 16	–	–
16 to 19	670	12
20 to 24	6,280	53
25 to 34	20,000	141
35 to 44	17,910	165
45 to 54	18,040	228
55 to 64	7,280	145
65 and older	520	62
Occupation		
Management, business, and financial	1,320	32
Professional and related	180	–
Service	600	8
Sales and related	190	–
Office and administrative support	410	–
Farming, fishing, and forestry	90	–
Construction and extractive	53,300	644
Installation, maintenance, and repair	10,590	45
Production	2,040	22
Transportation and material moving	2,920	54
Military occupations	–	–
Race or ethnic origin[b]		
White, non-Hispanic	40,330	518
Black, non-Hispanic	2,590	48
Hispanic	11,200	220
Other, multiple, and not reported	17,610	20
Nature of injury or illness		
Fractures	8,500	5
Sprains, strains, or tears	21,800	–
Amputations	590	–
Cuts, lacerations, or punctures	9,870	7
Bruises or contusions	4,540	–
Chemical burns and corrosions	200	–
Heat (thermal) burns	770	8
Multiple traumatic injuries	1,820	320
Soreness or pain	10,760	–
Carpal tunnel syndrome	190	–
Tendonitis	50	–
All other	12,640	464
Part of body affected		
Head	5,720	199
Eye	*3,080*	–
Neck	770	30
Trunk	17,280	103
Back	*11,690*	*8*
Upper extremities	22,800	–
Shoulder	*5,900*	–
Arm	*3,270*	–
Wrist	*1,820*	–
Hand	*11,280*	–
Lower extremities	17,760	–
Knee	*6,460*	–
Ankle	*4,050*	–
Foot or toe	*3,730*	–
Body systems	1,100	137
Multiple	5,740	332
All other	550	–

Characteristic	Nonfatal cases	Fatalities
Source of injury or illness		
Chemicals or chemical products	690	19
Containers	3,320	6
Furniture or fixtures	1,370	–
Machinery	5,450	89
Parts and materials	14,030	60
Worker motion or position	10,190	–
Health care patient	–	–
Floors, walkways, or ground surfaces	6,470	15
Handtools	6,460	–
Ladders	6,180	69
Vehicles	4,940	232
All other	12,630	309
Event or exposure		
Violence and other injuries by persons or animals	480	35
Intentional injury by other person	*30*	–
Injury by person unintentional or intent unknown	*30*	–
Transportation incidents	2,490	234
Roadway incidents involving motorized land vehicles	*1,700*	*124*
Fires or explosions	250	9
Falls, slips, or trips	18,400	290
Slips or trips without fall	*2,860*	–
Fall on same level	*6,140*	*9*
Fall to lower level	*8,860*	*279*
Exposed to harmful substances or environments	2,560	102
Contact with object or equipment	24,350	136
Struck by object	*14,300*	*79*
Struck against object	*5,340*	–
Caught in object, equipment, or material	*2,960*	*13*
Overexertion and bodily reaction	22,530	–
Overexertion in lifting or lowering	*7,570*	–
Repetitive motion involving microtasks	*620*	–
All other	670	–

Source: This research was conducted with restricted access to Bureau of Labor Statistics (BLS) data. The views expressed here do not necessarily reflect the views of the BLS.

Note: Because of rounding and data exclusion of nonclassifiable responses, data may not sum to the totals. Dashes (–) indicate data that do not meet publication guidelines.

[a]*Days away from work include those that result in days away from work with or without restricted work activity or job transfer.*

[b]*In the fatalities column, non-Hispanic categories include cases with Hispanic origin not reported.*

Manufacturing

The Manufacturing industry sector includes establishments engaged in the mechanical or chemical transformation of materials, substances, or components into new products. It includes durable and nondurable goods such as food, textiles, apparel, lumber, wood products, paper and paper products, printing, chemicals and pharmaceuticals, petroleum and coal products, rubber and plastics products, metals and metal products, machinery, electrical equipment, and transportation equipment.

Manufacturing employment in 2012 was 14,686,000 workers, of which 14,583,000 were private sector employees.

Number of nonfatal occupational injuries and illnesses involving days away from work[a] and fatal occupational injuries by selected worker and case characteristics, private industry, United States, Manufacturing, 2012

Characteristic	Nonfatal cases	Fatalities
Total	**125,280**	**327**
Sex		
Men	99,880	311
Women	25,350	16
Age		
Younger than 16	–	–
16 to 19	1,790	–
20 to 24	11,060	15
25 to 34	25,650	55
35 to 44	29,020	70
45 to 54	32,410	86
55 to 64	20,920	69
65 and older	2,510	28
Occupation		
Management, business, and financial	1,500	19
Professional and related	1,520	15
Service	2,220	5
Sales and related	610	–
Office and administrative support	3,630	–
Farming, fishing, and forestry	370	–
Construction and extractive	3,720	23
Installation, maintenance, and repair	9,220	43
Production	81,500	133
Transportation and material moving	20,930	81
Military occupations	–	–
Race or ethnic origin[b]		
White, non-Hispanic	62,350	232
Black, non-Hispanic	9,300	40
Hispanic	20,000	45
Other, multiple, and not reported	33,630	10
Nature of injury or illness		
Fractures	12,450	–
Sprains, strains, or tears	38,840	–
Amputations	2,100	–
Cuts, lacerations, or punctures	16,610	8
Bruises or contusions	8,990	–
Chemical burns and corrosions	870	–
Heat (thermal) burns	2,250	8
Multiple traumatic injuries	3,610	119
Soreness or pain	13,410	–
Carpal tunnel syndrome	2,590	–
Tendonitis	650	–
All other	22,910	188
Part of body affected		
Head	9,830	77
Eye	*4,880*	–
Neck	1,220	14
Trunk	27,020	54
Back	*18,740*	–
Upper extremities	54,430	–
Shoulder	*9,770*	–
Arm	*6,700*	–
Wrist	*6,930*	–
Hand	*28,430*	–
Lower extremities	23,590	7
Knee	*8,310*	–
Ankle	*4,130*	–
Foot or toe	*6,300*	–
Body systems	1,520	38
Multiple	6,980	136
All other	700	–

Characteristic	Nonfatal cases	Fatalities
Source of injury or illness		
Chemicals or chemical products	2,610	18
Containers	13,490	13
Furniture or fixtures	3,890	–
Machinery	15,500	61
Parts and materials	23,260	44
Worker motion or position	20,870	–
Health care patient	–	–
Floors, walkways, or ground surfaces	13,120	12
Handtools	8,400	–
Ladders	2,010	–
Vehicles	7,320	97
All other	14,810	74
Event or exposure		
Violence and other injuries by persons or animals	470	45
Intentional injury by other person	*60*	*20*
Injury by person unintentional or intent unknown	*170*	–
Transportation incidents	2,260	87
Roadway incidents involving motorized land vehicles	*690*	*50*
Fires or explosions	210	25
Falls, slips, or trips	22,040	39
Slips or trips without fall	*3,980*	–
Fall on same level	*12,240*	*7*
Fall to lower level	*5,190*	*29*
Exposed to harmful substances or environments	6,390	28
Contact with object or equipment	46,640	102
Struck by object	*22,540*	*60*
Struck against object	*8,890*	–
Caught in object, equipment, or material	*12,160*	*39*
Overexertion and bodily reaction	46,040	–
Overexertion in lifting or lowering	*13,310*	–
Repetitive motion involving microtasks	*8,010*	–
All other	1,230	–

Source: This research was conducted with restricted access to Bureau of Labor Statistics (BLS) data. The views expressed here do not necessarily reflect the views of the BLS.

Note: Because of rounding and data exclusion of nonclassifiable responses, data may not sum to the totals. Dashes (–) indicate data that do not meet publication guidelines.

[a]Days away from work include those that result in days away from work with or without restricted work activity or job transfer.

[b]In the fatalities column, non-Hispanic categories include cases with Hispanic origin not reported.

Wholesale Trade

Establishments in Wholesale Trade generally sell merchandise to other businesses. The merchandise includes the outputs of agriculture, mining, manufacturing, and certain information industries, such as publishing.

Wholesale Trade employed 3,693,000 people in 2012, of which 3,680,000 were private sector employees.

Number of nonfatal occupational injuries and illnesses involving days away from work[a] and fatal occupational injuries by selected worker and case characteristics, private industry, United States, Wholesale Trade, 2012

Characteristic	Nonfatal cases	Fatalities
Total	**58,330**	**204**
Sex		
Men	51,020	199
Women	7,310	5
Age		
Younger than 16	–	–
16 to 19	990	–
20 to 24	4,210	10
25 to 34	14,240	33
35 to 44	13,680	33
45 to 54	15,320	53
55 to 64	7,710	49
65 and older	1,180	23
Occupation		
Management, business, and financial	1,550	11
Professional and related	430	–
Service	980	–
Sales and related	2,690	29
Office and administrative support	5,980	–
Farming, fishing, and forestry	730	5
Construction and extractive	430	–
Installation, maintenance, and repair	7,350	26
Production	6,340	11
Transportation and material moving	31,800	110
Military occupations	–	–
Race or ethnic origin[b]		
White, non-Hispanic	27,910	139
Black, non-Hispanic	4,300	23
Hispanic	10,050	35
Other, multiple, and not reported	16,070	7
Nature of injury or illness		
Fractures	4,940	–
Sprains, strains, or tears	24,200	–
Amputations	350	–
Cuts, lacerations, or punctures	4,270	–
Bruises or contusions	4,410	–
Chemical burns and corrosions	120	–
Heat (thermal) burns	710	6
Multiple traumatic injuries	2,120	93
Soreness or pain	8,160	–
Carpal tunnel syndrome	410	–
Tendonitis	120	–
All other	8,510	103
Part of body affected		
Head	3,210	55
Eye	*1,080*	*–*
Neck	710	–
Trunk	16,550	25
Back	*13,150*	*–*
Upper extremities	17,310	–
Shoulder	*5,400*	*–*
Arm	*2,840*	*–*
Wrist	*1,950*	*–*
Hand	*6,020*	*–*
Lower extremities	14,090	–
Knee	*5,360*	*–*
Ankle	*2,490*	*–*
Foot or toe	*3,100*	*–*
Body systems	880	13
Multiple	4,900	104
All other	690	–

Characteristic	Nonfatal cases	Fatalities
Source of injury or illness		
Chemicals or chemical products	590	–
Containers	12,270	–
Furniture or fixtures	1,030	–
Machinery	3,050	15
Parts and materials	7,290	14
Worker motion or position	8,380	–
Health care patient	–	–
Floors, walkways, or ground surfaces	7,020	11
Handtools	2,120	–
Ladders	480	7
Vehicles	10,180	110
All other	5,920	39
Event or exposure		
Violence and other injuries by persons or animals	450	24
Intentional injury by other person	*90*	*11*
Injury by person unintentional or intent unknown	*80*	*–*
Transportation incidents	4,200	94
Roadway incidents involving motorized land vehicles	*2,070*	*70*
Fires or explosions	120	–
Falls, slips, or trips	11,970	33
Slips or trips without fall	*2,210*	*–*
Fall on same level	*5,590*	*9*
Fall to lower level	*3,450*	*24*
Exposed to harmful substances or environments	1,920	9
Contact with object or equipment	14,790	40
Struck by object	*8,140*	*32*
Struck against object	*3,030*	*–*
Caught in object, equipment, or material	*2,960*	*5*
Overexertion and bodily reaction	23,960	–
Overexertion in lifting or lowering	*9,550*	*–*
Repetitive motion involving microtasks	*1,420*	*–*
All other	920	–

Source: This research was conducted with restricted access to Bureau of Labor Statistics (BLS) data. The views expressed here do not necessarily reflect the views of BLS.

Note: Because of rounding and data exclusion of nonclassifiable responses, data may not sum to the totals. Dashes (–) indicate data that do not meet publication guidelines.

[a]*Days away from work include those that result in days away from work with or without restricted work activity or job transfer.*

[b]*In the fatalities column, non-Hispanic categories include cases with Hispanic origin not reported.*

Establishments in Retail Trade generally sell merchandise in small quantities for personal or household consumption. This sector includes both store and nonstore retailers.

Retail Trade employed 16,182,000 people in 2012, of which 16,069,000 were private sector employees.

Number of nonfatal occupational injuries and illnesses involving days away from work[a] and fatal occupational injuries by selected worker and case characteristics, private industry, United States, Retail Trade, 2012

Characteristic	Nonfatal cases	Fatalities
Total	**125,650**	**273**
Sex		
Men	71,010	232
Women	54,490	41
Age		
Younger than 16	30	–
16 to 19	5,190	5
20 to 24	18,120	18
25 to 34	25,190	34
35 to 44	24,340	35
45 to 54	27,340	75
55 to 64	18,430	58
65 and older	5,170	46
Occupation		
Management, business, and financial	4,280	–
Professional and related	1,320	–
Service	12,210	11
Sales and related	45,420	159
Office and administrative support	17,550	14
Farming, fishing, and forestry	160	–
Construction and extractive	930	–
Installation, maintenance, and repair	13,750	26
Production	6,340	–
Transportation and material moving	23,410	52
Military occupations	–	–
Race or ethnic origin[b]		
White, non-Hispanic	46,760	182
Black, non-Hispanic	6,300	24
Hispanic	7,750	33
Other, multiple, and not reported	64,840	34
Nature of injury or illness		
Fractures	8,180	5
Sprains, strains, or tears	48,960	–
Amputations	360	–
Cuts, lacerations, or punctures	12,350	5
Bruises or contusions	13,060	–
Chemical burns and corrosions	270	–
Heat (thermal) burns	1,280	5
Multiple traumatic injuries	3,760	49
Soreness or pain	17,130	–
Carpal tunnel syndrome	970	–
Tendonitis	280	–
All other	19,050	209
Part of body affected		
Head	10,370	79
Eye	*2,560*	–
Neck	1,710	16
Trunk	33,400	71
Back	*25,710*	*7*
Upper extremities	36,750	–
Shoulder	*8,350*	–
Arm	*5,440*	–
Wrist	*5,140*	–
Hand	*15,740*	–
Lower extremities	29,250	–
Knee	*11,570*	–
Ankle	*5,800*	–
Foot or toe	*7,310*	–
Body systems	2,490	18
Multiple	10,270	85
All other	1,410	–

Characteristic	Nonfatal cases	Fatalities
Source of injury or illness		
Chemicals or chemical products	1,340	8
Containers	24,870	–
Furniture or fixtures	8,000	–
Machinery	6,870	10
Parts and materials	11,140	8
Worker motion or position	17,360	–
Health care patient	30	–
Floors, walkways, or ground surfaces	19,260	20
Handtools	5,180	–
Ladders	3,840	5
Vehicles	12,230	84
All other	15,530	135
Event or exposure		
Violence and other injuries by persons or animals	2,090	129
Intentional injury by other person	*670*	*108*
Injury by person unintentional or intent unknown	*530*	*5*
Transportation incidents	3,820	67
Roadway incidents involving motorized land vehicles	*2,440*	*53*
Fires or explosions	350	6
Falls, slips, or trips	30,230	40
Slips or trips without fall	*4,630*	–
Fall on same level	*19,250*	*21*
Fall to lower level	*5,880*	*19*
Exposed to harmful substances or environments	3,880	10
Contact with object or equipment	35,450	20
Struck by object	*21,820*	*18*
Struck against object	*8,710*	–
Caught in object, equipment, or material	*3,500*	–
Overexertion and bodily reaction	48,530	–
Overexertion in lifting or lowering	*21,740*	–
Repetitive motion involving microtasks	*3,750*	–
All other	1,300	–

Source: This research was conducted with restricted access to Bureau of Labor Statistics (BLS) data. The views expressed here do not necessarily reflect the views of BLS.

Note: Because of rounding and data exclusion of nonclassifiable responses, data may not sum to the totals. Dashes (–) indicate data that do not meet publication guidelines.

[a]Days away from work include those that result in days away from work with or without restricted work activity or job transfer.

[b]In the fatalities column, non-Hispanic categories include cases with Hispanic origin not reported.

This industry sector includes transportation of cargo and passengers, warehousing and storage of goods, scenic and sightseeing transportation, and support activities related to transportation by rail, highway, air, water, or pipeline.

Employment in the Transportation and Warehousing industry sector totaled 6,081,000 in 2012, of which 5,016,000 were private sector employees.

Number of nonfatal occupational injuries and illnesses involving days away from work[a] and fatal occupational injuries by selected worker and case characteristics, private industry, United States, Transportation and Warehousing[b], 2012

Characteristic	Nonfatal cases	Fatalities
Total	**89,260**	**741**
Sex		
Men	68,400	715
Women	18,080	26
Age		
Younger than 16	–	–
16 to 19	590	7
20 to 24	4,980	22
25 to 34	14,660	100
35 to 44	20,380	137
45 to 54	27,930	216
55 to 64	15,910	176
65 and older	3,070	83
Occupation		
Management, business, and financial	380	14
Professional and related	130	–
Service	1,520	5
Sales and related	160	–
Office and administrative support	12,330	9
Farming, fishing, and forestry	–	–
Construction and extractive	720	5
Installation, maintenance, and repair	5,510	24
Production	1,110	–
Transportation and material moving	67,300	679
Military occupations	–	–
Race or ethnic origin[c]		
White, non-Hispanic	23,240	483
Black, non-Hispanic	4,770	129
Hispanic	5,170	92
Other, multiple, and not reported	56,080	37
Nature of injury or illness		
Fractures	6,210	–
Sprains, strains, or tears	39,140	–
Amputations	230	–
Cuts, lacerations, or punctures	3,980	–
Bruises or contusions	8,070	–
Chemical burns and corrosions	230	–
Heat (thermal) burns	230	29
Multiple traumatic injuries	2,690	387
Soreness or pain	14,170	–
Carpal tunnel syndrome	260	–
Tendonitis	460	–
All other	13,600	316
Part of body affected		
Head	4,950	114
Eye	*1,290*	–
Neck	1,900	30
Trunk	24,750	96
Back	*17,320*	*7*
Upper extremities	24,930	–
Shoulder	*9,180*	–
Arm	*4,700*	–
Wrist	*3,480*	–
Hand	*6,300*	–
Lower extremities	22,130	–
Knee	*8,150*	–
Ankle	*5,190*	–
Foot or toe	*4,300*	–
Body systems	1,350	67
Multiple	8,490	428
All other	750	–

Characteristic	Nonfatal cases	Fatalities
Source of injury or illness		
Chemicals or chemical products	710	15
Containers	17,860	6
Furniture or fixtures	2,610	–
Machinery	1,940	9
Parts and materials	9,110	7
Worker motion or position	12,270	–
Health care patient	80	–
Floors, walkways, or ground surfaces	11,620	8
Handtools	1,270	–
Ladders	640	–
Vehicles	22,440	603
All other	8,710	88
Event or exposure		
Violence and other injuries by persons or animals	1,050	76
Intentional injury by other person	*330*	*48*
Injury by person unintentional or intent unknown	*240*	–
Transportation incidents	10,230	548
Roadway incidents involving motorized land vehicles	*6,890*	*408*
Fires or explosions	80	8
Falls, slips, or trips	19,940	34
Slips or trips without fall	*4,050*	–
Fall on same level	*9,210*	*6*
Fall to lower level	*5,360*	*28*
Exposed to harmful substances or environments	2,150	19
Contact with object or equipment	18,410	53
Struck by object	*10,190*	*42*
Struck against object	*4,540*	–
Caught in object, equipment, or material	*2,700*	*8*
Overexertion and bodily reaction	36,180	–
Overexertion in lifting or lowering	*11,700*	–
Repetitive motion involving microtasks	*1,200*	–
All other	1,220	–

Source: This research was conducted with restricted access to Bureau of Labor Statistics (BLS) data. The views expressed here do not necessarily reflect the views of BLS.

Note: Because of rounding and data exclusion of nonclassifiable responses, data may not sum to the totals. Dashes (–) indicate data that do not meet publication guidelines.

[a]Days away from work include those that result in days away from work with or without restricted work activity or job transfer.

[b]Data for employees in railroad transportation are provided to BLS by the Federal Railroad Administration (FRA), U.S. Department of Transportation. FRA data do not reflect the changes in OSHA recordkeeping requirements in 2002.

[c]In the fatalities column, non-Hispanic categories include cases with Hispanic origin not reported.

Utilities

The Utilities sector includes establishments that provide electric power generation, transmission, and distribution; natural gas distribution; steam supply; water treatment and distribution; and sewage collection, treatment, and disposal.

The Utilities sector employed 1,189,000 people in 2012, of which 851,000 were private sector employees.

Number of nonfatal occupational injuries and illnesses involving days away from work[a] and fatal occupational injuries by selected worker and case characteristics, private industry, United States, Utilities, 2012

Characteristic	Nonfatal cases	Fatalities
Total	**4,280**	**23**
Sex		
Men	3,920	22
Women	350	–
Age		
Younger than 16	–	–
16 to 19	50	–
20 to 24	100	–
25 to 34	600	–
35 to 44	990	–
45 to 54	1,420	6
55 to 64	970	–
65 and older	90	–
Occupation		
Management, business, and financial	90	–
Professional and related	140	–
Service	140	–
Sales and related	–	–
Office and administrative support	410	–
Farming, fishing, and forestry	–	–
Construction and extractive	630	–
Installation, maintenance, and repair	2,140	14
Production	500	–
Transportation and material moving	180	–
Military occupations	–	–
Race or ethnic origin[b]		
White, non-Hispanic	1,970	20
Black, non-Hispanic	270	–
Hispanic	150	–
Other, multiple, and not reported	1,890	–
Nature of injury or illness		
Fractures	400	–
Sprains, strains, or tears	1,980	–
Amputations	20	–
Cuts, lacerations, or punctures	240	–
Bruises or contusions	200	–
Chemical burns and corrosions	30	–
Heat (thermal) burns	30	–
Multiple traumatic injuries	40	11
Soreness or pain	500	–
Carpal tunnel syndrome	40	–
Tendonitis	–	–
All other	790	11
Part of body affected		
Head	300	–
Eye	120	–
Neck	30	–
Trunk	1,060	–
Back	770	–
Upper extremities	1,210	–
Shoulder	430	–
Arm	200	–
Wrist	150	–
Hand	360	–
Lower extremities	1,230	–
Knee	650	–
Ankle	160	–
Foot or toe	160	–
Body systems	120	8
Multiple	300	11
All other	20	–

Characteristic	Nonfatal cases	Fatalities
Source of injury or illness		
Chemicals or chemical products	60	–
Containers	170	–
Furniture or fixtures	80	–
Machinery	110	–
Parts and materials	620	5
Worker motion or position	1,090	–
Health care patient	–	–
Floors, walkways, or ground surfaces	560	–
Handtools	380	–
Ladders	20	–
Vehicles	420	8
All other	770	6
Event or exposure		
Violence and other injuries by persons or animals	60	–
Intentional injury by other person	–	–
Injury by person unintentional or intent unknown	–	–
Transportation incidents	280	8
Roadway incidents involving motorized land vehicles	200	5
Fires or explosions	20	–
Falls, slips, or trips	1,030	–
Slips or trips without fall	350	–
Fall on same level	420	–
Fall to lower level	240	–
Exposed to harmful substances or environments	290	7
Contact with object or equipment	820	–
Struck by object	520	–
Struck against object	150	–
Caught in object, equipment, or material	120	–
Overexertion and bodily reaction	1,760	–
Overexertion in lifting or lowering	340	–
Repetitive motion involving microtasks	130	–
All other	30	–

Source: This research was conducted with restricted access to Bureau of Labor Statistics (BLS) data. The views expressed here do not necessarily reflect the views of BLS.
Note: Because of rounding and data exclusion of nonclassifiable responses, data may not sum to the totals. Dashes (–) indicate data that do not meet publication guidelines.
[a]Days away from work include those that result in days away from work with or without restricted work activity or job transfer.
[b]In the fatalities column, non-Hispanic categories include cases with Hispanic origin not reported.

Information

The Information sector includes establishments that produce and distribute information and cultural products, provide the means to transmit or distribute these products as well as data or communications, and process data. Included are both traditional and Internet publishing and broadcasting, motion pictures and sound recordings, telecommunications, Internet service providers, Web search portals, data processing, and information services.

The Information sector employed 2,971,000 people in 2012, of which 2,785,000 were private sector employees.

Number of nonfatal occupational injuries and illnesses involving days away from work[a] and fatal occupational injuries by selected worker and case characteristics, private industry, United States, Information, 2012

Characteristic	Nonfatal cases	Fatalities
Total	**15,350**	**42**
Sex		
Men	11,760	37
Women	3,590	5
Age		
Younger than 16	–	–
16 to 19	120	–
20 to 24	1,020	–
25 to 34	3,310	8
35 to 44	3,800	8
45 to 54	3,920	9
55 to 64	2,450	10
65 and older	320	–
Occupation		
Management, business, and financial	880	–
Professional and related	1,670	–
Service	510	–
Sales and related	580	5
Office and administrative support	1,670	–
Farming, fishing, and forestry	–	–
Construction and extractive	210	–
Installation, maintenance, and repair	7,960	10
Production	970	–
Transportation and material moving	840	16
Military occupations	–	–
Race or ethnic origin[b]		
White, non-Hispanic	4,140	27
Black, non-Hispanic	770	–
Hispanic	830	8
Other, multiple, and not reported	9,610	–
Nature of injury or illness		
Fractures	1,050	–
Sprains, strains, or tears	7,380	–
Amputations	60	–
Cuts, lacerations, or punctures	690	–
Bruises or contusions	1,070	–
Chemical burns and corrosions	–	–
Heat (thermal) burns	50	–
Multiple traumatic injuries	370	21
Soreness or pain	1,600	–
Carpal tunnel syndrome	190	–
Tendonitis	70	–
All other	2,820	18
Part of body affected		
Head	920	6
Eye	150	–
Neck	300	–
Trunk	3,940	5
Back	2,890	–
Upper extremities	3,980	–
Shoulder	1,040	–
Arm	610	–
Wrist	870	–
Hand	1,110	–
Lower extremities	3,930	–
Knee	1,750	–
Ankle	1,040	–
Foot or toe	660	–
Body systems	490	–
Multiple	1,720	22
All other	60	–

Characteristic	Nonfatal cases	Fatalities
Source of injury or illness		
Chemicals or chemical products	40	–
Containers	980	–
Furniture or fixtures	340	–
Machinery	840	–
Parts and materials	1,340	–
Worker motion or position	3,730	–
Health care patient	–	–
Floors, walkways, or ground surfaces	3,020	–
Handtools	280	–
Ladders	1,510	–
Vehicles	1,290	23
All other	1,980	15
Event or exposure		
Violence and other injuries by persons or animals	380	11
Intentional injury by other person	*50*	*6*
Injury by person unintentional or intent unknown	*20*	*–*
Transportation incidents	960	23
Roadway incidents involving motorized land vehicles	*800*	*19*
Fires or explosions	–	–
Falls, slips, or trips	4,560	–
Slips or trips without fall	*1,020*	*–*
Fall on same level	*2,550*	*–*
Fall to lower level	*900*	*–*
Exposed to harmful substances or environments	520	–
Contact with object or equipment	2,560	–
Struck by object	*1,300*	*–*
Struck against object	*810*	*–*
Caught in object, equipment, or material	*370*	*–*
Overexertion and bodily reaction	6,310	–
Overexertion in lifting or lowering	*1,730*	*–*
Repetitive motion involving microtasks	*580*	*–*
All other	70	–

Source: This research was conducted with restricted access to Bureau of Labor Statistics (BLS) data. The views expressed here do not necessarily reflect the views of BLS.

Note: Because of rounding and data exclusion of nonclassifiable responses, data may not sum to the totals. Dashes (–) indicate data that do not meet publication guidelines.

[a]Days away from work include those that result in days away from work with or without restricted work activity or job transfer.

[b]In the fatalities column, non-Hispanic categories include cases with Hispanic origin not reported.

Financial Activities

Financial Activities includes the Finance and Insurance sector and the Real Estate and Rental and Leasing sector. Included are banks and other savings institutions; securities and commodities brokers, dealers, exchanges, and services; insurance carriers, brokers, and agents; real estate operators, developers, agents, and brokers; and establishments that rent and lease goods, such as automobiles, computers, and household and industrial machinery and equipment.

Financial Activities had 9,590,000 workers in 2012, of which 9,363,000 were private sector employees.

Number of nonfatal occupational injuries and illnesses involving days away from work[a] and fatal occupational injuries by selected worker and case characteristics, private industry, United States, Financial Activities, 2012

Characteristic	Nonfatal cases	Fatalities
Total	25,790	85
Sex		
Men	16,020	73
Women	9,770	12
Age		
Younger than 16	–	–
16 to 19	170	–
20 to 24	3,030	5
25 to 34	5,940	10
35 to 44	5,640	10
45 to 54	5,650	29
55 to 64	4,500	18
65 and older	610	13
Occupation		
Management, business, and financial	3,140	37
Professional and related	510	–
Service	3,850	–
Sales and related	1,760	14
Office and administrative support	6,220	–
Farming, fishing, and forestry	–	–
Construction and extractive	570	7
Installation, maintenance, and repair	5,720	18
Production	370	–
Transportation and material moving	3,310	–
Military occupations	–	–
Race or ethnic origin[b]		
White, non-Hispanic	8,920	60
Black, non-Hispanic	2,620	–
Hispanic	3,000	15
Other, multiple, and not reported	11,250	8
Nature of injury or illness		
Fractures	1,960	–
Sprains, strains, or tears	10,040	–
Amputations	30	–
Cuts, lacerations, or punctures	2,250	–
Bruises or contusions	1,820	–
Chemical burns and corrosions	40	–
Heat (thermal) burns	70	–
Multiple traumatic injuries	740	23
Soreness or pain	3,710	–
Carpal tunnel syndrome	620	–
Tendonitis	80	–
All other	4,430	58
Part of body affected		
Head	1,820	23
Eye	*360*	–
Neck	290	–
Trunk	7,270	15
Back	*6,000*	–
Upper extremities	6,980	–
Shoulder	*1,430*	–
Arm	*950*	–
Wrist	*1,180*	–
Hand	*3,090*	–
Lower extremities	5,340	–
Knee	*1,960*	–
Ankle	*1,590*	–
Foot or toe	*810*	–
Body systems	870	7
Multiple	2,750	35
All other	470	–

Characteristic	Nonfatal cases	Fatalities
Source of injury or illness		
Chemicals or chemical products	260	–
Containers	1,680	–
Furniture or fixtures	2,170	–
Machinery	2,120	–
Parts and materials	1,200	–
Worker motion or position	4,950	–
Health care patient	50	–
Floors, walkways, or ground surfaces	4,670	5
Handtools	1,680	–
Ladders	580	7
Vehicles	2,140	23
All other	4,290	41
Event or exposure		
Violence and other injuries by persons or animals	780	30
Intentional injury by other person	*290*	*20*
Injury by person unintentional or intent unknown	*340*	–
Transportation incidents	1,350	20
Roadway incidents involving motorized land vehicles	*1,210*	*13*
Fires or explosions	–	–
Falls, slips, or trips	7,100	21
Slips or trips without fall	*1,480*	–
Fall on same level	*4,070*	–
Fall to lower level	*1,460*	*16*
Exposed to harmful substances or environments	1,110	5
Contact with object or equipment	5,200	6
Struck by object	*2,820*	*6*
Struck against object	*1,240*	–
Caught in object, equipment, or material	*750*	–
Overexertion and bodily reaction	9,710	–
Overexertion in lifting or lowering	*3,540*	–
Repetitive motion involving microtasks	*1,220*	–
All other	530	–

Source: This research was conducted with restricted access to Bureau of Labor Statistics (BLS) data. The views expressed here do not necessarily reflect the views of BLS.

Note: Because of rounding and data exclusion of nonclassifiable responses, data may not sum to the totals. Dashes (–) indicate data that do not meet publication guidelines.

[a]Days away from work include those that result in days away from work with or without restricted work activity or job transfer.

[b]In the fatalities column, non-Hispanic categories include cases with Hispanic origin not reported.

Professional and Business Services

The Professional and Business Services sector includes legal, accounting, architectural, engineering, computer, consulting, research, advertising, photographic, translation and interpretation, veterinary, and other professional scientific and technical services. Also included are business management and administrative and support activities and waste management and remediation services.

Professional and Business Services employed 16,539,000 people in 2012, of which 16,096,000 were private sector employees.

Number of nonfatal occupational injuries and illnesses involving days away from work[a] and fatal occupational injuries by selected worker and case characteristics, private industry, United States, Professional and Business Services, 2012

Characteristic	Nonfatal cases	Fatalities
Total	**70,330**	**409**
Sex		
Men	45,350	391
Women	24,960	18
Age		
Younger than 16	–	–
16 to 19	1,050	5
20 to 24	6,420	34
25 to 34	19,200	65
35 to 44	14,470	91
45 to 54	16,210	95
55 to 64	9,390	80
65 and older	2,600	39
Occupation		
Management, business, and financial	3,110	11
Professional and related	5,860	19
Service	30,810	241
Sales and related	1,810	–
Office and administrative support	6,320	6
Farming, fishing, and forestry	70	–
Construction and extractive	2,230	27
Installation, maintenance, and repair	4,520	13
Production	4,000	17
Transportation and material moving	11,460	71
Military occupations	–	–
Race or ethnic origin[b]		
White, non-Hispanic	25,840	245
Black, non-Hispanic	5,280	57
Hispanic	14,850	99
Other, multiple, and not reported	24,360	8
Nature of injury or illness		
Fractures	7,430	–
Sprains, strains, or tears	21,990	–
Amputations	330	–
Cuts, lacerations, or punctures	8,510	6
Bruises or contusions	4,740	–
Chemical burns and corrosions	510	–
Heat (thermal) burns	350	–
Multiple traumatic injuries	2,310	133
Soreness or pain	11,630	–
Carpal tunnel syndrome	400	–
Tendonitis	200	–
All other	11,930	263
Part of body affected		
Head	6,380	89
Eye	*1,680*	–
Neck	610	17
Trunk	17,270	67
Back	*13,670*	*6*
Upper extremities	20,100	–
Shoulder	*4,120*	–
Arm	*2,940*	–
Wrist	*3,400*	–
Hand	*8,620*	–
Lower extremities	15,470	6
Knee	*5,090*	–
Ankle	*3,510*	–
Foot or toe	*3,230*	–
Body systems	1,870	77
Multiple	7,520	153
All other	1,100	–

Characteristic	Nonfatal cases	Fatalities
Source of injury or illness		
Chemicals or chemical products	1,050	13
Containers	7,240	–
Furniture or fixtures	2,580	–
Machinery	3,940	41
Parts and materials	3,920	18
Worker motion or position	10,440	–
Health care patient	370	–
Floors, walkways, or ground surfaces	12,710	14
Handtools	2,770	5
Ladders	2,230	21
Vehicles	7,140	140
All other	15,940	151
Event or exposure		
Violence and other injuries by persons or animals	4,370	54
Intentional injury by other person	*520*	*29*
Injury by person unintentional or intent unknown	*470*	–
Transportation incidents	4,560	132
Roadway incidents involving motorized land vehicles	*3,490*	*78*
Fires or explosions	70	8
Falls, slips, or trips	19,570	80
Slips or trips without fall	*2,600*	–
Fall on same level	*11,500*	*6*
Fall to lower level	*4,710*	*73*
Exposed to harmful substances or environments	3,040	53
Contact with object or equipment	16,380	82
Struck by object	*9,170*	*64*
Struck against object	*4,330*	–
Caught in object, equipment, or material	*2,270*	*14*
Overexertion and bodily reaction	21,480	–
Overexertion in lifting or lowering	*6,340*	–
Repetitive motion involving microtasks	*2,010*	–
All other	860	–

Source: This research was conducted with restricted access to Bureau of Labor Statistics (BLS) data. The views expressed here do not necessarily reflect the views of BLS.
Note: Because of rounding and data exclusion of nonclassifiable responses, data may not sum to the totals. Dashes (–) indicate data that do not meet publication guidelines.
[a]Days away from work include those that result in days away from work with or without restricted work activity.
[b]In the fatalities column, non-Hispanic categories include cases with Hispanic origin not reported.

Educational and Health Services

Educational Services includes instruction and training through schools, colleges, universities, and training centers. Health Services includes ambulatory health care facilities, hospitals, nursing and residential care facilities, and social assistance for individuals, families, and communities.

Educational and Health Services employed 32,351,000 people in 2012, of which 22,080,000 were private sector employees.

Number of nonfatal occupational injuries and illnesses involving days away from work[a] and fatal occupational injuries by selected worker and case characteristics, private industry, United States, Educational and Health Services, 2012

Characteristic	Nonfatal cases	Fatalities
Total	**178,330**	**141**
Sex		
Men	36,600	89
Women	141,640	52
Age		
Younger than 16	50	–
16 to 19	2,400	–
20 to 24	14,200	9
25 to 34	38,500	23
35 to 44	38,210	23
45 to 54	44,260	37
55 to 64	32,710	27
65 and older	6,110	21
Occupation		
Management, business, and financial	6,580	17
Professional and related	62,810	–
Service	92,110	85
Sales and related	420	–
Office and administrative support	7,160	8
Farming, fishing, and forestry	–	–
Construction and extractive	870	–
Installation, maintenance, and repair	2,940	–
Production	1,350	–
Transportation and material moving	3,850	26
Military occupations	–	–
Race or ethnic origin[b]		
White, non-Hispanic	72,700	110
Black, non-Hispanic	24,810	15
Hispanic	13,320	6
Other, multiple, and not reported	67,500	10
Nature of injury or illness		
Fractures	9,560	–
Sprains, strains, or tears	84,330	–
Amputations	100	–
Cuts, lacerations, or punctures	6,590	5
Bruises or contusions	16,050	–
Chemical burns and corrosions	370	–
Heat (thermal) burns	1,480	–
Multiple traumatic injuries	6,060	50
Soreness or pain	29,270	–
Carpal tunnel syndrome	1,120	–
Tendonitis	510	–
All other	22,900	83
Part of body affected		
Head	10,340	27
Eye	*1,820*	–
Neck	3,850	6
Trunk	55,490	19
Back	*46,630*	–
Upper extremities	44,850	–
Shoulder	*13,540*	–
Arm	*6,840*	–
Wrist	*7,810*	–
Hand	*12,600*	–
Lower extremities	35,370	–
Knee	*15,400*	–
Ankle	*8,530*	–
Foot or toe	*5,690*	–
Body systems	3,610	24
Multiple	23,440	63
All other	1,400	–

Characteristic	Nonfatal cases	Fatalities
Source of injury or illness		
Chemicals or chemical products	2,290	10
Containers	8,570	–
Furniture or fixtures	8,990	–
Machinery	3,540	–
Parts and materials	2,170	–
Worker motion or position	22,220	–
Health care patient	49,030	–
Floors, walkways, or ground surfaces	34,910	15
Handtools	2,300	–
Ladders	830	–
Vehicles	10,060	64
All other	33,420	44
Event or exposure		
Violence and other injuries by persons or animals	20,590	39
Intentional injury by other person	*9,480*	*22*
Injury by person unintentional or intent unknown	*9,280*	–
Transportation incidents	6,690	60
Roadway incidents involving motorized land vehicles	*5,890*	*29*
Fires or explosions	40	–
Falls, slips, or trips	45,100	20
Slips or trips without fall	*6,570*	–
Fall on same level	*34,050*	*13*
Fall to lower level	*3,920*	*7*
Exposed to harmful substances or environments	6,550	18
Contact with object or equipment	21,330	–
Struck by object	*11,480*	–
Struck against object	*6,570*	–
Caught in object, equipment, or material	*1,990*	–
Overexertion and bodily reaction	77,100	–
Overexertion in lifting or lowering	*19,230*	–
Repetitive motion involving microtasks	*3,880*	–
All other	940	–

Source: This research was conducted with restricted access to Bureau of Labor Statistics (BLS) data. The views expressed here do not necessarily reflect the views of the BLS.

Note: Because of rounding and data exclusion of nonclassifiable responses, data may not sum to the totals. Dashes (–) indicate data that do not meet publication guidelines.

[a]Days away from work include those that result in days away from work with or without restricted work activity.

[b]In the fatalities column, non-Hispanic categories include cases with Hispanic origin not reported.

The Leisure sector includes establishments that provide arts, entertainment, and recreation experiences such as theatre, dance, music, and spectator sports, museums, zoos, amusement and theme parks, casinos, golf courses, ski areas, marinas, and fitness and sports centers. The Hospitality sector includes hotels and other traveler accommodations, food services, and drinking places.

The Leisure and Hospitality sector employed 13,192,000 people in 2012, of which 12,766,000 were private sector employees.

Number of nonfatal occupational injuries and illnesses involving days away from work[a] and fatal occupational injuries by selected worker and case characteristics, private industry, United States, Leisure and Hospitality, 2012

Characteristic	Nonfatal cases	Fatalities
Total	**89,480**	**232**
Sex		
Men	44,880	187
Women	44,570	45
Age		
Younger than 16	30	–
16 to 19	3,550	5
20 to 24	13,810	26
25 to 34	21,690	50
35 to 44	16,060	43
45 to 54	16,520	51
55 to 64	9,390	36
65 and older	3,400	21
Occupation		
Management, business, and financial	3,890	42
Professional and related	2,960	–
Service	68,600	129
Sales and related	3,270	7
Office and administrative support	1,580	10
Farming, fishing, and forestry	–	–
Construction and extractive	320	–
Installation, maintenance, and repair	3,370	11
Production	1,440	–
Transportation and material moving	3,550	31
Military occupations	–	–
Race or ethnic origin[b]		
White, non-Hispanic	29,500	130
Black, non-Hispanic	7,690	39
Hispanic	18,170	40
Other, multiple, and not reported	34,120	23
Nature of injury or illness		
Fractures	5,870	5
Sprains, strains, or tears	26,140	–
Amputations	430	–
Cuts, lacerations, or punctures	14,380	10
Bruises or contusions	7,120	–
Chemical burns and corrosions	380	–
Heat (thermal) burns	5,920	–
Multiple traumatic injuries	2,020	49
Soreness or pain	13,970	–
Carpal tunnel syndrome	480	–
Tendonitis	150	–
All other	12,610	165
Part of body affected		
Head	6,380	54
Eye	*1,250*	–
Neck	680	19
Trunk	18,330	50
Back	*13,910*	*6*
Upper extremities	34,460	–
Shoulder	*5,190*	–
Arm	*4,720*	–
Wrist	*3,440*	–
Hand	*19,410*	–
Lower extremities	19,770	6
Knee	*7,920*	–
Ankle	*4,650*	–
Foot or toe	*3,860*	–
Body systems	1,770	33
Multiple	7,290	68
All other	800	–

Characteristic	Nonfatal cases	Fatalities
Source of injury or illness		
Chemicals or chemical products	1,160	11
Containers	12,380	–
Furniture or fixtures	5,450	–
Machinery	5,880	7
Parts and materials	1,870	–
Worker motion or position	11,590	–
Health care patient	20	–
Floors, walkways, or ground surfaces	20,200	15
Handtools	6,610	–
Ladders	810	–
Vehicles	3,610	59
All other	19,900	137
Event or exposure		
Violence and other injuries by persons or animals	2,240	105
Intentional injury by other person	*770*	*79*
Injury by person unintentional or intent unknown	*680*	–
Transportation incidents	1,960	60
Roadway incidents involving motorized land vehicles	*1,270*	*28*
Fires or explosions	170	6
Falls, slips, or trips	26,530	27
Slips or trips without fall	*3,960*	–
Fall on same level	*18,900*	*13*
Fall to lower level	*3,320*	*12*
Exposed to harmful substances or environments	8,340	19
Contact with object or equipment	25,740	14
Struck by object	*16,980*	*8*
Struck against object	*5,840*	–
Caught in object, equipment, or material	*2,360*	–
Overexertion and bodily reaction	23,380	–
Overexertion in lifting or lowering	*7,390*	–
Repetitive motion involving microtasks	*1,740*	–
All other	1,120	–

Source: This research was conducted with restricted access to Bureau of Labor Statistics (BLS) data. The views expressed here do not necessarily reflect the views of the BLS.
Note: Because of rounding and data exclusion of nonclassifiable responses, data may not sum to the totals. Dashes (–) indicate data that do not meet publication guidelines.
[a]Days away from work include those that result in days away from work with or without restricted work activity or job transfer.
[b]In the fatalities column, non-Hispanic categories include cases with Hispanic origin not reported.

Other Services

The Other Services sector includes repair and maintenance of equipment and machinery and personal and household goods; personal care and laundry services; and religious, grant making, civic, professional, and similar organizations.

The Other Services sector employed 7,167,000 people in 2012, of which 7,129,000 were private sector employees.

Number of nonfatal occupational injuries and illnesses involving days away from work[a] and fatal occupational injuries by selected worker and case characteristics, private industry, United States, Other Services (except Public Administration), 2012

Characteristic	Nonfatal cases	Fatalities
Total	**26,820**	**199**
Sex		
Men	19,510	172
Women	7,320	27
Age		
Younger than 16	–	–
16 to 19	940	–
20 to 24	3,630	12
25 to 34	6,130	27
35 to 44	5,430	35
45 to 54	5,090	51
55 to 64	4,190	38
65 and older	1,200	35
Occupation		
Management, business, and financial	1,040	17
Professional and related	660	–
Service	6,020	56
Sales and related	540	–
Office and administrative support	760	8
Farming, fishing, and forestry	70	–
Construction and extractive	200	6
Installation, maintenance, and repair	9,450	75
Production	2,980	12
Transportation and material moving	5,060	24
Military occupations	–	–
Race or ethnic origin[b]		
White, non-Hispanic	13,270	130
Black, non-Hispanic	1,500	26
Hispanic	3,890	24
Other, multiple, and not reported	8,160	19
Nature of injury or illness		
Fractures	2,170	–
Sprains, strains, or tears	8,210	–
Amputations	240	–
Cuts, lacerations, or punctures	3,060	–
Bruises or contusions	1,760	–
Chemical burns and corrosions	130	–
Heat (thermal) burns	380	6
Multiple traumatic injuries	930	42
Soreness or pain	4,040	–
Carpal tunnel syndrome	190	–
Tendonitis	50	–
All other	5,660	145
Part of body affected		
Head	2,600	59
Eye	930	–
Neck	90	18
Trunk	5,650	39
Back	3,630	–
Upper extremities	10,510	–
Shoulder	2,110	–
Arm	1,000	–
Wrist	1,430	–
Hand	4,780	–
Lower extremities	5,140	–
Knee	1,900	–
Ankle	1,240	–
Foot or toe	970	–
Body systems	1,010	15
Multiple	1,690	62
All other	130	–

Characteristic	Nonfatal cases	Fatalities
Source of injury or illness		
Chemicals or chemical products	380	–
Containers	1,550	–
Furniture or fixtures	750	–
Machinery	1,540	11
Parts and materials	3,810	5
Worker motion or position	3,740	–
Health care patient	–	–
Floors, walkways, or ground surfaces	4,610	5
Handtools	1,790	–
Ladders	510	–
Vehicles	2,940	75
All other	5,200	92
Event or exposure		
Violence and other injuries by persons or animals	830	85
Intentional injury by other person	70	50
Injury by person unintentional or intent unknown	150	5
Transportation incidents	1,050	51
Roadway incidents involving motorized land vehicles	640	29
Fires or explosions	400	7
Falls, slips, or trips	7,230	13
Slips or trips without fall	1,360	–
Fall on same level	4,230	–
Fall to lower level	1,250	10
Exposed to harmful substances or environments	1,550	6
Contact with object or equipment	7,460	36
Struck by object	4,190	29
Struck against object	1,930	–
Caught in object, equipment, or material	890	6
Overexertion and bodily reaction	8,100	–
Overexertion in lifting or lowering	2,020	–
Repetitive motion involving microtasks	680	–
All other	200	–

Source: This research was conducted with restricted access to Bureau of Labor Statistics (BLS) data. The views expressed here do not necessarily reflect the views of the BLS.

Note: Because of rounding and data exclusion of nonclassifiable responses, data may not sum to the totals. Dashes (–) indicate data that do not meet publication guidelines.

[a]*Days away from work include those that result in days away from work with or without restricted work activity or job transfer.*

[b]*In the fatalities column, non-Hispanic categories include cases with Hispanic origin not reported.*

Government

Government includes public employees at all levels from federal (civilian and military) to state, county, and municipal.

Total government employment was 21,657,000 in 2012, of which 16,863,000 were state and local government employees.

Number of nonfatal occupational injuries and illnesses involving days away from work[a] and fatal occupational injuries by selected worker and case characteristics, United States, Government, 2012

Characteristic	State and local government nonfatal cases[b]	All government fatalities
Total	**248,290**	**453**
Sex		
Men	142,420	387
Women	104,370	66
Age		
Younger than 16	50	–
16 to 19	1,300	6
20 to 24	7,170	34
25 to 34	43,170	86
35 to 44	61,220	81
45 to 54	74,550	95
55 to 64	48,020	102
65 and older	7,060	49
Occupation		
Management, business, and financial	5,310	19
Professional and related	50,310	17
Service	122,920	229
Sales and related	750	–
Office and administrative support	11,200	26
Farming, fishing, and forestry	520	–
Construction and extractive	14,030	46
Installation, maintenance, and repair	13,500	28
Production	3,700	5
Transportation and material moving	24,260	49
Military occupations	–	31
Race or ethnic origin[c]		
White, non-Hispanic	92,680	347
Black, non-Hispanic	18,400	53
Hispanic	15,070	33
Other, multiple, and not reported	122,140	20
Nature of injury or illness		
Fractures	12,860	–
Sprains, strains, or tears	102,670	5
Amputations	180	–
Cuts, lacerations, or punctures	13,350	11
Bruises or contusions	23,390	–
Chemical burns and corrosions	310	–
Heat (thermal) burns	2,580	–
Multiple traumatic injuries	10,550	153
Soreness or pain	41,030	–
Carpal tunnel syndrome	1,070	–
Tendonitis	340	–
All other	39,960	275
Part of body affected		
Head	15,590	114
Eye	*3,530*	–
Neck	3,950	29
Trunk	52,720	73
Back	*40,080*	*10*
Upper extremities	61,910	–
Shoulder	*19,030*	–
Arm	*11,000*	–
Wrist	*8,530*	–
Hand	*18,480*	–
Lower extremities	59,500	13
Knee	*28,380*	–
Ankle	*13,110*	–
Foot or toe	*7,910*	–
Body systems	7,930	38
Multiple	43,070	183
All other	3,620	–

Characteristic	State and local government nonfatal cases[b]	All government fatalities
Source of injury or illness		
Chemicals or chemical products	2,130	10
Containers	14,410	–
Furniture or fixtures	11,360	–
Machinery	6,280	13
Parts and materials	9,510	5
Worker motion or position	40,520	–
Health care patient	16,210	–
Floors, walkways, or ground surfaces	45,270	19
Handtools	5,930	–
Ladders	2,080	7
Vehicles	25,050	221
All other	69,540	170
Event or exposure		
Violence and other injuries by persons or animals	38,100	137
Intentional injury by other person	*17,430*	*76*
Injury by person unintentional or intent unknown	*17,470*	*8*
Transportation incidents	3,020	217
Roadway incidents involving motorized land vehicles	*13,580*	*119*
Fires or explosions	500	11
Falls, slips, or trips	65,750	43
Slips or trips without fall	*12,520*	–
Fall on same level	*41,650*	*18*
Fall to lower level	*9,710*	*22*
Exposed to harmful substances or environments	11,500	22
Contact with object or equipment	34,250	21
Struck by object	*19,060*	*18*
Struck against object	*9,990*	–
Caught in object, equipment, or material	*2,930*	–
Overexertion and bodily reaction	77,630	–
Overexertion in lifting or lowering	*21,640*	–
Repetitive motion involving microtasks	*4,810*	–
All other	3,620	–

Source: Source: This research was conducted with restricted access to Bureau of Labor Statistics (BLS) data. The views expressed here do not necessarily reflect the views of BLS.

Note: Because of rounding and data exclusion of nonclassifiable responses, data may not sum to the totals. Dashes (–) indicate data that do not meet publication guidelines.

[a]Days away from work include those that result in days away from work with or without restricted work activity.

[b]Data for government entities is only collected for state and local governments in the BLS National Survey of Occupational Injuries and Illnesses.

[c]In the fatalities column, non-Hispanic categories include cases with Hispanic origin not reported.

Motor Vehicle

Motor Vehicle Crashes by Time of Day and Day of Week

More fatal crashes occurred on Saturday than any other day of the week in 2013, according to data from the National Highway Traffic Safety Administration. More than 18% of fatal crashes occurred on Saturday, compared with 15.9% on Sundays and 15.4% on Fridays. For all crashes, Friday had the highest percentage, with more than 16%.

Patterns by hour of day for fatal crashes show peaks during afternoon rush hour for weekdays and, especially, late at night during weekends. For all crashes, primary peaks occurred during afternoon rush hours, with secondary peaks during morning rush hours.

Percent of weekly crashes by hour of day and day of week, United States, 2013

| Time of day | Fatal crashes | | | | | | | | All crashes | | | | | | | |
	Total	Sun.	Mon.	Tues.	Wed.	Thurs.	Fri.	Sat.	Total	Sun.	Mon.	Tues.	Wed.	Thurs.	Fri.	Sat.
All hours	100.0%	15.9%	12.4%	12.6%	12.4%	13.1%	15.4%	18.1%	100.0%	10.4%	14.7%	15.4%	15.0%	15.2%	16.6%	12.7%
Midnight to 3:59 a.m.	14.7%	4.1%	1.3%	1.2%	1.1%	1.5%	1.9%	3.6%	5.4%	1.4%	0.5%	0.5%	0.4%	0.6%	0.7%	1.2%
4:00 to 7:59 a.m.	12.5%	1.8%	1.7%	1.8%	1.7%	1.7%	1.8%	1.9%	10.3%	0.8%	1.7%	1.8%	1.8%	1.7%	1.6%	0.9%
8:00 to 11:59 a.m.	12.7%	1.5%	1.8%	1.8%	1.9%	1.9%	1.9%	2.0%	18.8%	1.5%	3.1%	3.1%	2.9%	2.9%	3.0%	2.3%
Noon to 3:59 p.m.	18.1%	2.5%	2.5%	2.6%	2.4%	2.4%	2.8%	2.9%	25.7%	2.7%	3.8%	3.8%	3.6%	3.8%	4.5%	3.5%
4:00 to 7:59 p.m.	21.4%	3.2%	2.8%	2.8%	2.9%	2.9%	3.3%	3.5%	27.9%	2.4%	4.2%	4.5%	4.6%	4.5%	4.7%	2.9%
8:00 to 11:59 p.m.	19.9%	2.6%	2.2%	2.4%	2.3%	2.7%	3.6%	4.0%	11.5%	1.5%	1.3%	1.5%	1.6%	1.5%	2.0%	2.0%

Source: National Safety Council analysis of data from the National Highway Traffic Safety Administration - Fatality Analysis Reporting System (FARS) and General Estimates System (GES).
Note: Column and row totals may not equal sum of parts due to rounding and unreported time of day or day of week data.

Percent of crashes by time of day and day of week, United States, 2013

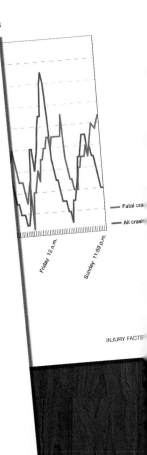

Fatal crashes
All crashes

Friday 12 a.m.
Sunday 11:59 p.m.

INJURY FACTS

Distracted Driving – pgs. 108-109

A recent study measuring brainwaves, eye movement, and other metrics assessed the impact to drivers' mental workload when attempting to complete multiple tasks. Results clearly showed that while simple tasks such as listening to the radio only minimally increased mental workload, more complex tasks such as listening and responding to in-vehicle, voice-activated email features substantially increased mental workload. Talking on cell phones (either hand-held or hands-free) was shown to moderately increase the level of mental workload.

National Safety Council

Motor Vehicle, 2013

Between 1912 and 2013, motor vehicle deaths per 10,000 registered vehicles decreased 96%, from 33 to 1.40. In 1912, 3,100 fatalities occurred when the number of registered vehicles totaled only 950,000. In 2013, 35,500 fatalities occurred, but registrations soared to 253 million. While mileage data were not available in 1912, the 2013 mileage death rate of 1.20 per 100,000,000 vehicle miles was down 11% from the revised 2012 rate of 1.35.

Beginning with the 2011 edition of *Injury Facts*®, the concept of medically consulted injury was adopted to replace disabling injury as the measure of nonfatal injuries. A medically consulted injury is an injury serious enough that a medical professional was consulted. Medically consulted injuries reported in this edition are not comparable to previous disabling injury estimates. Please see the Technical Appendix for a detailed description of this change. Medically consulted injuries in motor vehicle incidents totaled 4,300,000 in 2013, and total motor vehicle costs were estimated at $288.1 billion. Costs include wage and productivity losses, medical expenses, administrative expenses, motor vehicle property damage, and employer costs.

Motor vehicle deaths decreased 2% from 2012 to 2013 following an increase of 3% from 2011 to 2012. Miles traveled was up 10%, the number of registered vehicles decreased less than 0.5%, and the population increased 1%. As a result, the mileage rate was down 11% while the vehicle and population death rates were each down 3% from 2012 to 2013.

Compared to 2004, 2013 motor vehicle deaths decreased by about 21%. Mileage, registration, and population death rates also were sharply lower in 2013 compared with 2004 (see chart on next page).

The National Safety Council avoids using the word "accident." To some people, the word "accident" may imply a sense of inevitability. In contrast, the safety practice continually strives to decrease and ultimately prevent all unintentional injuries. NSC uses the terms "collision" and "crashes" in place of the word "accident."

Deaths	35,500
Medically consulted injuries	4,300,000
Cost	$288.1 billion
Motor vehicle mileage	2,966 billion
Registered vehicles in the United States	253,500,000
Licensed drivers in the United States	212,600,000
Death rate per 100,000,000 vehicle miles	1.20
Death rate per 10,000 registered vehicles	1.40
Death rate per 100,000 population	11.23

Motor vehicle crash outcomes, United States, 2013

Severity	Deaths or injuries	Crashes	Drivers (vehicles) involved
Fatal (within 1 year)	35,500	32,600	48,300
Medically consulted injury	4,300,000	3,000,000	5,500,000
Property damage (including unreported) and nondisabling injury		8,800,000	15,300,000
Total		**11,800,000**	**20,800,000**
Fatal (within 30 days)	32,719	30,057	44,574
Injury (disabling and nondisabling)	2,313,000	1,591,000	2,915,000
Police-reported property damage		4,066,000	7,083,000
Total		**5,687,000**	**10,043,000**

Source: National Safety Council estimates (top half) and National Highway Traffic Safety Administration (bottom half, with the exception of "Drivers (vehicles) involved," which are National Safety Council estimates).

Motor Vehicle, 2013

Travel, deaths, and death rates, United States, 1925-2013

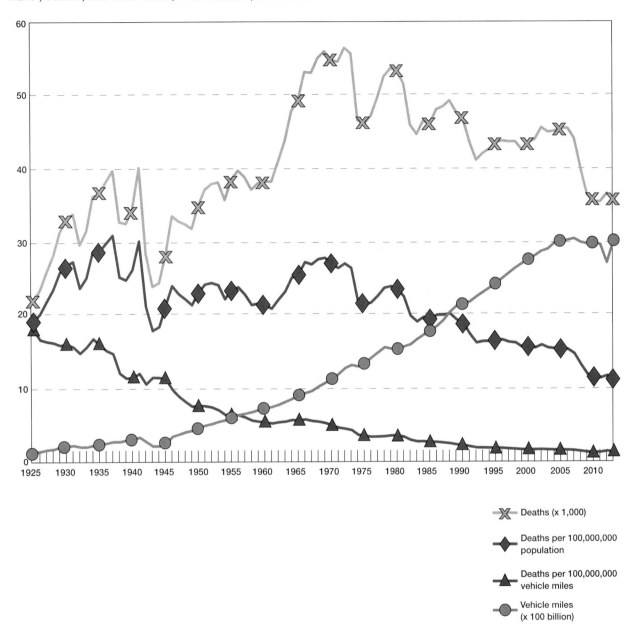

Deaths (x 1,000)

Deaths per 100,000,000
population

Deaths per 100,000,000
vehicle miles

Vehicle miles
(x 100 billion)

Deaths Due to Motor Vehicle Crashes, 2013

Type of crash and age of victim

All motor vehicle crashes

Includes deaths involving mechanically or electrically powered highway-transport vehicles in motion (except those on rails), both on and off the highway or street.

	Total	Change from 2012	Death rate[a]
Deaths	35,500	-2%	11.2
Nonfatal injuries[b]	4,300,000		

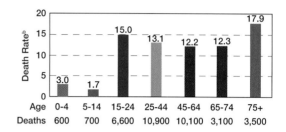

Age	0-4	5-14	15-24	25-44	45-64	65-74	75+
Death Rate[b]	3.0	1.7	15.0	13.1	12.2	12.3	17.9
Deaths	600	700	6,600	10,900	10,100	3,100	3,500

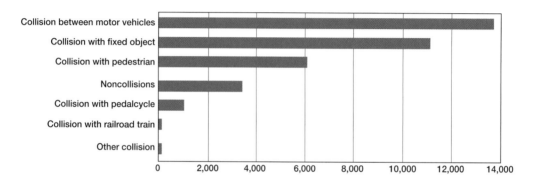

Collision between motor vehicles
Collision with fixed object
Collision with pedestrian
Noncollisions
Collision with pedalcycle
Collision with railroad train
Other collision

0   2,000   4,000   6,000   8,000   10,000   12,000   14,000

Collision between motor vehicles

Includes deaths from collisions of two or more motor vehicles. Motorized bicycles and scooters, trolley buses, and farm tractors or road machinery traveling on highways are motor vehicles.

	Total	Change from 2012	Death rate[a]
Deaths	13,700	-1%	4.3
Nonfatal injuries[b]	3,260,000		

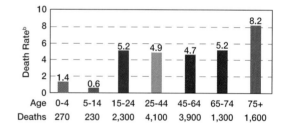

Age	0-4	5-14	15-24	25-44	45-64	65-74	75+
Death Rate[b]	1.4	0.6	5.2	4.9	4.7	5.2	8.2
Deaths	270	230	2,300	4,100	3,900	1,300	1,600

Collision with fixed object

Includes deaths from collisions in which the first harmful event is the striking of a fixed object such as a guardrail, abutment, impact attenuator, etc.

	Total	Change from 2012	Death rate[a]
Deaths	11,100	-3%	3.5
Nonfatal injuries[b]	590,000		

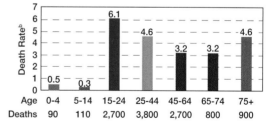

Age	0-4	5-14	15-24	25-44	45-64	65-74	75+
Death Rate[b]	0.5	0.3	6.1	4.6	3.2	3.2	4.6
Deaths	90	110	2,700	3,800	2,700	800	900

Collision with pedestrian

Includes all deaths of people struck by motor vehicles, either on or off a street or highway, regardless of the circumstances of the incident.

	Total	Change from 2012	Death rate[a]
Deaths	6,100	0%	1.9
Nonfatal injuries[b]	160,000		

See footnotes on page 107.

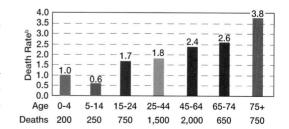

Age	0-4	5-14	15-24	25-44	45-64	65-74	75+
Death Rate[b]	1.0	0.6	1.7	1.8	2.4	2.6	3.8
Deaths	200	250	750	1,500	2,000	650	750

Type of crash and age of victim

Noncollisions

Includes deaths from noncollisions in which the first injury or damage-producing event was an overturn, jackknife, or other type of noncollision.

	Total	Change from 2012	Death rate[a]
Deaths	3,400	-10%	1.1
Nonfatal injuries[b]	150,000		

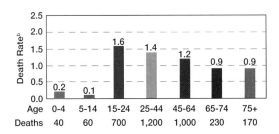

Collision with pedalcycle

Includes deaths of pedalcyclists and motor vehicle occupants from collisions between pedalcycles and motor vehicles on streets, highways, private driveways, parking lots, etc.

	Total	Change from 2012	Death rate[a]
Deaths	1,000	0%	0.3
Nonfatal injuries[b]	120,000		

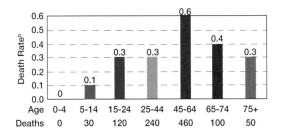

Collision with railroad train

Includes deaths from collisions of motor vehicles (moving or stalled) and railroad vehicles at public or private grade crossings. In other types of incidents, classification requires motor vehicle to be in motion.

	Total	Change from 2012	Death rate[a]
Deaths	100	-24%	(d)
Nonfatal injuries[b]	1,000		

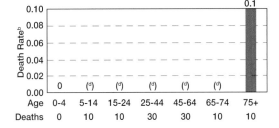

Other collision

Includes deaths from motor vehicle collisions not specified in other categories above. Most of the deaths arose from collisions involving animals or animal-drawn vehicles.

	Total	Change from 2012	Death rate[a]
Deaths	100	0%	(d)
Nonfatal injuries[b]	19,000		

Note: Procedures and benchmarks for estimating deaths by type of incident and age were changed in 1990.
Estimates for 1987 and later years are not comparable to earlier years. The noncollision and fixed-object categories were most affected by the changes.
[a]Deaths per 100,000 population.
[b]Nonfatal injury is defined as medically consulted injuries and is not comparable to estimates provided in earlier editions that used the definition of disabling injury.
Please see the Technical Appendix for more information regarding medically consulted injuries.
[c]Deaths per 100,000 population in each age group.
[d]Death rate was less than 0.05.

Motor vehicle crashes were the leading cause of death for people in the 5 to 24 age group in 2011. Motor vehicle crashes also were the leading cause of unintentional-injury-related death for people for each single year of age from 3 to 25, from ages 61 to 68 and for age 70. This is a summary of the most important issues that affect traffic safety.

Occupant protection. Safety belt use was a record-high 87% overall in 2013, statistically unchanged from the 86% use rate in 2012. Forty-nine states and the District of Columbia have mandatory safety belt use laws in effect, with laws in 33 of the states and the District of Columbia allowing standard (primary) enforcement. In 2013, safety belt use was significantly higher in states with standard (primary) enforcement (91%) than in states with secondary enforcement or no safety belt use law (80%). Half (50%) of the passenger vehicle occupants killed in 2013 were unrestrained. Reported helmet use rates for fatally injured motorcyclists in 2012 were 59% for operators and 48% for passengers, compared with the corresponding rates of 60% and 49%, respectively, in 2011. Safety belts saved an estimated 12,174 lives in 2012 among passenger vehicle occupants older than 4. Child passenger restraints saved an additional 284 lives while air bags saved approximately 2,213 lives.

Alcohol. From 2012 to 2013, traffic fatalities in alcohol-impaired crashes as a percentage of total traffic fatalities increased by less than 1% to 30.8%. Overall, 10,076 people were killed in alcohol-impaired crashes in 2013, a decrease of 2.5% from the 10,336 in 2012. Males continue to comprise the majority – 80% in 2013 – of all drivers involved in fatal crashes with a BAC of 0.08 g/dL or higher. All states and the District of Columbia have 21-year-old minimum-drinking-age laws and have created a threshold by law making it illegal to drive while impaired by alcohol (i.e., with a BAC of 0.08 g/dL or higher).

Speeding. Excessive speed was a factor in 29% of all traffic fatalities in 2013, killing an average of 26 people per day for a total of 9,613 speeding-related fatalities. Alcohol involvement is highly prevalent among drivers in speeding-related crashes. Thirty-seven percent of fatalities involving young drivers (ages 15-19) are speeding-related, compared with 28% of fatalities involving drivers older than 19. It has been estimated that speeding-related crashes cost the nation more than $40 billion annually.

Distracted driving. Epidemiological studies have found that cell phone use while driving is associated with a fourfold increase in crash risk. The results also showed no significant difference between handheld and hands-free phone use. A review of 33 cell phone driving studies concluded that cell phone use while driving lengthens driver reaction time by about 0.25 seconds – again with no significant difference between handheld and hands-free phones. The National Safety Council estimates that 26% of all traffic crashes are associated with drivers using cell phones and text messaging

(21% cell phones and 5% text messaging). Although the research cited above indicates there is no safety advantage of hands-free over handheld cell phone use, the 12 states and District of Columbia that have implemented bans impacting all drivers have focused on handheld bans.

Large trucks. In 2013, 3,964 fatalities resulted from traffic crashes involving a large truck (gross vehicle weight rating greater than 10,000 pounds), a 1.1% increase from 3,921 in 2012. The majority of these deaths (72%) were occupants of vehicles other than the large truck. Fatalities among non-occupants in large truck crashes increased 15% from 2012 to 2013, while fatalities among truck occupants and other vehicle occupants declined 1%. Large trucks are more likely to be involved in a multiple-vehicle fatal crash than passenger vehicles – 78% versus 35%, respectively, in 2013.

Motorcycles. Fatalities among motorcycle riders and passengers increased 16% between 2004 and 2013, from 4,028 to 4,668. Nonfatal injuries have increased as well, from 76,000 to 88,000 over the same period. The number of motorcycle fatalities decreased 6% from 2012 to 2013, while injuries decreased by 5%. The latest available mileage data show that motorcycle travel has more than doubled from 2003 to 2012, increasing from 9.6 billion miles to 21.3 billion over this period. As a result, the death rate has declined 40% from 2003 to 2012, going from 38.78 to 23.27 deaths per 100 million miles traveled. In 2012, speeding was a factor in 34% of motorcycle crashes compared with 22% for fatal passenger car crashes.

Young drivers. There were 4,333 fatalities in crashes involving young drivers ages 15-20 in 2013, a 7% decrease from 2012 and the ninth consecutive yearly decline. Motor vehicle crashes, however, remain the number one cause of death for U.S. teens and young driver fatalities per miles driven is still more than 3 times higher than for all drivers of passenger vehicles. With the advent of state graduated driver licensing programs, fatal crash risk among young drivers have decreased substantially since 1995. The fatal crash rate per 100,000,000 miles driven for 16 year old drivers decreased from 13.4 per 100 million miles driven in 1995-96 down to 9.1 in 2008.

Pedestrians. About 6,100 pedestrian deaths and 160,000 medically consulted injuries due to motor vehicle incidents occurred in 2013. Overall, nearly half (49%) of pedestrian deaths and injuries involve no improper action or circumstance. A further 23% of the deaths and injuries result from pedestrians darting or running into the street, 4.5% result from improper crossing of the roadway or intersection, and 3% involve pedestrians in the roadway improperly (standing, lying, working, or playing). Pedestrians in age groups beginning with those 15 and older are more likely to exhibit no improper action prior to the incident, while those in younger age groups are more likely to dart or run into the roadway.

Estimating Motor Vehicle Crash Costs

Two methods commonly are used to measure the costs of motor vehicle crashes. One is the economic cost framework and the other is the comprehensive cost framework.

Economic costs may be used by a community or state to estimate the economic impact of motor vehicle crashes that occurred within its jurisdiction in a given time period. It is a measure of the productivity lost and expenses incurred because of the crashes. Economic costs, however, should not be used for a cost-benefit analysis because they do not reflect what society is willing to pay to prevent a statistical fatality or injury.

There are five economic cost components: (1) wage and productivity losses, which include wages, fringe benefits, household production, and travel delay; (2) medical expenses, including emergency service costs; (3) administrative expenses, which include the administrative cost of private and public insurance plus police and legal costs; (4) motor vehicle damage, including the value of damage to property; and (5) uninsured employer costs for crashes involving workers.

The information below shows the average economic costs in 2013 per death (not per fatal crash), per injury (not per injury crash), and per property damage crash.

Economic costs, 2013

Death	**$1,500,000**
Nonfatal disabling injury	**$80,700**
Incapacitating injury[a]	*$74,900*
Non-incapacitating evident injury[a]	*$24,000*
Possible injury[a]	*$13,600*
Property damage crash (including minor injuries)	**$9,300**

Comprehensive costs include not only the economic cost components, but also a measure of the value of lost quality of life associated with the deaths and injuries – that is, what society is willing to pay to prevent them. The values of lost quality of life were obtained through empirical studies of what people actually pay to reduce their safety and health risks, such as through the purchase of air bags or smoke detectors. Comprehensive costs should be used for a cost-benefit analysis, but because the lost quality of life represents only a dollar equivalence of intangible qualities, they do not represent real economic losses and should not be used to determine the economic impact of past crashes.

The information below shows the average comprehensive costs in 2013 on a per-person basis.

Comprehensive costs, 2013

Death	**$4,628,000**
Incapacitating injury[a]	*$235,400*
Non-incapacitating evident injury[a]	*$60,000*
Possible injury[a]	*$28,600*
No injury	**$2,600**

Source: National Safety Council estimates (see the Technical Appendix) and Children's Safety Network Economics and Insurance Resource Center, Pacific Institute for Research and Evaluation.
Note: The National Safety Council's cost-estimating procedures were extensively revised for the 1993 edition, and additional revisions were made for the 2005-2006 edition. The costs are not comparable to those of prior years.

[a]National Safety Council. (2007). Manual on Classification of Motor Vehicle Traffic Accidents, ANSI D16.1-2007 *(7th ed.). Itasca, IL: Author.*

State Laws

No state has passed a total ban on cell phone use while driving, although 14 states and the District of Columbia have bans on handheld devices. Mandatory breath alcohol ignition interlock device laws are in effect in 26 states and four California counties for first-time DUI convictions. Mandatory safety belt use laws are in effect in 49 states and the District of Columbia, of which 21 states and the District of Columbia have primary enforcement for all seating positions. Graduated Driver Licensing is in effect in some form in all states and the District of Columbia, yet relatively few have optimum laws. Please see pages 124-125 for further details regarding young driver issues.

State laws

State	Distracted driving laws — Total cell phone ban	Total text messaging ban	Additional novice driver restrictions[c]	Alcohol law — Mandatory alcohol ignition interlock device[e]	Mandatory safety belt use law — Enforcement	Seating positions covered by law	Graduated Driver Licensing laws — Minimum instructional permit period[k]	Minimum hours of supervised driving[l]	No passengers younger than 20	10 p.m. or earlier nighttime driving restriction	Unrestricted license minimum age[m]
Alabama	no	yes	cell phone[b]	yes	primary	front	6 mo.	none	no	no	17 yrs.
Alaska	no	yes	no	yes	primary	all	6 mo.	40/10	no	no	16 yrs., 6 mo.
Arizona	no	no	no	yes	secondary	front[j]	6 mo.	30/10	no	no	16 yrs., 6 mo.
Arkansas	no	yes	cell phone[b]	yes	primary	front	6 mo.	none	no	no	18 yrs.
California	no[a]	yes	cell phone[b]	yes[h]	primary	all	6 mo.	50/10	yes	no	17 yrs.
Colorado	no	yes	cell phone	yes	secondary	front	12 mo.	50/10	yes	no	17 yrs.
Connecticut	no[a]	yes	cell phone	yes	primary	front	4 mo.	40/-	yes	no	18 yrs.
Delaware	no[a]	yes	cell phone	yes	primary	all	6 mo.	50/10	no	yes	17 yrs.
District of Columbia	no[a]	yes	cell phone	no	primary	all	6 mo.	40/10	yes	no	18 yrs.
Florida	no	yes[b]	no	yes[f, g]	primary	front[j]	12 mo.	50/10	no	no	18 yrs.
Georgia	no	yes	cell phone	yes[g]	primary	front[j]	12 mo.	40/6	yes	no	18 yrs.
Hawaii	no[a]	yes	cell phone	yes	primary	all	6 mo.	50/10	no	no	17 yrs.
Idaho	no	yes	no	yes[g]	secondary	all	6 mo.	50/10	no	yes	16 yrs.
Illinois	no[a]	yes	cell phone	yes	primary	all	9 mo.	50/10	no	no	18 yrs.
Indiana	no	yes	cell phone	yes[g]	primary	all	6 mo.	50/10	yes	no	18 yrs.
Iowa	no	yes[b]	cell phone	no	primary	front	12 mo.	20/2	no	no	17 yrs.
Kansas	no	yes	cell phone	yes	primary	all	12 mo.	50/10	no	yes	16 yrs., 6 mo.
Kentucky	no	yes	cell phone	yes[g]	primary	all	6 mo.	60/10	no	no	17 yrs.
Louisiana	no	yes	cell phone	yes	primary	all	6 mo.	50/15	no	no	17 yrs.
Maine	no	yes	cell phone	yes	primary	all	6 mo.	70/10	yes	no	16 yrs., 9 mo.
Maryland	no[a]	yes	cell phone	yes[f, g]	primary	all	9 mo.	60/10	no	no	18 yrs.
Massachusetts	no	yes	cell phone	yes[g]	secondary	all	6 mo.	40/-	no	no	18 yrs.
Michigan	no	yes	cell phone[d]	yes[f, g]	primary	front	6 mo.	50/10	no	yes	17 yrs.
Minnesota	no	yes	cell phone	yes	primary	all	6 mo.	40/15	no	no	17 yrs.
Mississippi	no	no	texting	yes	primary	front	12 mo.	none	no	no	16 yrs., 6 mo.
Missouri	no	no	texting	yes	secondary	front	6 mo.	40/10	no	no	17 yrs., 11 mo.
Montana	no	no	no	yes[g]	secondary	all	6 mo.	50/10	no	no	16 yrs.
Nebraska	no	yes[b]	cell phone[b]	yes	secondary	front	6 mo.	none	no	no	17 yrs.
Nevada	no[a]	yes	no	yes[f]	secondary	all	6 mo.	50/10	no	yes	18 yrs.
New Hampshire	no[a]	yes	cell phone	yes[f, g]	no law	no law	none	40/10	no	no	18 yrs.
New Jersey	no[a]	yes	cell phone	yes[f, g]	primary	all	6 mo.	none	no	no	18 yrs.
New Mexico	no	yes	cell phone	yes	primary	all	6 mo.	50/10	no	no	16 yrs., 6 mo.
New York	no[a]	yes	no	yes	primary	front	6 mo.	50/15	no	yes	17 yrs.
North Carolina	no	yes	cell phone	yes[f, g]	primary	all	12 mo.	72/16	no	yes	16 yrs., 6 mo.
North Dakota	no	yes	cell phone	no	secondary	front	6 mo.	none	no	yes	16 yrs.
Ohio	no	yes[b]	cell phone	no	secondary	front[j]	6 mo.	50/10	no	no	18 yrs.
Oklahoma	no	no	handheld and texting	yes[f, g]	primary	front	6 mo.	50/10	no	yes	16 yrs., 6 mo.
Oregon	no[a]	yes	cell phone	yes	primary	all	6 mo.	50/-	yes	no	17 yrs.
Pennsylvania	no	yes	no	yes[g]	secondary	front[j]	6 mo.	65/10	no	no	17 yrs.
Rhode Island	no	yes	cell phone	yes[f, g]	primary	all	6 mo.	50/10	no	no	17 yrs., 6 mo.
South Carolina	no	yes	no	yes[f, g]	primary	all	6 mo.	40/10	no	yes	16 yrs., 6 mo.
South Dakota	no	yes	cell phone[b]	no	secondary	front	3 mo.	none	no	yes	16 yrs.
Tennessee	no	yes	cell phone	yes[f]	primary	front	6 mo.	50/10	no	no	17 yrs.
Texas	no	no	cell phone and texting	yes[g, i]	primary	all	6 mo.	30/10	no	no	18 yrs.
Utah	no	yes	cell phone	yes	secondary	all	6 mo.	40/10	yes	no	17 yrs.
Vermont	no[a]	yes	cell phone	yes	secondary	all	12 mo.	40/10	yes	no	16 yrs., 6 mo.
Virginia	no	yes	cell phone[b]	yes	secondary	front	9 mo.	45/15	no	no	18 yrs.
Washington	no[a]	yes	cell phone	yes	primary	all	6 mo.	50/10	yes	no	17 yrs.
West Virginia	no[a]	yes	cell phone	yes	primary	front[j]	6 mo.	none	yes	yes	17 yrs.
Wisconsin	no	yes	cell phone	yes[f, g]	primary	all	6 mo.	30/10	no	no	16 yrs., 9 mo.
Wyoming	no	yes	no	yes[f, g]	secondary	all	10 days	50/10	no	no	16 yrs., 6 mo.

Source: Insurance Institute for Highway Safety data retrieved from www.iihs.org on September 26, 2014.

[a]Statewide handheld ban (effective 7/1/15 for New Hampshire).
[b]Secondary enforcement.
[c]Restrictions specific to novice drivers in addition to any other all-driver ban.
[d]Integrated voice-operated systems excepted.
[e]Instruments designed to prevent drivers from starting their cars when breath-alcohol content is at or above a set point. Mandatory in New Hampshire effective 1/1/16.
[f]Mandatory with a conviction for a BAC of at least .15 versus the lower limit of .08 found in other mandatory states.
[g]Mandatory with repeat convictions or upon reinstatement.
[h]Mandatory for all offenders in four counties.

[i]Mandatory as a condition of suspending the jail sentence for a high-BAC first-time offender.
[j]Required for certain ages at all seating positions.
[k]Minimum instructional periods often include time spent in driver's education classes.
[l]Figures shown as follows: Total hours/nighttime hours. For example, 25/5 means 25 hours of supervised driving, 5 of which must be at night. When states (Alabama, Arizona, Connecticut, Nebraska, Oregon, South Dakota, and West Virginia) have lower requirements if driver's education is taken, the lower requirement is reflected in the table. Pennsylvania additionally requires 5 of the total hours of supervised driving to be during inclement weather.
[m]Minimum age to obtain unrestricted license provided driver is crash and violation free. Alcohol restrictions still apply at least until age 21.

Occupant Protection Use

Safety belt use hit a record-high 87% overall in 2013, statistically unchanged from the 86% use rate in 2012. Significant increases in safety belt use from 2012 to 2013 occurred among occupants traveling in heavy traffic (89% to 90%) and in the Northeast (80% to 84%). Overall, seat belt use has shown an increasing trend since 1995 that has been accompanied by a steady decline in the percentage of unrestrained passenger vehicle occupant fatalities during the daytime (see graph below). These results are from the National Occupant Protection Use Survey (NOPUS) that is conducted annually by the National Highway Traffic Safety Administration. NOPUS includes the observation of drivers and right-front passengers of passenger vehicles with no commercial or governmental markings.

In 2013, safety belt use was significantly higher for drivers (88%) than right-front passengers (85%); for occupants in states with primary enforcement laws (91%) than those with secondary enforcement laws or no safety belt use law (80%); and for occupants traveling on expressways (91%) rather than on surface streets (84%). By vehicle type, safety belt use was significantly higher in vans and SUVs (90%) and in passenger cars (88%) than in pickup trucks (78%).

Safety belt use by state in 2013 ranged from 68.7% in South Dakota to 98.2% in Oregon. Nineteen states achieved use rates of 90% or higher, including Oregon, California, Alabama, Georgia, Minnesota, Nevada, Washington, Hawaii, Illinois, Michigan, Delaware, New Mexico, Iowa, South Carolina, Indiana, New York, New Jersey, Maryland, and Texas. Jurisdictions with stronger safety belt laws continue to exhibit generally higher use rates than those with weaker laws.

Results from the 2013 NOPUS Controlled Intersection Study show that safety belt use among black occupants increased significantly from 77% in 2012 to 81% in 2013. Belt use among drivers age 16 to 24 with passengers all from the same age group showed a significant increase from 76% to 85% over the same time period. In 2013, female occupants (89%) had higher use rates than male occupants (85%), members of other races (93%) had higher use rates than whites (87%) and blacks (81%), drivers with at least one passenger (90%) had higher use rates than drivers with no passengers (87%), and drivers age 16 to 24 with at least one passenger not age 16-24 (87%) had higher use rates than drivers age 16 to 24 with no passengers (84%) or passengers all age 16-24 (85%). Occupants age 25 to 69 had the highest use rates among all age groups, while occupants age 16 to 24 had the lowest use rates (83%). Drivers with passengers all under 8 years of age (90%), with passengers all age 8 and older (90%), and with a mixture of passengers from both groups (91%) had higher use rates than did drivers with no passengers (87%).

Child restraint use. Restraint use for child passengers younger than 8 was 89% in 2013, down a significant 2% from the 91% use rate observed in 2012. From 2012 to 2013, significant decreases in belt use were observed for child passengers driven by a belted driver (93% to 91%), a male driver (92% to 87%), and drivers age 16 to 24 (92% to 84%). Other significant reductions in belt use from 2012 to 2013 among child passengers included children in the rear seat (92% to 90%), child passengers on expressways (93% to 89%), traveling in slow traffic (92% to 85%), in pickup trucks (91% to 76%), in the South (88% to 81%), and traveling during weekends (92% to 88%).

Safety belt use by the driver strongly influences the restraint status of child passengers. When the driver was belted, a significantly high 91% of child passengers younger than 8 were restrained in 2013, compared to a significantly low 68% of children when the driver was unbelted. However, as noted above, belt use by children driven by a belted driver dropped by a significant two percentage points from 2012 to 2013.

Children ages 4-7 should be restrained in a front-facing safety seat or booster seat, depending on the child's height and weight. The results from 2013 National Survey of the Use of Booster Seats showed a non-significant decline in booster seat use among 4- to 7-year-old from 47% in 2011 to 46% in 2013, although restraint use for all children under 13 remained the same at 91% in 2013. The results also indicate that premature graduation continues to be a problem, but some improvements in the use of appropriate restraint types were noted from 2011 to 2013.

Source: Pickrell, T.M., & Liu, C. (2015, January). Occupant Restraint Use in 2013– Results from the National Occupant Protection Use Survey Controlled Intersection Study (DOT HS 812 080). Washington, DC: National Highway Traffic Safety Administration. Chen, Y.Y., & Ye, T.J. (2014, May). Seat belt use in 2013–use rates in the States and Territories. Traffic Safety Facts Crash Stats (DOT HS 812 809). Washington, DC: National Highway Traffic Safety Administration. Pickrell, T.M., & Choi, E. (2014, June). The 2013 National Survey of the Use of Booster Seats (DOT HS 812 037). Washington, DC: National Highway Traffic Safety Administration. Pickrell, T.M., & Liu, C. (2014, January). Seat belt use in 2013–overall results. Traffic Safety Facts Research Note (DOT HS 811 875). Washington, DC: National Highway Traffic Safety Administration.

Safety belt use rate and daytime percent of unrestrained passenger vehicle occupant fatalities, United States, 2000-2013

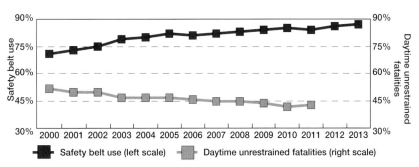

Safety belts

- When used properly, lap/shoulder safety belts reduce the risk of fatal injury to front-seat passenger car occupants by 45% and reduce the risk of moderate-to-critical injury by 50%.
- For light-truck occupants, safety belts reduce the risk of fatal injury by 60% and moderate-to-critical injury by 65%.
- Forty-nine states and the District of Columbia have mandatory safety belt use laws in effect, the only exception being New Hampshire. Sixteen of the states with safety belt use laws in effect in 2013 specified secondary enforcement (i.e., police officers are permitted to write a citation only after a vehicle is stopped for some other traffic infraction). Thirty-three states and the District of Columbia had laws that allowed primary enforcement, enabling officers to stop vehicles and write citations whenever they observe violations of the safety belt law. (See page 110 for additional information on state laws.)

- Safety belts saved an estimated 12,174 lives in 2012 among passenger vehicle occupants older than 4. An additional 3,031 lives could have been saved in 2012 if all passenger vehicle occupants older than 4 wore safety belts. From 1975 through 2012, an estimated 304,679 lives were saved by safety belts (see table on following page).
- A total of 21,132 occupants of passenger vehicles (cars, pickup trucks, vans, and SUVs) were killed in motor vehicle traffic crashes in 2013, 65% of the total traffic fatalities reported for the year. Of those for whom restraint use was known, 9,777 (50%) were unrestrained. The table below shows the number of driver and passenger fatalities in crashes by vehicle type and restraint use in 2013.

Drivers and passengers killed, by vehicle type and restraint use, 2013

Type of passenger vehicle	Restrained		Unrestrained		Unknown		Total		Known restrained (%)	Known unrestrained (%)
	Number	%	Number	%	Number	%	Number	%		
Drivers killed										
Passenger car	4,635	53	3,436	39	713	8	8,784	100	57	43
Pickup trucks	1,159	36	1,850	57	249	8	3,258	100	39	61
Sport utility vehicles	1,090	41	1,330	50	217	8	2,637	100	45	55
Vans	376	50	303	41	66	9	745	100	55	45
Other light trucks	10	43	10	43	3	13	23	100	50	50
Total	**7,270**	**47**	**6,929**	**45**	**1,248**	**8**	**15,447**	**100**	**51**	**49**
Passengers killed										
Passenger car	1,612	50	1,254	39	327	10	3,193	100	56	44
Pickup trucks	278	30	571	63	64	7	913	100	33	67
Sport utility vehicles	431	37	638	54	105	9	1,174	100	40	60
Vans	184	47	179	46	28	7	391	100	51	49
Other light trucks	2	14	9	64	3	21	14	100	18	82
Total	**2,507**	**44**	**2,651**	**47**	**527**	**9**	**5,685**	**100**	**49**	**51**

Source: National Safety Council analysis of NHTSA FARS data.

Air bags

- Air bags, combined with lap/shoulder belts, offer the best available protection for passenger vehicle occupants. Analyses indicate a fatality-reducing effectiveness for frontal air bags of 14% when no safety belt was used and 11% when a safety belt was used in conjunction with air bags.
- Lap/shoulder belts should always be used, even in a vehicle with an air bag. Air bags are a supplemental form of protection, and most are designed to deploy only in moderate-to-severe frontal crashes.
- Children in rear-facing child seats should not be placed in the

front seat of vehicles equipped with passenger-side air bags. The impact of the deploying air bag could result in serious injury to the child.
- An estimated 2,213 lives were saved by frontal air bags in 2012, and a total of 36,976 lives were saved from 1987 through 2012 (see table on following page).
- Beginning in September 1997, all new passenger cars were required to have driver and passenger-side air bags. In 1998, the same requirement went into effect for light trucks. Since 1999, driver and passenger-side air bags have been required in all cars, light trucks, and vans.

Child restraints

- Child restraints saved an estimated 284 lives in 2012 among children younger than 5. An additional 59 lives of such children could have been saved if all had used child safety seats.
- All states and the District of Columbia have had child restraint use laws in effect since 1985.
- Research has shown that child safety seats reduce fatal injury in passenger cars by 71% for infants (younger than 1) and by 54% for toddlers (1-4 years old). For infants and toddlers in light trucks, the corresponding reductions are 58% and 59%, respectively.
- In 2013, there were 214 occupant fatalities among children younger than 4. Of the 200 fatalities among children younger than 4 for which restraint use was known, 53 (26%) were completely unrestrained.
- An estimated 284 lives were saved by child restraints in 2012, and a total of 10,157 lives have been saved by child restraints from 1975 through 2012 (see table below).

Estimated number of lives saved by restraint systems, 1975-2012

Restraint type	1975-2003	2004	2005	2006	2007	2008	2009	2010	2011	2012	Total
Safety belts	179,948	15,548	15,688	15,458	15,223	13,312	12,763	12,582	11,983	12,174	304,679
Child restraints	7,021	455	424	427	388	286	307	303	262	284	10,157
Air bags	14,258[a]	2,660	2,752	2,824	2,800	2,557	2,387	2,315	2,210	2,213	36,976

Source: National Center for Statistics and Analysis. (2014, March). Traffic Safety Facts 2012 Data–Occupant Protection (DOT HS 811 892). Washington, DC: National Highway Traffic Safety Administration.
[a]Total is from 1987 to 2003. Frontal air bags did not exist prior to 1987.

Motorcycle helmets

- Motorcycle helmets are estimated to be 37% effective in preventing fatal injuries to motorcycle operators and 41% effective for motorcycle passengers.
- It is estimated that motorcycle helmets saved the lives of 1,699 motorcyclists in 2012. An additional 781 lives could have been saved in 2012 if all motorcyclists had worn helmets.
- Reported helmet use rates for fatally injured motorcyclists in 2012 were 59% for operators and 48% for passengers, compared with the corresponding rates of 60% and 49%, respectively, in 2011.
- As of January 2015, 19 states and the District of Columbia required helmet use by all motorcycle operators and passengers. Twenty-eight states only required helmet use by a subset of motorcyclists (typically motorcyclists under age 18) and 3 states (Illinois, Iowa, and New Hampshire) do not require helmet use by motorcyclists of any age. In states without universal helmet laws, 62% of motorcyclists killed in 2012 were not wearing helmets, as compared to 9% in states with universal helmet laws.
- According to the National Occupant Protection Use Survey, use of Department of Transportation-compliant helmets by all motorcyclists (riders and passengers) was 60% in 2013, unchanged from 2012. Although not statistically significant, the use rate for motorcycle passengers did increase from 46% to 50%. Observed helmet use in states with universal helmet laws was significantly higher than in states with weaker or no helmet laws at 88% versus 49%.
- The economic cost savings due to helmet use was approximately $2.9 billion in 2008, and an additional $1.3 billion could have been saved if all motorcyclists had worn helmets.

Source: National Center for Statistics and Analysis. (2011, March). Traffic Safety Facts Research Note – Determining Estimates of Lives and Costs Saved by Motorcycle Helmets (DOT HS 811 433). Washington, DC: National Highway Traffic Safety Administration.
National Center for Statistics and Analysis. (2014, March). Traffic Safety Facts 2012 Data – Occupant Protection (DOT HS 811 892). Washington, DC: National Highway Traffic Safety Administration.
National Center for Statistics and Analysis. (2013, May). Traffic Safety Facts 2011 Data – Motorcycles (DOT HS 811 765). Washington, DC: National Highway Traffic Safety Administration.
National Center for Statistics and Analysis. (2014, April). Traffic Safety Facts Research Note – Motorcycle Helmets Use in 2013 – Overall Results (DOT HS 812 010).
Current status of safety belt and motorcycle helmet use laws downloaded January 6, 2015, from the Insurance Institute for Highway Safety at http://www.iihs.org/iihs/topics/laws/helmetuse?topicName=motorcycles.

According to studies conducted by the National Highway Traffic Safety Administration, about 10,076 people were killed in alcohol-impaired crashes in 2013, a decrease of 2.5% from the 10,336 fatalities in 2012. Alcohol-impaired driving crashes involve at least one driver or motorcycle operator with a blood alcohol concentration (BAC) of 0.08 grams per deciliter (g/dL) or higher. The following data summarize the extent of alcohol involvement in motor vehicle crashes with at least one alcohol-impaired driver or motorcycle operator:

- The cost of alcohol-related motor vehicle crashes in 2013 is estimated by the National Highway Traffic Safety Administration at $49.8 billion.
- Traffic fatalities in alcohol-impaired driving crashes as a percentage of total traffic fatalities increased by less than 1% to 30.8% from 2012 to 2013 but decreased by nearly 9% from 2004 to 2013 (see corresponding chart on bottom of page).
- The 10,076 fatalities in alcohol-impaired driving crashes in 2013 represent an average of one alcohol-impaired driving fatality every 52 minutes.
- Since July 1988, all states and the District of Columbia have had a minimum legal drinking age of 21. The impact these laws had on alcohol-related fatalities was dramatic. Among fatally injured drivers 16-20 years old, the percentage with positive BACs declined from 61% in 1982 to 31% in 1995, a larger decline than for older age groups. These declines occurred among the ages directly affected by increasing the drinking age (ages 18-20) and among young teens not directly affected (ages 16-17).

- In 2013, while people ages 25-34 constituted 20% of all drivers involved in fatal crashes, they were overrepresented among the drivers with a BAC of 0.08 g/dL or higher, comprising 27% of such drivers involved in fatal crashes. Drivers 21-24 years old were similarly overrepresented, accounting for 10% of drivers in fatal crashes and 16% of those with a BAC of 0.08 g/dL or higher. The 35-44 age group also was slightly overrepresented, making up 16% of drivers in fatal crashes and 18% of those with a BAC of 0.08 g/dL or higher.
- Males continue to comprise the majority – 80% in 2013 – of all drivers involved in fatal crashes with a BAC of 0.08 g/dL or higher. Male drivers showed a 1% decrease while female drivers showed a 3% increase in the proportion of drivers involved in fatal crashes who were alcohol-impaired from 2004 to 2013.
- The proportion of drivers with BACs of 0.08 g/dL or higher has changed very little since 2004. In both years 21% of drivers involved in fatal crashes had a BAC of 0.08 g/dL or higher. The only age group that has shown some improvement is drivers aged 16 to 20. In this age group the prevalence of drivers with BACs of 0.08 g/dL or higher decreased from 18% to 17% (see corresponding chart on page 115).
- In 2013, the percentage of alcohol-impaired-driving fatalities by state varied from a low of 17% in Utah to a high of 44% in South Carolina (see corresponding chart on page 115).
- In 2013, all states and the District of Columbia had by law created a threshold making it illegal to drive with a BAC of 0.08 g/dL or higher.

Percent of alcohol-impaired driving fatalities, United States, 1990-2013

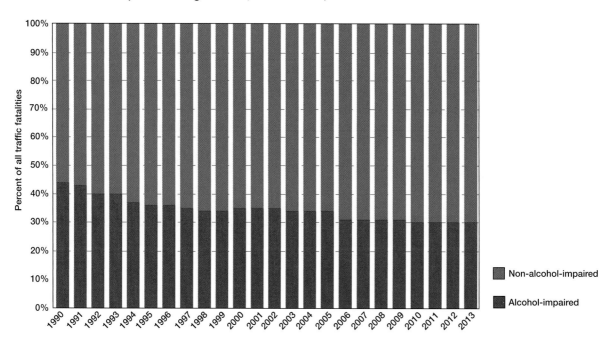

 Alcohol (cont.)

Percent of drivers with BACs of 0.08 or higher involved in fatal crashes by age, 2004 and 2013

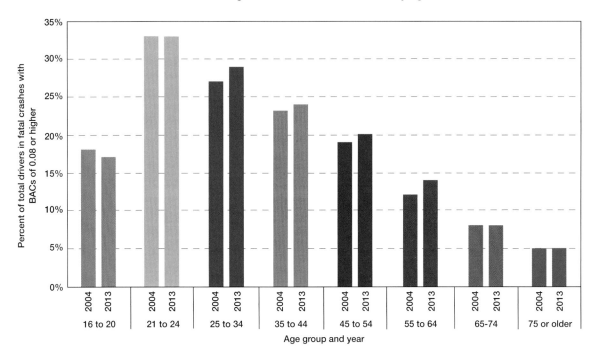

Percent of fatalities involved in fatal crashes with BAC of 0.08+, by state, 2013

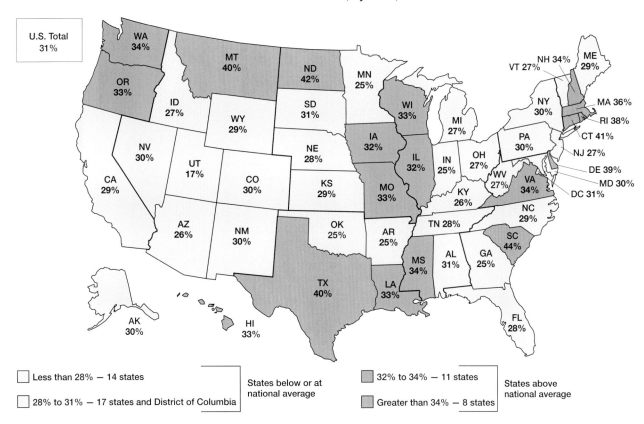

U.S. Total
31%

WA 34%
OR 33%
MT 40%
ND 42%
MN 25%
NH 34%
VT 27%
ME 29%
ID 27%
WY 29%
SD 31%
WI 33%
NY 30%
MA 36%
RI 38%
NV 30%
UT 17%
CO 30%
NE 28%
IA 32%
MI 27%
PA 30%
CT 41%
NJ 27%
CA 29%
KS 29%
IL 32%
IN 25%
OH 27%
WV 27%
VA 34%
DE 39%
MD 30%
DC 31%
MO 33%
KY 26%
NC 29%
AZ 26%
NM 30%
OK 25%
AR 25%
TN 28%
SC 44%
TX 40%
LA 33%
MS 34%
AL 31%
GA 25%
AK 30%
HI 33%
FL 28%

Less than 28% — 14 states

28% to 31% — 17 states and District of Columbia

States below or at national average

32% to 34% — 11 states

Greater than 34% — 8 states

States above national average

Source: National Center for Statistics and Analysis. (2014, December). Traffic Safety Facts Research Note: 2013 Motor Vehicle Crashes: Overview (DOT HS 812 101). Washington, DC: National Highway Traffic Safety Administration. National Center for Statistics and Analysis. (2014, December). Traffic Safety Facts 2013 Data: Alcohol-Impaired Driving (DOT HS 812 102). Washington, DC: National Highway Traffic Safety Administration. McCartt, A.T., Hellinga, L.A., & Kirley, B.B. (2010). The effect of minimum legal drinking age 21 laws on alcohol-related driving in the United States. Journal of Safety Research, Vol. 41, pp. 173-181.

Type of Motor Vehicle Crash

Although motor vehicle deaths occur more often in collisions between motor vehicles than any other type of incident, this type represents only about 39% of the total. Collisions between a motor vehicle and a fixed object were the next most common type, with about 31% of deaths, followed by pedestrian incidents and noncollisions (rollovers, etc.).

While collisions between motor vehicles accounted for less than half of motor vehicle fatalities, this crash type represented 76% of injuries, 70% of injury crashes, and 71% of all incidents. Single-vehicle crashes involving collisions with fixed objects,

pedestrians, and noncollisions, on the other hand, accounted for a greater proportion of fatalities and fatal crashes compared to less-serious crashes. These three crash types made up 58% of fatalities and 60% of fatal crashes, but only 26% or less of injuries, injury crashes, or all crashes.

Of collisions between motor vehicles, angle collisions cause the greatest number of deaths, about 6,600 in 2013, and also the greatest number of fatal crashes. The table below shows the estimated number of deaths, injuries, fatal crashes, injury crashes, and all crashes for various types of motor vehicle crashes.

Motor vehicle deaths, injuries, and number of crashes by type of crash, 2013

Type of crash	Deaths	Nonfatal injuries[a]	Fatal crashes	Injury crashes	All crashes
Total	**35,500**	**4,300,000**	**32,600**	**3,000,000**	**11,800,000**
Collision with...					
Pedestrian	6,100	160,000	5,600	130,000	140,000
Other motor vehicle	13,700	3,260,000	11,900	2,100,000	8,410,000
Angle collision	*6,600*	*1,334,000*	*5,900*	*819,000*	*2,580,000*
Head-on collision	*3,800*	*242,000*	*3,100*	*132,000*	*290,000*
Rear-end collision	*2,200*	*1,449,000*	*2,000*	*980,000*	*3,980,000*
Sideswipe and other two-vehicle collisions	*1,100*	*235,000*	*900*	*169,000*	*1,560,000*
Railroad train	100	1,000	100	1,000	1,000
Pedalcycle	1,000	120,000	900	110,000	119,000
Animal, animal-drawn vehicle	100	19,000	100	19,000	590,000
Fixed or other object	11,100	590,000	10,900	520,000	2,290,000
Noncollision	**3,400**	**150,000**	**3,100**	**120,000**	**250,000**

Source: National Safety Council estimates, based on data from the National Highway Traffic Safety Administration Fatality Analysis Reporting System and General Estimates System. Procedures for estimating the number of incidents by type were changed for the 1998 edition and are not comparable to estimates in previous editions (see Technical Appendix).

[a]Nonfatal injury is defined as a medically consulted injury and is not comparable to estimates provided in earlier editions that used the definition of disabling injury. Please see the Technical Appendix for more information regarding medically consulted injuries.

Speeding

Speeding is one of the major factors contributing to the occurrence of deaths, injuries, and property damage related to motor vehicle crashes. The role of speeding in crash causation can be described in terms of its effect on the driver, the vehicle, and the road. Excessive-speed driving reduces the amount of time the driver has to react in a dangerous situation to avoid a crash. Speeding increases vehicle stopping distance and also reduces the ability of road safety structures such as guardrails, impact attenuators, crash cushions, median dividers, and concrete barriers to protect vehicle occupants in a crash.

The National Highway Traffic Safety Administration (NHTSA) estimates that speeding-related crashes[a] cost the nation $40.4 billion in 2000, or 18% of the entire cost of motor vehicle crashes in the United States. This economic loss is equivalent to $110.7 million per day or $4.6 million per hour.

Speeding was a factor in 29% of all traffic fatalities in 2013, killing an average of 26 people per day for a total of 9,613 speeding-related fatalities. The total number of fatal motor vehicle crashes attributable to speeding was 8,660. Among young drivers, the impact of speeding is even more severe. Thirty-seven percent of fatalities involving young drivers (ages 15-19) are speeding-related, compared with 28% of fatalities involving drivers older than 19. The figure below shows that the proportion of fatalities by day of the week associated with speeding is greater for young drivers than for older drivers. This speeding related disparity is greatest during the middle of the week, Tuesday through Thursday, and decreases on the weekends.

Speeding as typically reported by NHTSA combines both "driving too fast for conditions" and "exceeding posted speed limit," as well as other speed-related offenses including racing. A recent NHTSA study using data from six states whose police incident reports record these components separately found that more-severe crashes are more often associated with exceeding the posted speed limit, while less-severe crashes are associated with driving too fast for conditions:

Fatal crashes:
- 55% attributed to exceeding posted speed limit
- 45% attributed to driving too fast for conditions

Injury crashes:
- 26% attributed to exceeding posted speed limit
- 74% attributed to driving too fast for conditions

Property damage only:
- 18% attributed to exceeding posted speed limit
- 82% attributed to driving too fast for conditions

Percent of fatalities associated with speeding by young driver involvement and day of week, 2013

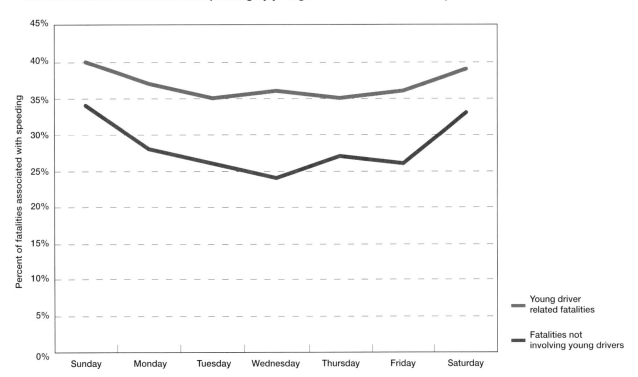

Source: National Safety Council analysis of NHTSA FARS data.
National Center for Statistics and Analysis. (2010). An Analysis of Speeding-Related Crashes: Definitions and the Effects of Road Environments (DOT HS 811 090). Washington, DC: National Highway Traffic Safety Administration.
[a]A crash is considered speeding-related if the driver was charged with a speeding-related offense or if racing, driving too fast for conditions, or exceeding the posted speed limit was indicated as a contributing factor in the crash.

Distracted driving as defined by the National Highway Traffic Safety Administration (NHTSA) is a specific type of inattention that occurs when drivers divert their attention away from the driving task to focus on another activity. These distractions can be from electronic sources, such as cell phones or navigation devices, or more conventional distractions such as interacting with passengers and eating. Distracting tasks can affect drivers in different ways, and can be categorized into the following types:

- **Visual distraction:** Tasks that require the driver to look away from the roadway to visually obtain information;
- **Manual distraction:** Tasks that require the driver to take a hand off the steering wheel and manipulate a device;
- **Cognitive distraction:** Tasks that are defined as the mental workload associated with a task that involves thinking about something other than the driving task (NHTSA, 2010).

The impact of distraction on driving is determined not just by the type of distraction, but also the frequency and duration of the task. Because of this, even if a task is less distracting, a driver who engages in it frequently or for long durations may increase the crash risk to a level comparable to that of much more difficult tasks performed less often.

A recent study measuring brainwaves, eye movement, and other metrics assessed the impact to drivers' mental workload when attempting to complete multiple tasks. Results clearly showed that while simple tasks such as listening to the radio only minimally increased mental workload, more complex tasks such as listening and responding to in-vehicle, voice-activated email features substantially increased mental workload. Talking on cell phones (either hand-held or hands-free) was shown to moderately increase the level of mental workload.

A second phase of this study investigated the mental workload associated with operating original equipment manufacturers' voice-based infotainment systems. Six vehicles representing model years 2013 or 2012 were tested: a Ford equipped with MyFord Touch, a Chevrolet equipped with MyLink, a Chrysler equipped with Uconnect, a Toyota equipped with Entune, a Mercedes equipped with COMAND, and a Hyundai equipped with Blue Link. Drivers in the study were asked to perform a number of simple tasks using voice commands while driving in a residential setting. The tasks included dialing a phone number, calling a contact, changing the radio station, or playing a CD. The workload associated with operating the voice-based systems in each vehicle were assessed using the same scale as the original study (discussed in the last paragraph). As shown in the graph below, the cognitive workload required to operate the voice-based systems varies substantially across the different vehicles tested.

Cognitive Workload Scale

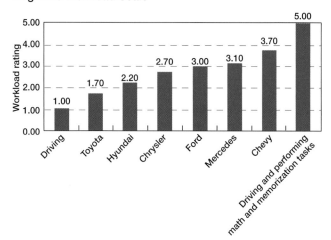

Cognitive Workload Scale

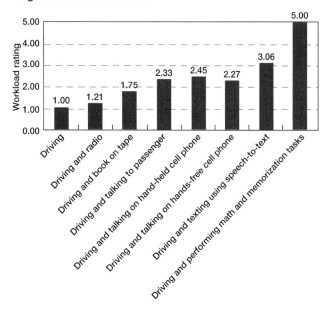

Cell phone Driving Prevalence

Nationally, about 9% of drivers are using hand-held or hands-free cell phones at any given daylight moment. This figure from the National Occupant Protection Use Survey (NOPUS) conducted by the National Highway Traffic Safety Administration is the only national estimate of driver cell phone use based on actual driver observations. As shown in the graph on the facing page, the percentage of drivers likely to be on either hand-held or hands-free cell phones decreased from 11% in 2007 and 2008 down to 9% starting in 2009 and continuing through 2012. The corresponding hand-held cell phone use estimate has also remained constant at 5% of drivers for the last three years. However, the percent of drivers observed manipulating hand-held electronic devices increased from 1.3% in 2011 to 1.5% in 2012. Among other activities, this observation would include text messaging as well as manipulating devices such as MP3 players.

A national phone survey conducted by NHTSA in 2012 on distracted driving attitudes and behaviors found that almost half of drivers (48%) report answering their phone while driving, while 24% report making calls. Results also

found that 10% of drivers reported sending text messages or e-mails while driving at least sometimes, while almost 80% of respondents stated that they never do so.

Cell phone Driving Risk

Two epidemiological studies have found that cell phone use while driving is associated with approximately a quadrupling of crash risk. Researchers in Western Australia analyzed cell phone records of drivers who went to hospital emergency departments due to injuries sustained in a crash. A second group of researchers in Canada analyzed cell phone records of drivers who reported property damage only crashes. Both studies compared cell phone use during a 10-minute period prior to the time of the crash and during non-crash periods, and found cell phone use while driving was associated with a slightly more than four-fold increase in crash risk. Results also showed no significant difference between hand-held and hands-free phone use.

A review of 33 cell phone driving studies published representing a total sample size of approximately 2,000 participants revealed the following:

- Cell phone conversation while driving increases driver reaction time. The total mean increase in reaction time is 0.25 sec.
- Use of hand-held and hands-free phones results in similar increases in reaction time.

Driver use of cell phones 2002-2012

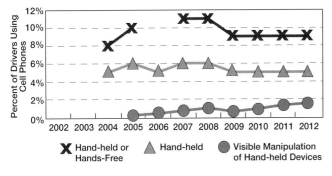

The National Safety Council estimates that 26% of all traffic crashes are associated with drivers using cell phones and text messaging (21% cell phone and 5% text messaging). The percent crash estimates are based on a population attributable risk percent calculation that factors in the relative risk of an activity and the prevalence of the activity. The data inputs for the 21% of crashes associated with cell phones included epidemiological studies that have found that cell phone use results in a four fold increase in the risk of crashes as well as NHTSA's NOPUS results showing that 9% of drivers are talking on cell phones at any given daylight moment. The 5% of crashes associated with text messaging is based on an eight times relative risk while text messaging

estimate and a NOPUS estimate that about 1.5% of drivers at any given daylight moment are observed manipulating hand-held electronic devices. For additional details on the National Safety Council's crash estimates please visit: *http://www.nsc.org/DistractedDrivingDocuments/Attributable-Risk-Estimate.pdf*

State Laws

Although research findings indicate that there is little to no safety advantage of hands-free over hand-held cell phone use, the states that have implemented bans impacting all drivers have focused on hand-held bans. As of September 2013, 12 states and the District of Columbia ban hand-held devices for all drivers while 41 states and the District of Columbia have passed total text ban laws. The only state laws banning any use of cell phones while driving are limited to either young drivers or bus drivers. Thirty-seven states and the District of Columbia ban young or novice drivers from using cell phones. See page 110 for additional information regarding state motor vehicle laws.

Cooper, J.M., Ingebretsen, H., & Strayer, D. (2014). *Mental workload of common voice-based vehicle interactions across six different vehicle systems.* Washington, DC: AAA Foundation for Traffic Safety. Downloaded from: https://www.aaafoundation.org/measuring-cognitive-distraction-part-ii-2-new-reports.

McEvoy, S.P., Stevenson, M.R., McCartt, A.T., Woodward, M., Haworth, C., Palamar, P., & Cercarelli, R. (2005). *Role of mobile phones in motor vehicle crashes resulting in hospital attendance: A case-crossover study.* British Medical Journal. *Online First BMJ, doi:10.1136/bmj.38537.397512.55 (published online 12 July 2005).*

National Highway Traffic Safety Administration [NHTSA]. (2002 - 2014). *Traffic Safety Fact Sheets.* Available at http://www.nrd.nhtsa.dot.gov/cats/index.aspx.

National Safety Council. (2010). *Understanding the distracted brain, why driving while using hands-free cellphones is risky behavior.* Downloaded on September 1, 2010 from: http://www.nsc.org/safety_road/Distracted_Driving/Pages/distracted_driving.aspx.

Ranney, T.A. (2008, April). *Driver distraction: A review of the current state-of-knowledge (Report No. DOT HS 810 787).* Washington, DC: National Highway Traffic Safety Administration.

Redelmeier, D.A., & Tibshirani, R.J. (1997). *Association between cellular-telephone calls and motor vehicle collisions.* New England Journal of Medicine, 336 (7), 453-458.

Schroeder, P., Meyers, M., & Kostyniuk, L. (2013, April). *National survey on distracted driving attitudes and behaviors – 2012 (Report No. DOT HS 811 729).* Washington, DC: National Highway Traffic Safety Administration. Downloaded from: http://www.nhtsa.gov/staticfiles/nti/pdf/811729.pdf.

Strayer, D.L., Cooper, J.M., Turril, J., Medeiros-Ward, N., & Biondi, F. (2013). *Measuring cognitive distraction in the automobile.* Washington, DC: AAA Foundation for Traffic Safety. Downloaded from: https://www.aaafoundation.org/measuring-cognitive-distractions.

Improper Driving

In most motor vehicle crashes, factors are present relating to the driver, the vehicle, and the road, and it is the interaction of these factors that often sets up the series of events that result in a crash. The table below relates only to the driver, and shows the principal kinds of improper driving in crashes in 2013 as reported by police. The "Other improper driving" category in the table includes driver inattention – however, see page 118 for a discussion of distracted driving issues.

Exceeding the posted speed limit or driving at an unsafe speed was the most common primary error in fatal crashes.

Right-of-way violations predominated in the "Injury crashes" and "All crashes" categories.

While some drivers were under the influence of alcohol or other drugs, this represents the driver's physical condition – not a driving error. See page 114 for a discussion of alcohol involvement in traffic incidents.

Correcting the improper practices listed below could reduce the number of crashes. This does not mean, however, that road and vehicle conditions can be disregarded.

Primary improper driving reported in crashes, 2013

Kind of improper driving	Fatal crashes	Injury crashes	All crashes
Total	100.0%	100.0%	100.0%
Improper driving	**55.9**	**62.5**	**55.7**
Speed too fast or unsafe	16.1	14.6	11.7
Right of way	11.9	18.4	14.1
Failed to yield	*8.1*	*13.2*	*10.6*
Passed stop sign	*2.4*	*2.2*	*1.5*
Disregarded signal	*1.5*	*3.0*	*1.9*
Drove left of center	6.2	1.2	1.0
Improper overtaking	1.4	1.1	1.3
Made improper turn	3.8	3.9	3.0
Followed too closely	0.8	6.8	7.6
Other improper driving	15.7	15.5	17.0
No improper driving stated	**44.1**	**38.5**	**44.3**

Source: Based on reports from 20 state traffic authorities. Percents may not add to totals due to rounding.

Large Trucks

In 2013, 3,964 fatalities resulted from a traffic crash involving a large truck, a 1.1% increase from 3,921 in 2012. About 72% of these deaths were occupants of vehicles other than the large truck (see figure below). Fatalities among non-occupants in large truck crashes increased 15% from 2012 to 2013, while fatalities among truck occupants declined 1% and other vehicle occupants fatalities remained relatively stable. A large truck is one with a gross vehicle weight rating greater than 10,000 pounds.

Large trucks are more likely to be involved in a multiple-vehicle fatal crash than passenger vehicles. In 2013, 78% of large truck fatal crashes were multiple-vehicle crashes, compared with 35% of other fatal crashes.

In two-vehicle fatal crashes involving a large truck, 58% of the vehicles were struck in the front compared with 64% in two-vehicle fatal crashes not involving large trucks. Trucks are more likely to be struck in the rear during a fatal crash than other vehicle types – 21% and 15%, respectively.

Source: National Safety Council analysis of NHTSA FARS data.

Fatalities in crashes involving large trucks, United States, 2013

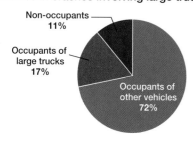

Motorcycles

Although motorcycles make up 3% of all registered vehicles and only 0.7% of all vehicle miles traveled in the United States, motorcyclists accounted for 15% of total traffic fatalities, 18% of all occupant fatalities, and 4% of all occupant injuries in 2012.

Fatalities among motorcycle riders and passengers have increased 16% between 2004 and 2013, from 4,028 to 4,668. Nonfatal injuries have increased as well, from 76,000 to 88,000 during the same period. The number of motorcycle fatalities decreased 6% from 2012 to 2013, while injuries decreased by 5%.

Exposure also has increased. From 2003 through 2012 (the latest year available), the number of registered motorcycles increased nearly 57% to 8.5 million from 5.4 million. Miles traveled is up 122%, from 9.6 billion to 21.3 billion in 2012 (latest available data). Consequently, the death rate from 2003 to 2012 has decreased 40%, from 38.78 to 23.27 deaths per 100 million miles traveled.

In 2012, speeding was a factor in 34% of fatal motorcycle crashes compared with 22% for fatal passenger car crashes.

Twenty-seven percent of motorcycle operators involved in fatal crashes were alcohol-impaired (blood-alcohol content greater than or equal to 0.08 g/dL), compared with 23% for passenger cars, 22% for light trucks, and 2% for large trucks.

Motorcycle helmets are estimated to be 37% effective in preventing fatal injuries to motorcycle operators and 41% effective for motorcycle passengers. The National Highway Traffic Safety Administration estimated helmets saved 1,699 motorcyclists' lives in 2012, and an additional 781 lives could have been saved if all motorcyclists wore helmets. Helmet use decreased in 2012 to 60% from 66% in 2011. The 2012 helmet use rate is substantially lower than the high of 71% achieved in 2000.

In 2014, 19 states and the District of Columbia had laws requiring helmet use by all motorcyclists. Other states either required only a subset of motorcyclists to use helmets (such as those younger than 18) or had no helmet requirement.

An analysis by the National Safety Council shows a strong relationship between retail gasoline prices and motorcycle fatalities. After correcting for general inflation, as retail gasoline prices go up, so do motorcycle fatalities. The inverse also appears to be true; when gasoline prices trend down, so do motorcycle fatalities. These trends have been consistent for more than 30 years (see chart).

National Center for Statistics and Analysis. (2014). Traffic Safety Facts 2012 Data: Motorcycles. (DOT HS 811 765.) Washington, DC: National Highway Traffic Safety Administration.
Insurance Institute for Highway Safety. (November 2013). Motorcycle and bicycle helmet use laws. Downloaded on January 2, 2015 from www.iihs.org/laws/HelmetUseOverview.aspx.
U.S. Department of Energy, Historical Gas Prices. Downloaded on January. 2, 2015 from www.eia.gov/forecasts/steo/realprices.

Motorcycle fatality and gasoline price trends, United States, 1976-2013

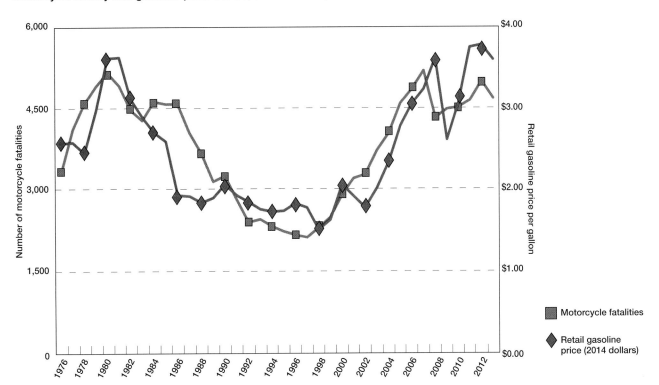

School Bus Transportation

School bus-related crashes killed 130 people nationwide in 2013, according to National Safety Council tabulations of data from the National Highway Traffic Safety Administration (NHTSA).

A school bus-related crash is defined by NHTSA to be any crash in which a vehicle, regardless of body design, used as a school bus is directly or indirectly involved, such as a crash involving school children alighting from a vehicle.

From 2007 to 2013, about 71% of the deaths in school bus-related crashes were occupants of vehicles other than the school bus and 17% were pedestrians. About 5% were school bus passengers, 4% were school bus drivers, and another 3% were pedalcyclists.

Out of the people injured in school bus-related crashes from 2007 to 2012, about 35% were school bus passengers, 8% were school bus drivers, and an additional 48% were occupants of other vehicles. The remainder were pedestrians, pedalcyclists, and other or unknown type persons.

Characteristics of school bus transportation

According to the American School Bus Council, an estimated 480,000 yellow school buses provide transportation service daily nationwide and travel approximately 5.8 billion miles each school year. Approximately 26 million elementary and secondary school children ride school buses to and from school each day throughout the United States. This compares to projections from the U.S. Department of Education of enrollments in fall 2013 in grades K-12 of about 50.1 million public school pupils and 5.2 million private school pupils nationwide.

Deaths and injuries in school bus-related crashes, United States, 2007-2013

	2007	2008	2009	2010	2011	2012	2013
Deaths							
Total	142	152	118	130	123	131	130
School bus driver	4	4	2	6	7	6	4
School bus passenger	1	15	3	10	4	8	4
Pedestrian	19	21	21	26	21	27	22
Pedalcyclist	6	8	1	3	4	3	3
Occupant of other vehicle	112	104	91	84	86	87	95
Other non-occupants	0	0	0	1	1	0	2
Injuries							
Total	9,000	13,000	13,000	10,000	12,000	9,000	[b]
School bus driver	1,000	1,000	1,000	1,000	[a]	1,000	[b]
School bus passenger	2,000	6,000	6,000	3,000	4,000	2,000	[b]
Pedestrian	[a]	[a]	1,000	[a]	[a]	[a]	[b]
Pedalcyclist	[a]	[a]	[a]	[a]	[a]	[a]	[b]
Occupant of other vehicle	5,000	5,000	5,000	5,000	6,000	6,000	[b]
Other non-occupants	[a]	[a]	[a]	[a]	[a]	[a]	[b]

Source: Deaths for 2007-2012 – National Center for Statistics and Analysis. (2014). Traffic Safety Facts 2002-2012 Data – School Transportation-Related Crashes (DOT HS 811 746). Washington, DC: National Highway Traffic Safety Administration. Fatality data for 2013 and pedalcyclist deaths are National Safety Council tabulations of Fatality Analysis Reporting System (FARS) data. Injuries – National Center for Statistics and Analysis. (2007-2012). Traffic Safety Facts, 2007-2012 editions. Washington, DC: National Highway Traffic Safety Administration. School bus transportation data accessed Jan. 2, 2015 from American School Bus Council at http://www.americanschoolbuscouncil.org/issues/environmental-benefits. *Student enrollment data from the* Digest of Education Statistics: 2013, *accessed Jan. 2, 2015 from the National Center for Education Statistics at* http://nces.ed.gov/programs/digest/d12/tables/dt12_002.asp?referrer=report.
[a]*Fewer than 500.*
[b]*Nonfatal injury data not available.*

Pedestrians

In 2013, an estimated 6,100 pedestrian deaths and 160,000 medically consulted nonfatal injuries[a] occurred among pedestrians in motor vehicle incidents. About 23% of these deaths and injuries occurred when pedestrians darted or ran into streets. Pedestrians improperly crossing roadways or intersections accounted for 4.5% of deaths and injuries, while being in the roadway improperly (standing, working, or playing) accounted for over 3%. Nearly half of pedestrian deaths and injuries involved no improper action or circumstance.

The distribution of pedestrian deaths and injuries by action varies for people of different ages. Darting or running into the road was the leading specified type for individuals younger than 15, accounting for about 70% of pedestrian deaths or injuries for those from 5 to 9 years old and about 47% of incidents for those aged 10 to 14. No improper action or circumstance was the leading specified type for all other age groups, ranging from 37% for those 15-19 years old to 57% for those aged 65 or older.

[a]Medically consulted injuries are not comparable to estimates provided in earlier editions that used the definition of disabling injury. Please see the Technical Appendix for more information regarding medically consulted injuries

Deaths and injuries of pedestrians by age and action/circumstance, United States, 2013

Action or circumstance	Total[a]	Age of people killed or injured							
		Younger than 5	5-9	10-14	15-19	20-24	25-44	45-64	65 or older
Totals[a]	115.0%	113.9%	127.6%	124.1%	116.4%	112.6%	111.3%	116.9%	109.5%
No improper action or circumstance	49.1%	64.3%	18.8%	29.6%	37.2%	49.2%	54.8%	53.9%	57.1%
Darting or running into roadway	23.0%	32.5%	70.0%	47.2%	34.0%	20.1%	19.8%	13.3%	6.4%
Other action or circumstance	20.9%	14.6%	15.0%	22.1%	19.1%	25.7%	19.1%	20.3%	25.3%
In roadway improperly (standing, lying, working, playing)	3.3%	0.0%	5.0%	5.5%	4.0%	1.3%	3.8%	3.8%	1.5%
Improper crossing of roadway or intersection	4.5%	1.3%	0.0%	2.1%	4.1%	2.9%	2.9%	8.0%	7.8%
Failure to obey traffic signs, signals, or officer	3.2%	0.0%	1.2%	7.5%	5.6%	2.4%	2.1%	3.9%	1.1%
Not visible (dark clothing, no lighting, etc.)	4.9%	1.1%	1.2%	5.7%	9.1%	5.0%	3.1%	4.9%	8.2%
Inattentive – talking, eating, etc.	1.5%	0.0%	15.8%	1.7%	1.4%	0.5%	0.9%	0.6%	0.7%
Not reported/unknown	4.6%	0.0%	0.7%	2.8%	1.8%	5.4%	4.8%	8.3%	1.2%

Source: National Safety Council tabulations of National Highway Traffic Safety Administration General Estimates System data.
[a]Totals are greater than 100% as multiple actions/circumstances may be entered for each case. Columns may not sum to totals because of rounding.

Pedestrian deaths and death rates by sex and age group, United States, 2012

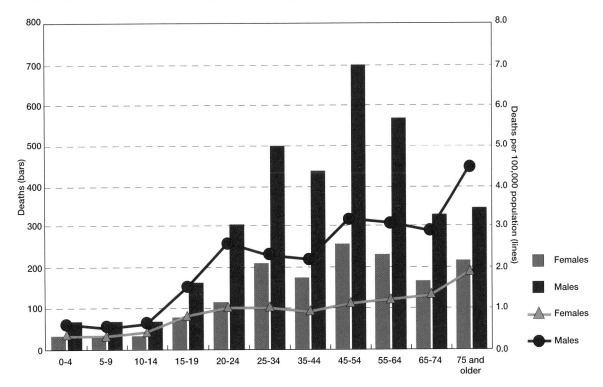

Source: National Safety Council tabulations based on U.S. Census Bureau and National Center for Health Statistics data.

Young Drivers

According to the latest data available from the National Highway Traffic Safety Administration, 2013 marked the 12th consecutive year in which the number of teen motor vehicle occupant fatalities has decreased in the United States, now at 2,176. However, motor vehicle crashes are still the number one cause of death for U.S. teens. The total death toll, including pedestrian and bicycle incidents, among teens ages 13 to 19 was 2,524 in 2013, and is equivalent to nearly seven deaths per day.

A strategy shown to help prevent young driver crashes is the passage and enforcement of state Graduated Driver Licensing (GDL) programs. GDL programs allow for a gradual phasing in of full driving privileges using a three-step process comprising an initial learner's permit phase; an intermediate, or provisional, license phase; and a full licensure phase.

With the advent of state graduated driver licensing programs, fatal crash risk among young drivers have decreased substantially since 1995. Based on mileage estimates from the National Household Travel Survey, the fatal crash rate per 100,000,000 miles driven for 16 year old drivers decreased from 13.4 per 100 million miles driven in 1995-96 down to 9.1 in 2008. Smaller improvements are also evident among other young drivers from ages 17 through 19 years of age (see chart on the right). However, all of the young driver fatal crash rates remain significantly higher than for the core population of adult drivers, those 30 to 59 years of age.

Crashes involving young drivers impact people of all ages. The bottom chart clearly shows that young driver fatalities account for less than half of the overall fatalities associated with young driver crashes. In 2013, there were 1,691 young driver fatalities, 1,051 fatalities among passengers of young drivers, 1,128 fatalities to occupants of all other vehicles, and 463 non-occupant fatalities.

Mileage-based fatal crash rate per 100,000,000 miles driven by young driver ages compared to the core population of adult drivers by select years

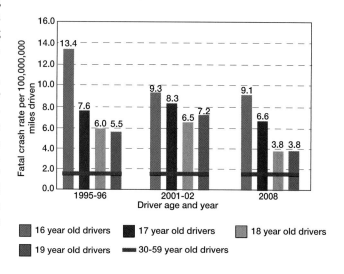

Historical trend of young driver-related fatalities, United States, 1982-2013

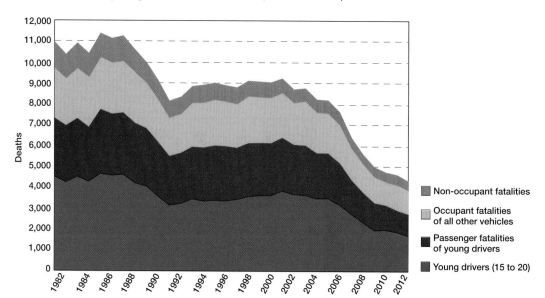

Source: National Safety Council analysis of National Highway Traffic Safety Administration data.

During the period when GDL programs were being implemented, improvement among some young driver safety indicators are evident. Improvements are in general larger for the 16 and 17 year old drivers than for the 18 and 19 year old drivers, perhaps reflecting GDL's focus on the 16 and 17 year old age groups. For example, the percentage of fatal crashes involving 16 year old drivers occurring at night has dropped from 32.2% in 1996 down to 28.6% in 2012, compared to the 43.9% to 40.9% drop among 19 year old drivers. Provided below are four graphs that chart the trends regarding night-time driving, teen passengers, driver error, and speeding.

Percentage of passenger vehicle fatal crashes involving nightime driving (9 p.m. to 5:59 a.m.) by young driver age compared to core population of adult drivers by select years

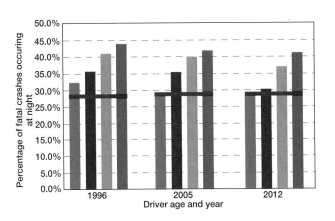

Percentage of passenger vehicle fatal crashes involving two or more teenage passengers by young driver age compared to the core population of adult drivers by select years

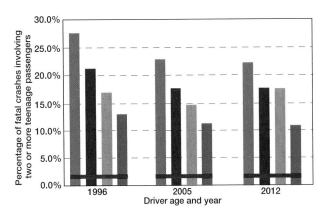

Percentage of passenger vehicle fatal crashes involving driver error by young driver age compared to the core population of adult drivers by select years

Percentage of passenger vehicle fatal crashes involving speeding by young driver age compared to core population of adult drivers by select years

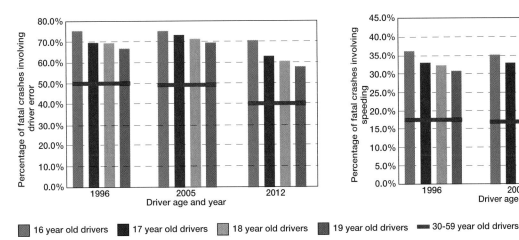

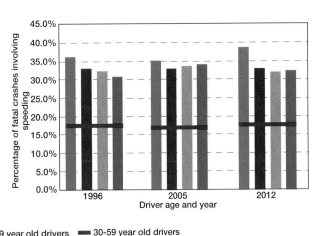

■ 16 year old drivers ■ 17 year old drivers ■ 18 year old drivers ■ 19 year old drivers ■— 30-59 year old drivers

Source: McCartt, A.T., & Teoh, E.R. (2014). Tracking progress in teenage crash risk in the United States since the advent of graduated driver licensing programs. Downloaded on Oct. 13,2014 from: http://www.iihs.org/frpmtemd/iihs/documents/masterfiledocs.ashx?id=2069.

The table below shows the total number of licensed drivers and drivers involved in crashes by selected ages and age groups. Also shown is the rate of crash involvement on the basis of the number of drivers in each age group. The fatal crash involvement rates per 100,000 licensed drivers in each age group ranged from a low of 16 for drivers in the 65-74 age group to a high of 40 for drivers age 18. The all-incident involvement rates per 100 drivers in each age group ranged from five for drivers in the 75 and older age group to 36 for drivers age 16.

On the basis of miles driven by each age group, however, involvement rates (not shown in the table) are highest for the youngest drivers. The rates of fatal crashes per mile driven for 16-19 year-olds are about 3 times the rates for drivers age 20 and older. Passenger vehicle drivers age 16 had the highest fatal crash involvement rate at 9.1 fatal crashes per 100 million vehicle miles traveled in 2008, more than 7 times the rate of 1.2 for drivers aged 30-59.

For more details of this mileage-based analysis, please see pages 124 and 125.

Source: National Safety Council estimates based on NHTSA FARS data. Involvement rates per mile driven. McCartt, A.T., & Teoh, E.R., (March 2014). Tracking Progress in Teenage Crash Risk in the United States Since the Advent of Graduated Driver Licensing Programs. Arlington, VA: Insurance Institute for Highway Safety.

Licensed drivers and number in crashes by age of driver, United States, 2013

Age group	Licensed drivers		Drivers in...					
	Number	Percent	Fatal crashes			All crashes		
			Number	Percent	Rate[a]	Number	Percent	Rate[b]
Total	212,600,000	100.0%	48,300	100.0%	23	20,800,000	100.0%	10
Younger than 16	256,000	0.1	200	0.4	(c)	60,000	0.3	(c)
16	1,165,000	0.5	400	0.8	34	420,000	2.0	36
17	1,900,000	0.9	600	1.2	32	450,000	2.2	24
18	2,514,000	1.2	1,000	2.1	40	570,000	2.7	22
19	2,958,000	1.4	1,100	2.3	37	560,000	2.7	19
19 and younger	8,793,000	4.1	3,300	6.8	38	2,060,000	9.9	23
20	3,164,000	1.5	1,200	2.5	38	610,000	2.9	19
21	3,341,000	1.6	1,300	2.7	39	610,000	2.9	18
22	3,592,000	1.7	1,300	2.7	36	550,000	2.6	15
23	3,751,000	1.8	1,300	2.7	35	590,000	2.8	16
24	3,704,000	1.7	1,200	2.5	32	620,000	3.0	17
20-24	17,552,000	8.3	6,300	13.0	36	2,980,000	14.3	17
25-34	36,920,000	17.4	9,700	20.1	26	4,460,000	21.4	12
35-44	36,211,000	17.0	7,900	16.4	22	3,440,000	16.5	9
45-54	39,877,000	18.8	8,100	16.8	20	3,400,000	16.3	9
55-64	36,181,000	17.0	6,500	13.5	18	2,490,000	12.0	7
65-74	22,686,000	10.7	3,700	7.7	16	1,250,000	6.0	6
75 and older	14,380,000	6.8	2,800	5.8	19	720,000	3.5	5

Source: National Safety Council estimates. Drivers in incidents based on data from the National Highway Traffic Safety Administration's Fatality Analysis Reporting System and General Estimates System. Total licensed drivers and age distribution estimated by the National Safety Council based on data from the Federal Highway Administration.
Note: Percents may not add to total due to rounding.
[a]Drivers in fatal incidents per 100,000 licensed drivers in each age group.
[b]Drivers in all incidents per 100 licensed drivers in each age group.
[c]Rates for drivers younger than 16 are substantially overstated due to the high proportion of unlicensed drivers involved.

Driveway and Parking Lot Crashes, 2011

Crashes occurring on driveways and parking lots are not always counted in overall crash totals (see page 131 for details). Starting in 2007 the National Highway Traffic Safety Administration implemented the Not-in-Traffic Surveillance system to estimate the number of crashes not occurring on public roads. From this surveillance data the National Safety Council estimates that 76,000 people were injured and another 961 people died in 2011 resulting from collisions occurring on driveways and parking lots. As shown in the table below, the vast majority of injuries occur in parking lots (either commercial or parking lots of unknown type). Fatalities, on the other hand, are evenly split among residential driveways, commercial parking lots, and parking lots of unknown type.

Number of injuries and injury crashes by driveway and parking lot type, 2011

| | Crashes | | Injuries | |
	Non-fatal[a]	Fatal[b]	Non-fatal[a]	Fatal[b]
Total	**66,000**	**939**	**76,000**	**961**
Residential driveway	5,000	263	5,000	263
Residential parking lot	2,000	77	2,000	82
Commercial driveway	1,000	17	1,000	17
Commercial parking lot	29,000	252	33,000	269
Parking garage structure	1,000	34	1,000	34
Parking lot (unknown type)	27,000	274	33,000	274
Unknown Driveway Type	1,000	22	1,000	22

Of the total 961 fatalities occurring on driveways and parking lots, 152 deaths occurred to pedestrians in collisions involving vehicles in the process of backing up. As shown in the table below, over half of these backup pedestrian fatalities occur on residential driveways. In 2011, a total of 63 pedestrians under the age of five died in this type of collision occurring on residential driveways, while an additional 19 children died from backup collisions occurring in parking lots. A total of 41 pedestrians over the age of 74 also died in parking lots and driveways as a result of collisions with vehicles backing up.

Number[b] of fatal pedestrian injuries resulting from vehicles backup collisions by driveway and parking lot type, 2011

| | Age | | | | | | | | | |
	Age 1-4	Age 5-14	15-24	25-34	35-44	45-54	55-64	65-74	75+	Total
Total	**82**	**5**	**0**	**14**	**0**	**5**	**5**	**0**	**41**	**152**
Residential driveway	63	5	0	9	0	0	0	0	9	**86**
Residential parking lot	5	0	0	0	0	0	0	0	0	**5**
Commercial driveway	0	0	0	5	0	0	0	0	0	**5**
Commercial parking lot	5	0	0	0	0	5	0	0	18	**28**
Parking lot (unknown type)	9	0	0	0	0	0	5	0	9	**23**
Unknown Driveway Type	0	0	0	0	0	0	0	0	5	**5**

In 2011, residential driveway pedestrian fatalities associated with vehicles backing up peaked in May while fatalities occurring in other types of driveways and parking lots peaked in August (see illustration below).

Pedestrian fatalities[b] resulting from in vehicle backup collisions by location, United States, 2011

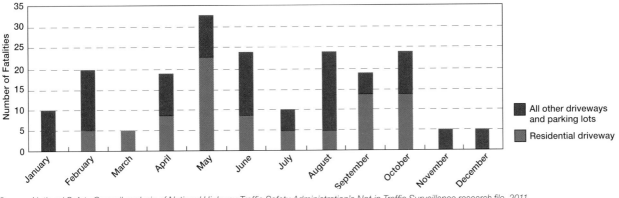

Source: National Safety Council analysis of National Highway Traffic Safety Administration's Not in Traffic Surveillance research file, 2011.
[a]Estimates rounded to the nearest thousand; the column entries may not sum to the totals shown.
[b]Estimated. Since a complete record of all nontraffic crash fatalities from state and police jurisdictions is not available, adjusted weights are used to obtain national estimates.

Motor Vehicle Crashes by Time of Day and Day of Week

More fatal crashes occurred on Saturday than any other day of the week in 2013, according to data from the National Highway Traffic Safety Administration. More than 18% of fatal crashes occurred on Saturday, compared with 15.9% on Sundays and 15.4% on Fridays. For all crashes, Friday had the highest percentage, with more than 16%.

Patterns by hour of day for fatal crashes show peaks during afternoon rush hour for weekdays and, especially, late at night during weekends. For all crashes, primary peaks occurred during afternoon rush hours, with secondary peaks during morning rush hours.

Percent of weekly crashes by hour of day and day of week, United States, 2013

Time of day	Fatal crashes								All crashes							
	Total	Sun.	Mon.	Tues.	Wed.	Thurs.	Fri.	Sat.	Total	Sun.	Mon.	Tues.	Wed.	Thurs.	Fri.	Sat.
All hours	100.0%	15.9%	12.4%	12.6%	12.4%	13.1%	15.4%	18.1%	100.0%	10.4%	14.7%	15.4%	15.0%	15.2%	16.6%	12.7%
Midnight to 3:59 a.m.	14.7%	4.1%	1.3%	1.2%	1.1%	1.5%	1.9%	3.6%	5.4%	1.4%	0.5%	0.5%	0.4%	0.6%	0.7%	1.2%
4:00 to 7:59 a.m.	12.5%	1.8%	1.7%	1.8%	1.7%	1.7%	1.8%	1.9%	10.3%	0.8%	1.7%	1.8%	1.8%	1.7%	1.6%	0.9%
8:00 to 11:59 a.m.	12.7%	1.5%	1.8%	1.8%	1.9%	1.9%	1.9%	2.0%	18.8%	1.5%	3.1%	3.1%	2.9%	2.9%	3.0%	2.3%
Noon to 3:59 p.m.	18.1%	2.5%	2.5%	2.6%	2.4%	2.4%	2.8%	2.9%	25.7%	2.7%	3.8%	3.8%	3.6%	3.8%	4.5%	3.5%
4:00 to 7:59 p.m.	21.4%	3.2%	2.8%	2.8%	2.9%	2.9%	3.3%	3.5%	27.9%	2.4%	4.2%	4.5%	4.6%	4.5%	4.7%	2.9%
8:00 to 11:59 p.m.	19.9%	2.6%	2.2%	2.4%	2.3%	2.7%	3.6%	4.0%	11.5%	1.5%	1.3%	1.5%	1.6%	1.5%	2.0%	2.0%

Source: National Safety Council analysis of data from the National Highway Traffic Safety Administration - Fatality Analysis Reporting System (FARS) and General Estimates System (GES).
Note: Column and row totals may not equal sum of parts due to rounding and unreported time of day or day of week data.

Percent of crashes by time of day and day of week, United States, 2013

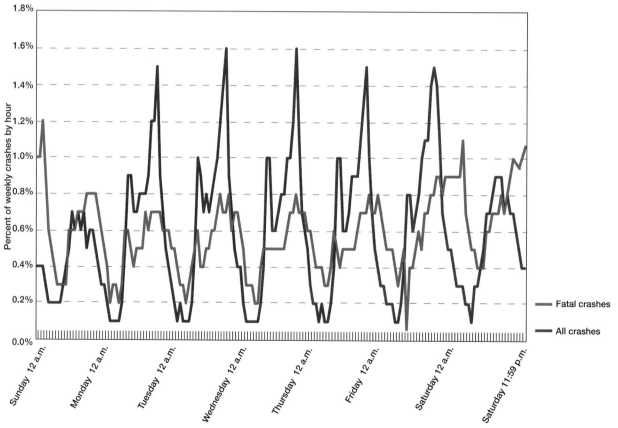

Note: Each daily column represents 24 hours.

Deaths and Mileage Death Rates by Month

Motor vehicle deaths in 2013 were at their lowest level in February and increased to their highest level in August. In 2013, the highest monthly mileage death rate of 1.32 deaths per 100,000,000 vehicle miles occurred in September. The overall rate for the year was 1.20.

Motor vehicle deaths and mileage death rates by month, United States, 2013

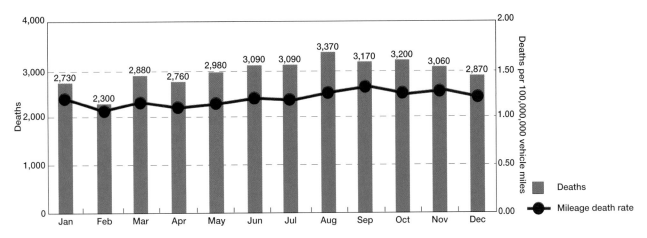

Source: Deaths – National Safety Council estimates. Mileage – Federal Highway Administration, Traffic Volume Trends.

Holidays

Holidays traditionally are a time of travel for families across the United States. Many choose the automobile – with the highest fatality rate of any of the major forms of transportation based on fatalities per passenger mile (see page 156) – as their mode of travel, therefore increasing their risk of dying in a motor vehicle crash. In addition, holidays are often the cause for celebrations that include drinking alcohol, which is a major contributing factor to motor vehicle crashes. Nationwide, alcohol-impaired (blood-alcohol content of 0.08 g/dL or higher) fatalities in 2013 represented 31% of the total traffic fatalities. The table below shows the number of fatalities for each major holiday period and the percent of those fatalities that were alcohol-impaired.

Motor vehicle deaths and percent alcohol-impaired during holiday periods, United States, 2009-2013

Year	Holiday period[a]											
	New Year's Day		Memorial Day		Independence Day		Labor Day		Thanksgiving Day		Christmas Day	
	Deaths[b]	Alcohol-impaired[c] (%)	Deaths[b]	Alcohol-impaired[c] (%)	Deaths[b]	Alcohol-impaired[c] (%)	Deaths[b]	Alcohol-impaired[c] (%)	Deaths[b]	Alcohol-impaired[c] (%)	Deaths[b]	Alcohol-impaired[c] (%)
2009	458 (4)	40	462 (3)	42	398 (3)	39	351 (3)	38	401 (4)	34	248 (3)	36
2010	286 (3)	48	389 (3)	40	365 (3)	38	390 (3)	35	417 (4)	40	249 (3)	35
2011	304 (3)	43	389 (3)	40	405 (3)	37	373 (3)	37	375 (4)	32	256 (3)	36
2012	348 (3)	39	367 (3)	44	157 (1)	44	378 (3)	38	405 (4)	42	351 (4)	37
2013	343 (4)	—	334 (3)	—	461 (4)	—	371 (3)	—	360 (4)	—	88 (1)	—

Source: Deaths – National Safety Council tabulations of National Highway Traffic Safety Administration (NHTSA), Fatality Analysis Reporting System data. Percent alcohol impaired – NHTSA, Traffic Safety Facts, 2012 edition.

Note: Dashes indicate data not available.

[a]The length of the holiday period depends on the day of the week on which the holiday falls. Memorial Day and Labor Day are always 3.25 days; Thanksgiving is always 4.25 days; and New Year's Day, Independence Day, and Christmas are 3.25 days if the holiday falls on Friday through Monday, 4.25 days if on Tuesday or Thursday, and 1.25 days if on Wednesday.

[b]Number in parentheses refers to the number of whole days in the holiday period.

[c]Highest blood alcohol concentration (BAC) among drivers or motorcycle riders involved in the crash was 0.08 grams per deciliter (g/dL) or higher. The holiday periods used to calculate the percentages conform to the NHTSA holiday period definitions that add another quarter day to the periods noted in footnote (a).

Work Zone Deaths and Injuries

In 2013, 579 people were killed and 24,680 people were injured in work zone crashes (see table below). Of the 579 killed in work zones, 384 were in construction zones, 73 were in maintenance zones, 12 were in utility zones, and 110 were in an unknown type of work zone.

From 2004 through 2013, work zone deaths have ranged from 576 to 1,074 and averaged 773 per year.

According to the Governors Highway Safety Association, nearly all states have laws that increase the penalties for speeding or committing other traffic violations while in a construction work.[a] The penalties often involve doubled fines, but also can be a fixed dollar amount. In some cases, the penalty is applicable only when workers are present and/or if signs are posted. Presently, 32 states and the District of Columbia double the fine for speeding or other traffic violations in a work zone. Twenty-four states and the District of Columbia require workers to be present in the construction zone for the increased penalties to take effect.

[a]Retrieved January. 5, 2015 from www.ghsa.org/html/stateinfo/laws/sanctions_laws.html.

People killed or injured in work zones, United States, 2013

	Total	Vehicle occupants	Pedestrians	Pedalcyclists	Other nonmotorists
Killed	579	473	101	5	0
Injured	24,680	23,800	743	137	0

Source: National Safety Council analysis of data from National Highway Traffic Safety Administration Fatality Analysis Reporting System and General Estimates Systems.

Work zone deaths, United States, 2000-2013

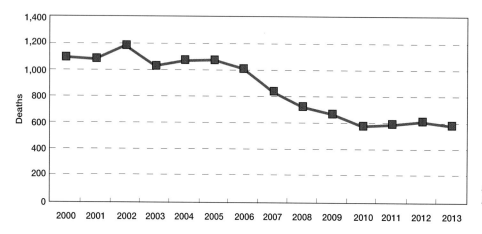

Source: NSC analysis of NHTSA FARS data files.

Emergency Vehicles

Crashes involving emergency vehicles, United States, 2013

	Ambulance		Fire truck/car		Police car	
	Total	Emergency use[a]	Total	Emergency use[a]	Total	Emergency use[a]
Emergency vehicles in fatal crashes	17	5	12	7	75	21
Emergency vehicles in injury crashes	1,506	701	379	210	8,083	2,924
Emergency vehicles in all crashes	**5,747**	**3,167**	**2,508**	**1,730**	**34,821**	**10,657**
Emergency vehicle drivers killed	3	1	2	1	18	3
Emergency vehicle passengers killed	4	2	0	0	0	0
Other vehicle occupants killed	11	4	8	4	41	15
Nonmotorists killed	3	0	2	2	28	5
Total killed in crashes	**21**	**7**	**12**	**7**	**87**	**23**
Total injured in crashes	**3,236**	**1,898**	**1,430**	**465**	**12,362**	**5,185**

Source: National Safety Council analysis of data from National Highway Traffic Safety Administration Fatality Analysis Reporting System and General Estimates Systems.
[a]Vehicle being used as an emergency vehicle at the time of the crash with or without the use of emergency warning equipment.

The National Safety Council (NSC) and the National Highway Traffic Safety Administration (NHTSA) count motor vehicle crash deaths using somewhat different criteria. NSC counts total motor vehicle-related fatalities – both traffic and nontraffic – that occur within one year of the crash. This is consistent with the data compiled from death certificates by the National Center for Health Statistics (NCHS). NSC uses NCHS death certificate data less intentional fatalities as the final count of unintentional deaths from all causes.

NHTSA counts only traffic fatalities that occur within 30 days of the crash in its Fatality Analysis Reporting System (FARS). This means that the FARS count omits about 800 to 1,000 motor vehicle-related deaths each year that occur more than 30 days after the crash. Nontraffic fatalities (those that do not occur on public highways; e.g., parking lots, private roads, and driveways), which account for 900 to 1,900 deaths annu-

ally, also are omitted. By using a 30-day cutoff, NHTSA can issue a "final" count about eight months after the reference year.

Because of the time it takes to process 2.4 million death certificates, the NCHS data are not available up to 22 months after the reference year. This means, for example, that this edition of *Injury Facts* includes the 2012 NCHS final counts by cause of death including motor vehicle crashes and estimates of the totals for 2013. For motor vehicle deaths, these estimates are based on data supplied by traffic authorities in all 50 states and the District of Columbia. See the Technical Appendix for more information on all of NSC's estimation procedures.

The graph below shows the NCHS death certificate counts of unintentional motor vehicle deaths through 2012 and NSC's estimate for 2013 compared to the NHTSA FARS counts of traffic deaths.

Motor vehicle deaths: NSC and NHTSA, 1992-2013

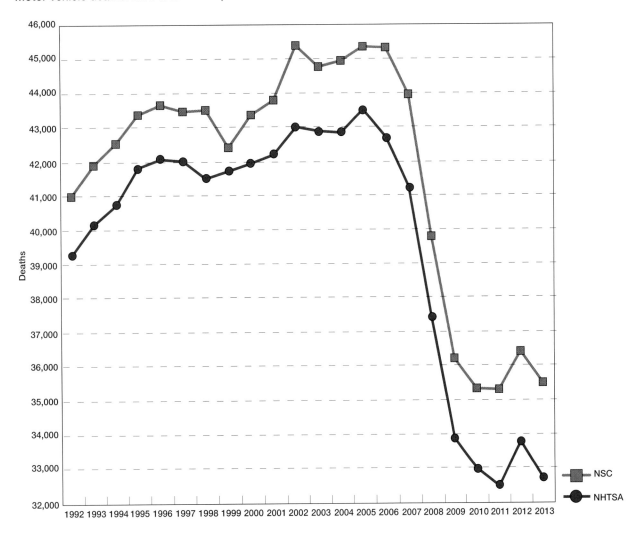

Motor Vehicle Deaths and Rates

Motor vehicle deaths and rates, United States, 1913-2013

Year	No. of deaths	Estimated no. of vehicles (millions)	Estimated vehicle miles (billions)	Estimated no. of drivers (millions)	Death rates		
					Per 10,000 motor vehicles	Per 100,000,000 vehicle miles	Per 100,000 population
1913	4,200	1.3	(a)	2.0	33.38	(a)	4.4
1914	4,700	1.8	(a)	3.0	26.65	(a)	4.8
1915	6,600	2.5	(a)	3.0	26.49	(a)	6.6
1916	8,200	3.6	(a)	5.0	22.66	(a)	8.1
1917	10,200	5.1	(a)	7.0	19.93	(a)	10.0
1918	10,700	6.2	(a)	9.0	17.37	(a)	10.3
1919	11,200	7.6	(a)	12.0	14.78	(a)	10.7
1920	12,500	9.2	(a)	14.0	13.53	(a)	11.7
1921	13,900	10.5	(a)	16.0	13.25	(a)	12.9
1922	15,300	12.3	(a)	19.0	12.47	(a)	13.9
1923	18,400	15.1	85	22.0	12.18	21.65	16.5
1924	19,400	17.6	104	26.0	11.02	18.65	17.1
1925	21,900	20.1	122	30.0	10.89	17.95	19.1
1926	23,400	22.2	141	33.0	10.54	16.59	20.1
1927	25,800	23.3	158	34.0	11.07	16.33	21.8
1928	28,000	24.7	173	37.0	11.34	16.18	23.4
1929	31,200	26.7	197	40.0	11.69	15.84	25.7
1930	32,900	26.7	206	40.0	12.32	15.97	26.7
1931	33,700	26.1	216	39.0	12.91	15.60	27.2
1932	29,500	24.4	200	36.0	12.09	14.75	23.6
1933	31,363	24.2	201	35.0	12.96	15.60	25.0
1934	36,101	25.3	216	37.0	14.27	16.71	28.6
1935	36,369	26.5	229	39.0	13.72	15.88	28.6
1936	38,089	28.5	252	42.0	13.36	15.11	29.7
1937	39,643	30.1	270	44.0	13.19	14.68	30.8
1938	32,582	29.8	271	44.0	10.93	12.02	25.1
1939	32,386	31.0	285	46.0	10.44	11.35	24.7
1940	34,501	32.5	302	48.0	10.63	11.42	26.1
1941	39,969	34.9	334	52.0	11.45	11.98	30.0
1942	28,309	33.0	268	49.0	8.58	10.55	21.1
1943	23,823	30.9	208	46.0	7.71	11.44	17.8
1944	24,282	30.5	213	45.0	7.97	11.42	18.3
1945	28,076	31.0	250	46.0	9.05	11.22	21.2
1946	33,411	34.4	341	50.0	9.72	9.80	23.9
1947	32,697	37.8	371	53.0	8.64	8.82	22.8
1948	32,259	41.1	398	55.0	7.85	8.11	22.1
1949	31,701	44.7	424	59.3	7.09	7.47	21.3
1950	34,763	49.2	458	62.2	7.07	7.59	23.0
1951	36,996	51.9	491	64.4	7.13	7.53	24.1
1952	37,794	53.3	514	66.8	7.10	7.36	24.3
1953	37,956	56.3	544	69.9	6.74	6.97	24.0
1954	35,586	58.6	562	72.2	6.07	6.33	22.1
1955	38,426	62.8	606	74.7	6.12	6.34	23.4
1956	39,628	65.2	631	77.9	6.07	6.28	23.7
1957	38,702	67.6	647	79.6	5.73	5.98	22.7
1958	36,981	68.8	665	81.5	5.37	5.56	21.3
1959	37,910	72.1	700	84.5	5.26	5.41	21.5
1960	38,137	74.5	719	87.4	5.12	5.31	21.2
1961	38,091	76.4	738	88.9	4.98	5.16	20.8
1962	40,804	79.7	767	92.0	5.12	5.32	22.0
1963	43,564	83.5	805	93.7	5.22	5.41	23.1
1964	47,700	87.3	847	95.6	5.46	5.63	25.0
1965	49,163	91.8	888	99.0	5.36	5.54	25.4
1966	53,041	95.9	930	101.0	5.53	5.70	27.1
1967	52,924	98.9	962	103.2	5.35	5.50	26.8
1968	54,862	103.1	1,016	105.4	5.32	5.40	27.5
1969	55,791	107.4	1,071	108.3	5.19	5.21	27.7
1970	54,633	111.2	1,120	111.5	4.92	4.88	26.8
1971	54,381	116.3	1,186	114.4	4.68	4.57	26.3
1972	56,278	122.3	1,268	118.4	4.60	4.43	26.9
1973	55,511	129.8	1,309	121.6	4.28	4.24	26.3
1974	46,402	134.9	1,290	125.6	3.44	3.59	21.8
1975	45,853	137.9	1,330	129.8	3.33	3.45	21.3
1976	47,038	143.5	1,412	133.9	3.28	3.33	21.6

See source and footnotes on page 133.

Motor vehicle deaths and rates, United States, 1913-2013 (cont.)

Year	No. of deaths	Estimated no. of vehicles (millions)	Estimated vehicle miles (billions)	Estimated no. of drivers (millions)	Death rates Per 10,000 motor vehicles	Per 100,000,000 vehicle miles	Per 100,000 population
1977	49,510	148.8	1,477	138.1	3.33	3.35	22.5
1978	52,411	153.6	1,548	140.8	3.41	3.39	23.6
1979	53,524	159.6	1,529	143.3	3.35	3.50	23.8
1980	53,172	161.6	1,521	145.3	3.29	3.50	23.4
1981	51,385	164.1	1,556	147.1	3.13	3.30	22.4
1982	45,779	165.2	1,592	150.3	2.77	2.88	19.8
1983	44,452	169.4	1,657	154.2	2.62	2.68	19.0
1984	46,263	171.8	1,718	155.4	2.69	2.69	19.6
1985	45,901	177.1	1,774	156.9	2.59	2.59	19.3
1986	47,865	181.4	1,835	159.5	2.63	2.60	19.9
1987	48,290	183.9	1,924	161.8	2.63	2.51	19.9
1988	49,078	189.0	2,026	162.9	2.60	2.42	20.1
1989	47,575	191.7	2,107	165.6	2.48	2.26	19.3
1990	46,814	192.9	2,148	167.0	2.43	2.18	18.8
1991	43,536	192.5	2,172	169.0	2.26	2.00	17.3
1992	40,982	194.4	2,240	173.1	2.11	1.83	16.1
1993	41,893	198.0	2,297	173.1	2.12	1.82	16.3
1994	42,524	201.8	2,360	175.4	2.11	1.80	16.3
1995	43,363	205.3	2,423	176.6	2.11	1.79	16.5
1996	43,649	210.4	2,486	179.5	2.07	1.76	16.5
1997	43,458	211.5	2,562	182.7	2.05	1.70	16.2
1998	43,501	215.0	2,632	185.2	2.02	1.65	16.1
1999	42,401	220.5	2,691	187.2	1.92	1.58	15.5
2000	43,354	225.8	2,747	190.6	1.92	1.58	15.8
2001	43,788	235.3	2,797	191.3	1.86	1.57	15.4
2002	45,380	234.6	2,856	194.3	1.93	1.59	15.8
2003	44,757	236.8	2,890	196.2	1.89	1.55	15.4
2004	44,933	243.0	2,965	199.0	1.85	1.52	15.3
2005	45,343	247.4	2,989	200.5	1.83	1.52	15.3
2006	45,316	250.8	3,014	202.8	1.81	1.50	15.2
2007	43,945	254.4	3,032	205.7	1.73	1.45	14.6
2008	39,790	255.9	2,976	208.3	1.55	1.34	13.1
2009	36,216	254.2	2,957	209.6	1.42	1.22	11.8
2010	35,332	250.3	2,967	210.1	1.41	1.19	11.4
2011[b]	35,303	253.2	2,950	211.9	1.39	1.20	11.3
2012[b]	36,415	253.6	2,699	211.8	1.44	1.35	11.6
2013[c]	35,500	253.5	2,966	212.6	1.40	1.20	11.2
Changes							
2004 to 2013	-21%	4%	(d)	7%	-24%	-21%	-27%
2012 to 2013	-2%	(d)	10%	(d)	-3%	-11%	-3%

Source: Deaths from National Center for Health Statistics except 1964 and 2013, which are National Safety Council estimates based on data from the National Highway Traffic Safety Administration's Fatality Analysis Reporting System. See Technical Appendix for comparability. Motor vehicle registrations, mileage, and drivers estimated by Federal Highway Administration except for 2013 registrations and drivers, which are National Safety Council estimates.
[a]*Mileage data inadequate prior to 1923.*
[b]*Revised.*
[c]*Preliminary.*
[d]*Less than 0.5%.*

Motor Vehicle Deaths by Type of Incident

Motor vehicle deaths by type of incident, United States, 1913-2013

Year	Total deaths	Deaths from collision with...							Deaths from noncollision incidents	Nontraffic deaths[a]
		Pedestrians	Other motor vehicles	Railroad trains	Streetcars	Pedalcycles	Animal-drawn vehicle or animal	Fixed objects		
1913	4,200	(b)	(b)	(b)	(b)	(b)	(b)	(b)	(b)	(c)
1914	4,700	(b)	(b)	(b)	(b)	(b)	(b)	(b)	(b)	(c)
1915	6,600	(b)	(b)	(b)	(b)	(b)	(b)	(b)	(b)	(c)
1916	8,200	(b)	(b)	(b)	(b)	(b)	(b)	(b)	(b)	(c)
1917	10,200	(b)	(b)	(b)	(b)	(b)	(b)	(b)	(b)	(c)
1918	10,700	(b)	(b)	(b)	(b)	(b)	(b)	(b)	(b)	(c)
1919	11,200	(b)	(b)	(b)	(b)	(b)	(b)	(b)	(b)	(c)
1920	12,500	(b)	(b)	(b)	(b)	(b)	(b)	(b)	(b)	(c)
1921	13,900	(b)	(b)	(b)	(b)	(b)	(b)	(b)	(b)	(c)
1922	15,300	(b)	(b)	(b)	(b)	(b)	(b)	(b)	(b)	(c)
1923	18,400	(b)	(b)	(b)	(b)	(b)	(b)	(b)	(b)	(c)
1924	19,400	(b)	(b)	1,130	410	(b)	(b)	(b)	(b)	(c)
1925	21,900	(b)	(b)	1,410	560	(b)	(b)	(b)	(b)	(c)
1926	23,400	(b)	(b)	1,730	520	(b)	(b)	(b)	(b)	(c)
1927	25,800	10,820	3,430	1,830	520	(b)	(b)	(b)	(b)	(c)
1928	28,000	11,420	4,310	2,140	570	(b)	(b)	540	8,070	(c)
1929	31,200	12,250	5,400	2,050	530	(b)	(b)	620	9,380	(c)
1930	32,900	12,900	5,880	1,830	480	(b)	(b)	720	9,970	(c)
1931	33,700	13,370	6,820	1,710	440	(b)	(b)	870	9,570	(c)
1932	29,500	11,490	6,070	1,520	320	350	400	800	8,500	(c)
1933	31,363	12,840	6,470	1,437	318	400	310	900	8,680	(c)
1934	36,101	14,480	8,110	1,457	332	500	360	1,040	9,820	(c)
1935	36,369	14,350	8,750	1,587	253	450	250	1,010	9,720	(c)
1936	38,089	15,250	9,500	1,697	269	650	250	1,060	9,410	(c)
1937	39,643	15,500	10,320	1,810	264	700	200	1,160	9,690	(c)
1938	32,582	12,850	8,900	1,490	165	720	170	940	7,350	(c)
1939	32,386	12,400	8,700	1,330	150	710	200	1,000	7,900	(c)
1940	34,501	12,700	10,100	1,707	132	750	210	1,100	7,800	(c)
1941	39,969	13,550	12,500	1,840	118	910	250	1,350	9,450	(c)
1942	28,309	10,650	7,300	1,754	124	650	240	850	6,740	(c)
1943	23,823	9,900	5,300	1,448	171	450	160	700	5,690	(c)
1944	24,282	9,900	5,700	1,663	175	400	140	700	5,600	(c)
1945	28,076	11,000	7,150	1,703	163	500	130	800	6,600	(c)
1946	33,411	11,600	9,400	1,703	174	450	130	950	8,900	(c)
1947	32,697	10,450	9,900	1,736	102	550	150	1,000	8,800	(c)
1948	32,259	9,950	10,200	1,474	83	500	100	1,000	8,950	(c)
1949	31,701	8,800	10,500	1,452	56	550	140	1,100	9,100	838
1950	34,763	9,000	11,650	1,541	89	440	120	1,300	10,600	900
1951	36,996	9,150	13,100	1,573	46	390	100	1,400	11,200	966
1952	37,794	8,900	13,500	1,429	32	430	130	1,450	11,900	970
1953	37,956	8,750	13,400	1,506	26	420	120	1,500	12,200	1,026
1954	35,586	8,000	12,800	1,289	28	380	90	1,500	11,500	1,004
1955	38,426	8,200	14,500	1,490	15	410	90	1,600	12,100	989
1956	39,628	7,900	15,200	1,377	11	440	100	1,600	13,000	888
1957	38,702	7,850	15,400	1,376	13	460	80	1,700	11,800	1,016
1958	36,981	7,650	14,200	1,316	9	450	80	1,650	11,600	929
1959	37,910	7,850	14,900	1,202	6	480	70	1,600	11,800	948
1960	38,137	7,850	14,800	1,368	5	460	80	1,700	11,900	995
1961	38,091	7,650	14,700	1,267	5	490	80	1,700	12,200	1,065
1962	40,804	7,900	16,400	1,245	3	500	90	1,750	12,900	1,029
1963	43,564	8,200	17,600	1,385	10	580	80	1,900	13,800	990
1964	47,700	9,000	19,600	1,580	5	710	100	2,100	14,600	1,123
1965	49,163	8,900	20,800	1,556	5	680	120	2,200	14,900	1,113
1966	53,041	9,400	22,200	1,800	2	740	100	2,500	16,300	1,108
1967	52,924	9,400	22,000	1,620	3	750	100	2,350	16,700	1,165
1968	54,862	9,900	22,400	1,570	4	790	100	2,700	17,400	1,061
1969	55,791	10,100	23,700	1,495	2	800	100	3,900[d]	15,700[d]	1,155
1970	54,633	9,900	23,200	1,459	3	780	100	3,800	15,400	1,140
1971	54,381	9,900	23,100	1,378	2	800	100	3,800	15,300	1,015
1972	56,278	10,300	23,900	1,260	2	1,000	100	3,900	15,800	1,064
1973	55,511	10,200	23,600	1,194	2	1,000	100	3,800	15,600	1,164
1974	46,402	8,500	19,700	1,209	1	1,000	100	3,100	12,800	1,088
1975	45,853	8,400	19,550	979	1	1,000	100	3,130	12,700	1,033
1976	47,038	8,600	20,100	1,033	2	1,000	100	3,200	13,000	1,026

See source and footnotes on page 135.

MOTOR VEHICLE

Motor Vehicle Deaths by Type of Incident (cont.)

Motor vehicle deaths by type of incident, United States, 1913-2013 (cont.)

| Year | Total deaths | Deaths from collision with... | | | | | | | Deaths from noncollision incidents | Nontraffic deaths[a] |
		Pedestrians	Other motor vehicles	Railroad trains	Streetcars	Pedalcycles	Animal-drawn vehicle or animal	Fixed objects		
1977	49,510	9,100	21,200	902	3	1,100	100	3,400	13,700	1,053
1978	52,411	9,600	22,400	986	1	1,200	100	3,600	14,500	1,074
1979	53,524	9,800	23,100	826	1	1,200	100	3,700	14,800	1,271
1980	53,172	9,700	23,000	739	1	1,200	100	3,700	14,700	1,242
1981	51,385	9,400	22,200	668	1	1,200	100	3,600	14,200	1,189
1982	45,779	8,400	19,800	554	1	1,100	100	3,200	12,600	1,066
1983	44,452	8,200	19,200	520	1	1,100	100	3,100	12,200	1,024
1984	46,263	8,500	20,000	630	0	1,100	100	3,200	12,700	1,055
1985	45,901	8,500	19,900	538	2	1,100	100	3,200	12,600	1,079
1986	47,865	8,900	20,800	574	2	1,100	100	3,300	13,100	998
1987	48,290	7,500[e]	20,700	554	1	1,000[e]	100	13,200[e]	5,200[e]	993
1988	49,078	7,700	20,900	638	2	1,000	100	13,400	5,300	1,054
1989	47,575	7,800	20,300	720	2	900	100	12,900	4,900	989
1990	46,814	7,300	19,900	623	2	900	100	13,100	4,900	987
1991	43,536	6,600	18,200	541	1	800	100	12,600	4,700	915
1992	40,982	6,300	17,600	521	2	700	100	11,700	4,100	997
1993	41,893	6,400	18,300	553	3	800	100	11,500	4,200	994
1994	42,524	6,300	18,900	549	1	800	100	11,500	4,400	1,017
1995	43,363	6,400	19,000	514	(c)	800	100	12,100	4,400	1,032
1996	43,649	6,100	19,600	373	(c)	800	100	12,100	4,600	1,127
1997	43,458	5,900	19,900	371	(c)	800	100	12,000	4,400	1,118
1998	43,501	5,900	19,700	309	(c)	700	100	12,200	4,600	1,310
1999	42,401	6,100	18,600	314	1	800	100	11,800	4,700	1,436
2000	43,354	5,900	19,100	321	(c)	800	100	12,300	4,800	1,360
2001	43,788	6,100	18,800	324	3	800	100	12,800	4,900	1,345
2002	45,380	6,100	19,200	283	(c)	800	100	13,600	5,300	1,315
2003	44,757	6,000	19,300	245	(c)	800	100	13,100	5,200	1,417
2004	44,933	6,000	19,600	253	(c)	900	100	13,000	5,100	1,501
2005	45,343	6,100	19,000	250	(c)	1,000	100	13,600	5,300	1,676
2006	45,316	6,200	18,500	264	(c)	1,000	100	13,900	5,400	1,652
2007	43,945	6,000	17,700	211	(c)	900	100	13,800	5,200	1,914
2008	39,790	5,600	15,500	199	(c)	900	100	12,900	4,600	1,805
2009	36,216	5,300	14,100	154	(c)	800	100	11,700	4,100	1,731
2010	35,332	5,500	13,600	139	(c)	800	100	11,300	3,900	1,645
2011[f]	35,303	5,700	13,500	139	(c)	900	100	11,200	3,800	1,520
2012[f]	36,415	6,100	13,900	132	(c)	1,000	100	11,400	3,800	1,480
2013[g]	35,500	6,100	13,700	100	(c)	1,000	100	11,100	3,400	(c)
Changes in deaths										
2004 to 2013	-21%	2%	-30%	-60%	–	11%	0%	-15%	-33%	–
2012 to 2013	-3%	0%	-1%	-24%	–	0%	0%	-3%	-11%	–

Source: Total deaths from National Center for Health Statistics except 1964 and 2013, which are National Safety Council estimates based on data from the National Highway Traffic Safety Administration's Fatality Analysis Reporting System. Most totals by type are estimated and may not add to the total deaths. See Technical Appendix for comparability.

[a]*See definition, page 207. Nontraffic deaths are included in appropriate incident-type totals in the table. In 2011, 31% of the nontraffic deaths were pedestrians, while in 2012 pedestrians accounted for 35% of nontraffic deaths.*

[b]*Insufficient data for approximations.*

[c]*Data not available.*

[d]*1969 through 1986 totals are not comparable to previous years.*

[e]*Procedures and benchmarks for estimating deaths for certain types of incidents were changed for the 1990 edition. Estimates for 1987 and later years are not comparable to earlier years.*

[f]*Revised.*

[g]*Preliminary.*

Motor vehicle deaths by age, United States, 1913-2013

Year	All ages	Younger than 5 years	5-14 years	15-24 years	25-44 years	45-64 years	65-74 years	75 and older[a]
1913	4,200	300	1,100	600	1,100	800	300	
1914	4,700	300	1,200	700	1,200	900	400	
1915	6,600	400	1,500	1,000	1,700	1,400	600	
1916	8,200	600	1,800	1,300	2,100	1,700	700	
1917	10,200	700	2,400	1,400	2,700	2,100	900	
1918	10,700	800	2,700	1,400	2,500	2,300	1,000	
1919	11,200	900	3,000	1,400	2,500	2,100	1,300	
1920	12,500	1,000	3,300	1,700	2,800	2,300	1,400	
1921	13,900	1,100	3,400	1,800	3,300	2,700	1,600	
1922	15,300	1,100	3,500	2,100	3,700	3,100	1,800	
1923	18,400	1,200	3,700	2,800	4,600	3,900	2,200	
1924	19,400	1,400	3,800	2,900	4,700	4,100	2,500	
1925	21,900	1,400	3,900	3,600	5,400	4,800	2,800	
1926	23,400	1,400	3,900	3,900	5,900	5,200	3,100	
1927	25,800	1,600	4,000	4,300	6,600	5,800	3,500	
1928	28,000	1,600	3,800	4,900	7,200	6,600	3,900	
1929	31,200	1,600	3,900	5,700	8,000	7,500	4,500	
1930	32,900	1,500	3,600	6,200	8,700	8,000	4,900	
1931	33,700	1,500	3,600	6,300	9,100	8,200	5,000	
1932	29,500	1,200	2,900	5,100	8,100	7,400	4,800	
1933	31,363	1,274	3,121	5,649	8,730	7,947	4,642	
1934	36,101	1,210	3,182	6,561	10,232	9,530	5,386	
1935	36,369	1,253	2,951	6,755	10,474	9,562	5,374	
1936	38,089	1,324	3,026	7,184	10,807	10,089	5,659	
1937	39,643	1,303	2,991	7,800	10,877	10,475	6,197	
1938	32,582	1,122	2,511	6,016	8,772	8,711	5,450	
1939	32,386	1,192	2,339	6,318	8,917	8,292	5,328	
1940	34,501	1,176	2,584	6,846	9,362	8,882	5,651	
1941	39,969	1,378	2,838	8,414	11,069	9,829	6,441	
1942	28,309	1,069	1,991	5,932	7,747	7,254	4,316	
1943	23,823	1,132	1,959	4,522	6,454	5,996	3,760	
1944	24,282	1,203	2,093	4,561	6,514	5,982	3,929	
1945	28,076	1,290	2,386	5,358	7,578	6,794	4,670	
1946	33,411	1,568	2,508	7,445	8,955	7,532	5,403	
1947	32,697	1,502	2,275	7,251	8,775	7,468	5,426	
1948	32,259	1,635	2,337	7,218	8,702	7,190	3,173	2,004
1949	31,701	1,667	2,158	6,772	8,892	7,073	3,116	2,023
1950	34,763	1,767	2,152	7,600	10,214	7,728	3,264	2,038
1951	36,996	1,875	2,300	7,713	11,253	8,276	3,444	2,135
1952	37,794	1,951	2,295	8,115	11,380	8,463	3,472	2,118
1953	37,956	2,019	2,368	8,169	11,302	8,318	3,508	2,271
1954	35,586	1,864	2,332	7,571	10,521	7,848	3,247	2,203
1955	38,426	1,875	2,406	8,656	11,448	8,372	3,455	2,214
1956	39,628	1,770	2,640	9,169	11,551	8,573	3,657	2,268
1957	38,702	1,785	2,604	8,667	11,230	8,545	3,560	2,311
1958	36,981	1,791	2,710	8,388	10,414	7,922	3,535	2,221
1959	37,910	1,842	2,719	8,969	10,358	8,263	3,487	2,272
1960	38,137	1,953	2,814	9,117	10,189	8,294	3,457	2,313
1961	38,091	1,891	2,802	9,088	10,212	8,267	3,467	2,364
1962	40,804	1,903	3,028	10,157	10,701	8,812	3,696	2,507
1963	43,564	1,991	3,063	11,123	11,356	9,506	3,786	2,739
1964	47,700	2,120	3,430	12,400	12,500	10,200	4,150	2,900
1965	49,163	2,059	3,526	13,395	12,595	10,509	4,077	3,002
1966	53,041	2,182	3,869	15,298	13,282	11,051	4,217	3,142
1967	52,924	2,067	3,845	15,646	12,987	10,902	4,285	3,192
1968	54,862	1,987	4,105	16,543	13,602	11,031	4,261	3,333
1969	55,791	2,077	4,045	17,443	13,868	11,012	4,210	3,136
1970	54,633	1,915	4,159	16,720	13,446	11,099	4,084	3,210
1971	54,381	1,885	4,256	17,103	13,307	10,471	4,108	3,251
1972	56,278	1,896	4,258	17,942	13,758	10,836	4,138	3,450
1973	55,511	1,998	4,124	18,032	14,013	10,216	3,892	3,236
1974	46,402	1,546	3,332	15,905	11,834	8,159	3,071	2,555
1975	45,853	1,576	3,286	15,672	11,969	7,663	3,047	2,640
1976	47,038	1,532	3,175	16,650	12,112	7,770	3,082	2,717

See source and footnotes on page 137.

Motor vehicle deaths by age, United States, 1913-2013 (cont.)

Year	All ages	Younger than 5 years	5-14 years	15-24 years	25-44 years	45-64 years	65-74 years	75 and older[a]
1977	49,510	1,472	3,142	18,092	13,031	8,000	3,060	2,713
1978	52,411	1,551	3,130	19,164	14,574	8,048	3,217	2,727
1979	53,524	1,461	2,952	19,369	15,658	8,162	3,171	2,751
1980	53,172	1,426	2,747	19,040	16,133	8,022	2,991	2,813
1981	51,385	1,256	2,575	17,363	16,447	7,818	3,090	2,836
1982	45,779	1,300	2,301	15,324	14,469	6,879	2,825	2,681
1983	44,452	1,233	2,241	14,289	14,323	6,690	2,827	2,849
1984	46,263	1,138	2,263	14,738	15,036	6,954	3,020	3,114
1985	45,901	1,195	2,319	14,277	15,034	6,885	3,014	3,177
1986	47,865	1,188	2,350	15,227	15,844	6,799	3,096	3,361
1987	48,290	1,190	2,397	14,447	16,405	7,021	3,277	3,553
1988	49,078	1,220	2,423	14,406	16,580	7,245	3,429	3,775
1989	47,575	1,221	2,266	12,941	16,571	7,287	3,465	3,824
1990	46,814	1,123	2,059	12,607	16,488	7,282	3,350	3,905
1991	43,536	1,076	2,011	11,664	15,082	6,616	3,193	3,894
1992	40,982	1,020	1,904	10,305	14,071	6,597	3,247	3,838
1993	41,893	1,081	1,963	10,500	14,283	6,711	3,116	4,239
1994	42,524	1,139	2,026	10,660	13,966	7,097	3,385	4,251
1995	43,363	1,004	2,055	10,600	14,618	7,428	3,300	4,358
1996	43,649	1,035	1,980	10,576	14,482	7,749	3,419	4,408
1997	43,458	933	1,967	10,208	14,167	8,134	3,370	4,679
1998	43,501	921	1,868	10,026	14,095	8,416	3,410	4,765
1999	42,401	834	1,771	10,128	13,516	8,342	3,276	4,534
2000	43,354	819	1,772	10,560	13,811	8,867	3,038	4,487
2001	43,788	770	1,686	10,725	14,020	9,029	2,990	4,568
2002	45,380	733	1,614	11,459	14,169	9,701	3,113	4,591
2003	44,757	766	1,642	10,972	13,794	10,032	2,967	4,584
2004	44,933	778	1,653	10,987	13,699	10,369	2,974	4,473
2005	45,343	763	1,447	10,908	13,987	10,851	3,110	4,277
2006	45,316	728	1,339	11,015	14,025	11,133	2,916	4,160
2007	43,945	675	1,285	10,568	13,457	10,889	2,940	4,131
2008	39,790	566	1,027	8,946	12,242	10,457	2,826	3,726
2009	36,216	574	974	7,688	10,953	9,777	2,693	3,557
2010	35,332	528	890	7,250	10,491	9,727	2,676	3,770
2011[b]	35,303	520	881	7,105	10,352	9,866	2,913	3,666
2012[b]	36,415	531	820	7,062	10,933	10,270	3,112	3,687
2013[c]	35,500	600	700	6,600	10,900	10,100	3,100	3,500
Changes in deaths								
2004 to 2013	-21%	-23%	-58%	-40%	-20%	-3%	4%	-22%
2012 to 2013	-3%	13%	-15%	-7%	(d)	-2%	(d)	-5%

Source: 1913 to 1932 calculated from National Center for Health Statistics data for registration states; 1933 to 1963 and 1965 to 2012 are NCHS totals. All other figures are National Safety Council estimates. See Technical Appendix for comparability.

[a]Includes "age unknown." In 2011, these deaths numbered 4 and in 2012 they numbered 5.

[b]Revised.

[c]Preliminary.

[d]Less than 0.5%.

Motor vehicle death rates[a] by age, United States, 1913-2013

Year	All ages	Younger than 5 years	5-14 years	15-24 years	25-44 years	45-64 years	65-74 years	75 and older
1913	4.4	2.3	5.5	3.1	3.8	5.3	8.5	
1914	4.8	2.5	5.7	3.5	4.1	6.2	9.3	
1915	6.6	3.5	7.3	5.0	5.6	8.8	13.5	
1916	8.1	4.7	8.6	6.0	7.0	10.7	15.8	
1917	10.0	5.6	10.6	7.4	8.6	12.6	18.6	
1918	10.3	6.9	12.3	7.7	8.3	13.7	21.2	
1919	10.7	7.5	13.9	7.5	8.1	12.4	24.1	
1920	11.7	8.6	14.6	8.7	8.8	13.5	27.0	
1921	12.9	9.0	14.5	9.2	10.2	15.4	31.0	
1922	13.9	9.2	15.0	10.8	11.1	17.2	34.9	
1923	16.5	9.7	15.6	13.4	13.6	21.0	40.5	
1924	17.1	11.1	16.1	14.3	13.7	21.8	43.7	
1925	19.1	11.0	15.6	17.2	15.8	25.0	48.9	
1926	20.1	11.0	15.9	18.6	17.1	26.3	51.4	
1927	21.8	12.8	16.0	20.0	18.8	28.9	56.9	
1928	23.4	12.7	15.5	21.9	20.2	32.4	62.2	
1929	25.7	13.4	15.6	25.6	22.3	35.6	68.6	
1930	26.7	13.0	14.7	27.4	23.9	37.0	72.5	
1931	27.2	13.3	14.5	27.9	24.8	37.4	70.6	
1932	23.6	11.3	12.0	22.6	22.0	32.9	63.6	
1933	25.0	12.0	12.7	24.8	23.4	34.7	63.1	
1934	28.6	11.7	13.0	28.6	27.2	40.7	71.0	
1935	28.6	12.3	12.2	29.2	27.6	39.9	68.9	
1936	29.7	13.2	12.6	30.8	28.2	41.3	70.5	
1937	30.8	13.0	12.7	33.2	28.2	42.0	75.1	
1938	25.1	11.0	10.8	25.4	22.5	34.3	64.1	
1939	24.7	11.2	10.4	26.5	22.6	32.2	60.2	
1940	26.1	11.1	11.5	28.7	23.5	33.9	62.1	
1941	30.0	12.7	12.6	35.7	27.5	37.0	68.6	
1942	21.1	9.5	8.8	25.8	19.2	26.9	44.5	
1943	17.8	9.4	8.6	20.6	16.1	21.9	37.6	
1944	18.3	9.6	9.1	22.5	16.6	21.6	38.2	
1945	21.2	10.0	10.3	27.8	19.7	24.2	44.1	
1946	23.9	11.9	10.8	34.4	21.1	26.4	49.6	
1947	22.8	10.5	9.7	32.8	20.3	25.7	48.2	
1948	22.1	11.0	9.8	32.5	19.8	24.3	39.6	55.4
1949	21.3	10.7	9.0	30.7	19.9	23.4	37.8	53.9
1950	23.0	10.8	8.8	34.5	22.5	25.1	38.8	52.4
1951	24.1	10.9	9.2	36.0	24.7	26.5	39.5	53.0
1952	24.3	11.3	8.7	38.6	24.7	26.7	38.5	50.8
1953	24.0	11.5	8.5	39.1	24.5	25.8	37.7	52.6
1954	22.1	10.4	8.1	36.2	22.6	24.0	33.9	49.0
1955	23.4	10.2	8.0	40.9	24.5	25.2	35.1	47.1
1956	23.7	9.4	8.4	42.9	24.6	25.3	36.2	46.4
1957	22.7	9.2	8.0	39.7	23.9	24.8	34.4	45.5
1958	21.3	9.1	8.1	37.0	22.3	22.6	33.5	42.3
1959	21.5	9.1	7.9	38.2	22.2	23.2	32.3	41.8
1960	21.2	9.6	7.9	37.7	21.7	22.9	31.3	41.1
1961	20.8	9.2	7.6	36.5	21.8	22.5	30.7	40.5
1962	22.0	9.3	8.1	38.4	22.9	23.7	32.2	41.7
1963	23.1	9.8	8.0	40.0	24.3	25.2	32.6	44.3
1964	25.0	10.5	8.8	42.6	26.8	26.6	35.5	45.2
1965	25.4	10.4	8.9	44.2	27.0	27.0	34.6	45.4
1966	27.1	11.4	9.7	48.7	28.5	27.9	35.4	46.2
1967	26.8	11.2	9.5	48.4	27.8	27.1	35.6	45.4
1968	27.5	11.1	10.1	49.8	28.8	27.0	35.1	46.0
1969	27.7	12.0	9.9	50.7	29.1	26.6	34.3	42.0
1970	26.8	11.2	10.2	46.7	27.9	26.4	32.7	42.2
1971	26.3	10.9	10.5	45.7	27.4	24.7	32.4	41.3
1972	26.9	11.1	10.7	47.1	27.4	25.3	32.0	42.6
1973	26.3	11.9	10.5	46.3	27.2	23.6	29.4	39.1
1974	21.8	9.4	8.6	40.0	22.4	18.8	22.6	30.1
1975	21.3	9.8	8.6	38.7	22.1	17.5	21.9	30.1
1976	21.6	9.8	8.4	40.3	21.8	17.6	21.6	30.1

See source and footnotes on page 139.

Motor vehicle death rates^a by age, United States, 1913-2013 (cont.)

Year	All ages	Younger than 5 years	5-14 years	15-24 years	25-44 years	45-64 years	65-74 years	75 and older
1977	22.5	9.5	8.5	43.3	22.7	18.1	20.9	29.3
1978	23.6	9.9	8.6	45.4	24.6	18.2	21.5	28.7
1979	23.8	9.1	8.3	45.6	25.6	18.4	20.7	28.1
1980	23.4	8.7	7.9	44.8	25.5	18.0	19.1	28.0
1981	22.4	7.4	7.5	41.1	25.2	17.6	19.4	27.5
1982	19.8	7.5	6.7	36.8	21.5	15.5	17.5	25.2
1983	19.0	7.0	6.6	34.8	20.6	15.0	17.2	26.0
1984	19.6	6.4	6.7	36.4	21.0	15.6	18.2	27.7
1985	19.3	6.7	6.9	35.7	20.5	15.4	17.9	27.5
1986	19.9	6.6	7.0	38.5	21.0	15.2	18.1	28.3
1987	19.9	6.6	7.1	37.1	21.3	15.7	18.8	29.1
1988	20.1	6.7	7.1	37.8	21.2	15.9	19.5	30.2
1989	19.3	6.6	6.5	34.6	20.8	15.9	19.4	29.8
1990	18.8	6.0	5.8	34.2	20.4	15.7	18.5	29.7
1991	17.3	5.6	5.6	32.1	18.3	14.2	17.5	28.9
1992	16.1	5.2	5.2	28.5	17.1	13.6	17.6	27.8
1993	16.3	5.5	5.3	29.1	17.3	13.5	16.7	30.0
1994	16.3	5.8	5.4	29.5	16.8	13.9	18.1	29.4
1995	16.5	5.1	5.4	29.3	17.5	14.2	17.6	29.4
1996	16.5	5.4	5.2	29.2	17.3	14.4	18.3	29.0
1997	16.2	4.9	5.1	27.9	17.0	14.7	18.2	29.9
1998	16.1	4.9	4.8	26.9	16.9	14.7	18.5	29.8
1999	15.5	4.4	4.5	26.8	16.3	14.1	18.0	27.8
2000	15.7	4.3	4.5	27.5	16.8	14.5	16.7	27.0
2001	15.4	4.0	4.1	26.8	16.5	14.0	16.3	26.8
2002	15.8	3.7	3.9	28.2	16.8	14.6	17.0	26.5
2003	15.4	3.9	4.0	26.6	16.4	14.6	16.2	26.0
2004	15.3	3.9	4.1	26.4	16.3	14.7	16.1	25.1
2005	15.3	3.8	3.6	25.9	16.6	14.9	16.7	23.6
2006	15.2	3.6	3.3	26.1	16.8	14.9	15.4	22.7
2007	14.6	3.3	3.2	24.9	16.1	14.2	15.2	22.2
2008	13.1	2.7	2.5	20.8	14.7	13.4	14.0	20.0
2009	11.8	2.7	2.4	17.8	13.2	12.3	13.0	18.9
2010	11.4	2.5	2.2	16.8	12.6	12.0	12.5	19.9
2011^b	11.3	2.6	2.1	16.2	12.6	11.9	13.0	19.4
2012^b	11.6	2.7	2.0	16.1	13.2	12.4	13.8	19.2
2013^c	11.2	3.0	1.7	15.0	13.1	12.2	12.3	17.9
Changes in rates								
2004 to 2013	-27%	-23%	-59%	-43%	-20%	-17%	-24%	-29%
2012 to 2013	-3%	11%	-15%	-7%	-1%	-2%	-11%	-7%

Source: 1913 to 1932 calculated from National Center for Health Statistics data for registration states; 1933 to 1963 and 1965 to 2012 are NCHS totals. All other figures are National Safety Council estimates. See Technical Appendix for comparability.
^aDeath rates are deaths per 100,000 population in each group that were calculated using population data from the U.S. Census Bureau.
^bRevised.
^cPreliminary.

Home and Community

Weather

■ *Weather-related deaths down 4% in 2013.*

Deaths in 2013 are down 4% from 2012. A variety of weather events resulted in 586 deaths in the United States in 2013, compared with 613 deaths in 2012. Temperature extremes accounted for 22% of the deaths, snow and ice accounted for 18%, while floods accounted for 15%. Both 2012 and 2013 experienced typical levels of weather related deaths compared to 2011, which experienced a total of 1,012 deaths dominated by 587 tornado related deaths.

Data on weather-related deaths were compiled by t National Climatic Data Center (NCDC), which is part of National Oceanic and Atmospheric Administration. NCI data may differ from data based on death certificates t appear elsewhere in *Injury Facts*.

Weather-related deaths, United States, 2013

Event	Total	Jan.	Feb.	March	April	May	June	July	Aug.	Sept.	Oct.	Nov.	D
Total	586	48	34	23	27	89	65	119	38	21	27	38	
Thunderstorm/high winds	42	2	1	1	0	7	6	3	5	0	5	9	
Tornado	55	1	1	0	1	41	1	0	0	0	0	8	
Temperature extremes	129	12	3	1	0	1	13	80	11	2	0	2	
Ocean/lake surf/rip current	67	5	2	1	3	7	16	22	4	1	0	3	
Flood	85	3	1	2	6	28	5	5	8	10	8	1	
Lightning	25	0	0	0	1	5	2	7	4	6	0	0	
Avalanche	21	5	1	4	9	0	0	0	0	0	0	0	
Wild/forest fire	21	0	0	0	0	0	19	0	1	0	0	0	
Hurricane/tropical storm	1	0	0	0	0	0	1	0	0	0	6	12	
Snow/ice	104	17	20	9	5	0	0	0	0	0	1	1	
Fog	15	2	5	3	1		1	2	3	1	4	1	
Precipitation							0	0	0	0	0	0	

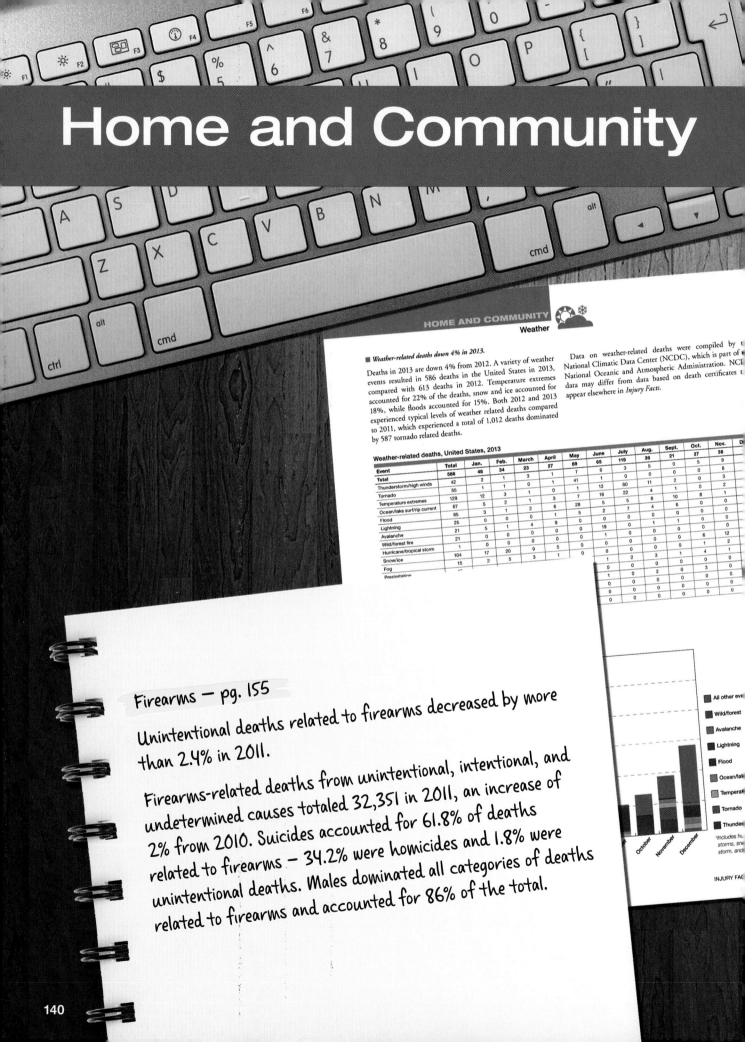

All other eve
Wild/forest
Avalanche
Lightning
Flood
Ocean/lal
Temperat
Tornado
Thunder

*Includes hu
storms, sne
storm, and

INJURY FAC

October November December

Firearms — pg. 155

Unintentional deaths related to firearms decreased by more than 2.4% in 2011.

Firearms-related deaths from unintentional, intentional, and undetermined causes totaled 32,351 in 2011, an increase of 2% from 2010. Suicides accounted for 61.8% of deaths related to firearms — 34.2% were homicides and 1.8% were unintentional deaths. Males dominated all categories of deaths related to firearms and accounted for 86% of the total.

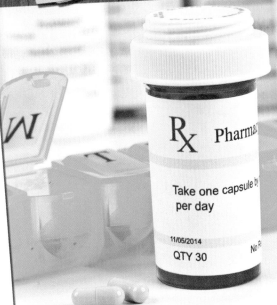

National Safety Council

The home and community venue is the combination of the home class and the public class. Home and community, together with the occupational and transportation venues, make up the totality of unintentional injuries. Home and community includes all unintentional injuries that are not work-related and do not involve motor vehicles on streets and highways.

In 2013, an estimated 93,200 unintentional-injury-related deaths occurred in the home and community venue, or 71% of all unintentional-injury-related deaths that year. The number of deaths was up about 4% from the revised 2012 total of 89,400. An additional 30,600,000 people suffered nonfatal medically consulted injuries. The death rate per 100,000 population was 29.5 – about 3% higher than the revised 2012 rate.

About 1 out of 11 people experienced an unintentional injury in the home and community venue, and about 1 out of 3,500 people died from such an injury, in 2013. About 39% of the deaths and injuries involved workers while they were away from work (off the job).

The graph on the next page shows the five leading causes of unintentional-injury-related deaths in the home and community venue and the broad age groups (children, youths and adults, and the elderly) affected by them. This is one way to prioritize issues in this venue. Below is a graph of the trend in deaths and death rates from 1999 to present. Similar graphs for the home and public classes appear on pages 144 and 148.

The National Safety Council adopted the Bureau of Labor Statistics' Census of Fatal Occupational Injuries count for work-related unintentional injuries beginning with 1992 data. Because of the lower work class total resulting from this change, adjustments were made to the home and public classes. Long-term historical comparisons for these three classes should be made with caution. Also, beginning with 1999 data, deaths are now classified according to the 10th revision of the *International Classification of Diseases*. Caution should be used in comparing data classified under the 10th revision with prior revisions. See the Technical Appendix for more information about both changes.

Deaths **93,200**
Medically consulted injuries **30,600,000**
Death rate per 100,000 population **29.5**
Costs .... **$350.3 billion**

Home and community deaths and death rates, United States, 1999-2013

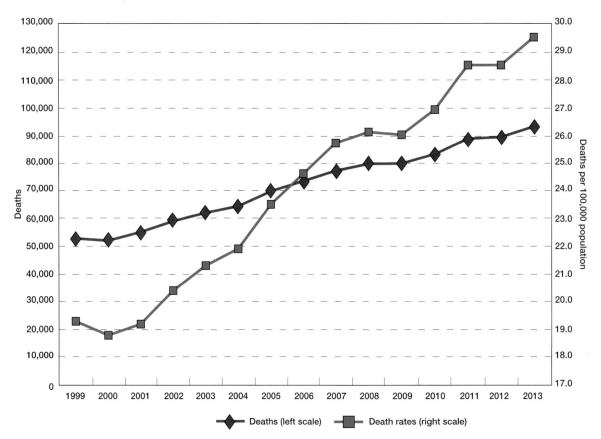

Leading causes of unintentional-injury-related deaths in home and community, United States, 2013

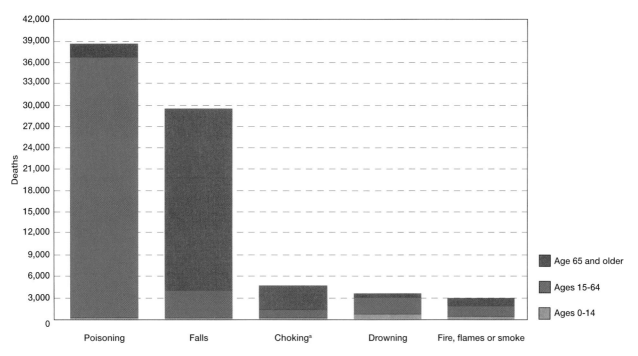

Deaths

	Age 65 and older
	Ages 15-64
	Ages 0-14

Poisoning   Falls   Choking^a   Drowning   Fire, flames or smoke

^aInhalation and ingestion of food or other object that obstructs breathing.

Causes of unintentional-injury-related deaths in home and community, United States, 2013

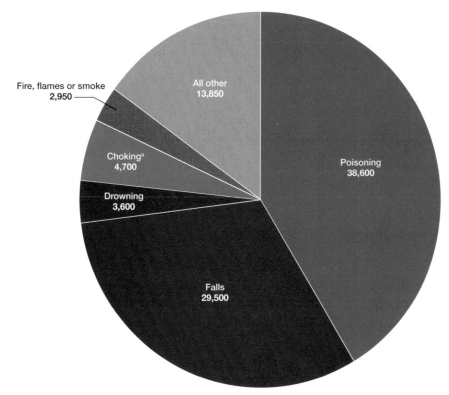

Fire, flames or smoke
2,950

All other
13,850

Choking^a
4,700

Drowning
3,600

Poisoning
38,600

Falls
29,500

^aInhalation and ingestion of food or other object that obstructs breathing.

Between 1912 and 2013, unintentional-home-injury-related deaths per 100,000 population were reduced 25% from 28 to 20.9 (after adjusting for the 1948 classification change). In 1912, when there were 21 million households, an estimated 26,000 to 28,000 people were killed by unintentional-home-related injuries. In 2013, with 122 million households and the population tripled, home-related deaths numbered 66,000. However, the number and rate of unintentional-home-injury-related deaths has been steadily increasing since 2000. This increase in deaths is largely driven by increases in both unintentional poisonings and falls.

The injury total of 19,900,000 means that 1 person in 16 in the United States experienced an unintentional injury in the home in 2013 that was serious enough to consult with a medical professional. The number of medically consulted injuries

occurring in the home is nearly equal to the total number of medically consulted injuries that occur in public places, the workplace, and motor vehicle crashes combined. The National Health Interview Survey estimates that about 52% of all medically attended injuries occurred at home.

The National Safety Council adopted the Bureau of Labor Statistics' Census of Fatal Occupational Injuries count for work-related unintentional injuries beginning with 1992 data. This affected long-term historical comparisons for the work, home, and public classes. Beginning with 1999 data, deaths are classified according to the 10th revision of the *International Classification of Diseases*. Caution should be used in comparing current data with data classified under prior revisions. See the Technical Appendix for more information.

Deaths	66,000
Medically consulted injuries	19,900,000
Death rate per 100,000 population	20.9
Costs	$226.1 billion

Home deaths and death rates, United States, 1999-2013

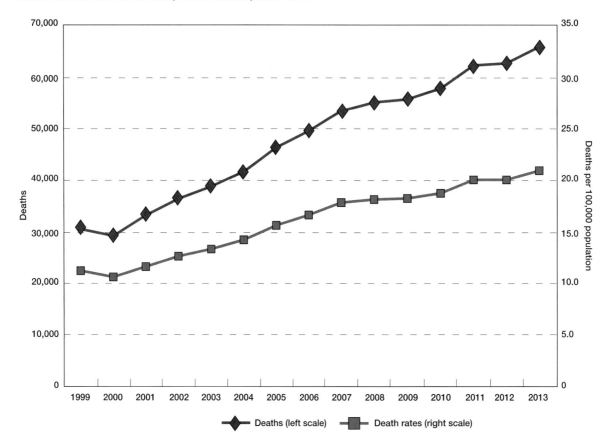

Principal types of unintentional-home-related injury deaths, United States, 1987-2013

Year	Total home	Poisoning	Falls	Fire, flames, or smoke[a]	Choking[b]	Mechanical suffocation	Drowning	Natural heat or cold	Firearms	Other
1987	21,400	4,100	6,300	3,900	2,500	600	700	(c)	800	2,500
1988	22,700	4,800	6,600	4,100	2,600	600	700	(c)	800	2,500
1989	22,500	5,000	6,600	3,900	2,500	600	700	(c)	800	2,400
1990	21,500	4,500	6,700	3,400	2,300	600	900	(c)	800	2,300
1991	22,100	5,000	6,900	3,400	2,200	700	900	(c)	800	2,200
1992	24,000	5,200	7,700	3,700	1,500	700	900	(c)	1,000	3,300
1993	26,100	6,500	7,900	3,700	1,700	700	900	(c)	1,100	3,600
1994	26,300	6,800	8,100	3,700	1,600	800	900	(c)	900	3,500
1995	27,200	7,000	8,400	3,500	1,500	800	900	(c)	900	4,200
1996	27,500	7,300	9,000	3,500	1,500	800	900	(c)	800	3,700
1997	27,700	7,800	9,100	3,200	1,500	800	900	(c)	700	3,500
1998	29,000	8,400	9,500	2,900	1,800	800	1,000	(c)	600	4,000
1999[d]	30,500	9,300	7,600	3,000	1,900	1,100	900	700	600	5,400
2000	29,200	9,800	7,100	2,700	2,100	1,000	1,000	400	500	4,600
2001	33,200	11,300	8,600	3,000	2,000	1,100	900	400	600	5,300
2002	36,400	13,900	9,700	2,800	1,900	1,100	900	400	500	5,200
2003	38,800	15,900	10,300	2,900	2,100	1,000	800	400	500	4,900
2004	41,700	17,500	11,300	2,900	2,200	1,200	900	400	400	4,900
2005	46,400	20,000	12,000	2,900	2,300	1,300	900	500	500	6,000
2006	49,600	23,300	12,800	2,800	2,300	1,400	1,000	600	400	5,000
2007	53,500	25,800	14,200	3,000	2,100	1,400	1,000	500	400	5,100
2008	55,200	26,800	15,100	2,600	2,300	1,500	900	400	400	5,200
2009	55,800	27,500	15,700	2,600	2,300	1,300	1,000	500	400	4,500
2010	57,900	28,800	16,500	2,500	2,200	1,400	1,000	600	400	4,500
2011[e]	62,400	31,400	17,400	2,400	2,500	1,400	900	700	400	5,300
2012[e]	62,800	31,400	17,900	2,300	2,600	1,400	1,000	500	400	5,300
2013[f]	66,000	33,600	19,000	2,200	2,500	1,500	1,000	600	400	5,200

Source: National Safety Council estimates based on National Center for Health Statistics (NCHS)–Mortality Data compiled from data provided by the 57 vital statistics jurisdictions through the Vital Statistics Cooperative Program. Rates are National Safety Council estimates based on data from NCHS. The Council adopted the Bureau of Labor Statistics Census of Fatal Occupational Injuries count for work-related unintentional injuries retroactive to 1992 data. Because of the lower work class total resulting from this change, several thousand unintentional-injury-related deaths that had been classified by the Council as work-related had to be reassigned to the home and public classes. For this reason, long-term historical comparisons for these three classes should be made with caution. See the Technical Appendix for an explanation of the methodological changes.
[a]*Includes deaths resulting from conflagration, regardless of nature of injury.*
[b]*Inhalation and ingestion of food or other object that obstructs breathing.*
[c]*Included in "Other."*
[d]*In 1999, a revision was made in the* International Classification of Diseases. *See the Technical Appendix for comparability with earlier years.*
[e]*Revised.*
[f]*Preliminary.*

Principal types of home unintentional-injury-related deaths, United States, 2013

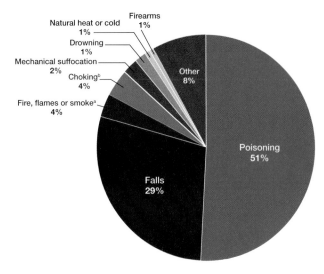

Firearms 1%
Natural heat or cold 1%
Drowning 1%
Mechanical suffocation 2%
Choking[b] 4%
Fire, flames or smoke[a] 4%
Other 8%
Poisoning 51%
Falls 29%

[a]*Includes deaths resulting from conflagration, regardless of nature of injury.*
[b]*Inhalation and ingestion of food or other object that obstructs breathing.*

Type of event and age of victim

All home

Includes deaths in the home and on home premises to occupants, guests, and trespassers. Also includes hired household workers but excludes other people working on home premises.

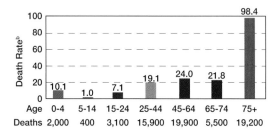

	Total	Change from 2012	Death rate[a]
Deaths	66,000	+5%	20.9

Age	0-4	5-14	15-24	25-44	45-64	65-74	75+
Death Rate[b]	10.1	1.0	7.1	19.1	24.0	21.8	98.4
Deaths	2,000	400	3,100	15,900	19,900	5,500	19,200

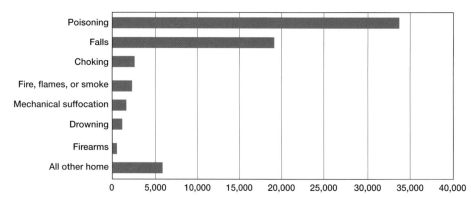

Poisoning

Includes deaths from drugs, medicines, other solid and liquid substances, and gases and vapors. Excludes poisonings from spoiled foods, *Salmonella*, etc., which are classified as disease deaths.

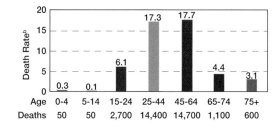

	Total	Change from 2012	Death rate[a]
Deaths	33,600	+7%	10.6

Age	0-4	5-14	15-24	25-44	45-64	65-74	75+
Death Rate[b]	0.3	0.1	6.1	17.3	17.7	4.4	3.1
Deaths	50	50	2,700	14,400	14,700	1,100	600

Falls

Includes deaths from falls from one level to another or on the same level in the home or on home premises.

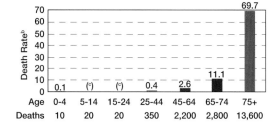

	Total	Change from 2012	Death rate[a]
Deaths	19,000	+6%	6.0

Age	0-4	5-14	15-24	25-44	45-64	65-74	75+
Death Rate[b]	0.1	(c)	(c)	0.4	2.6	11.1	69.7
Deaths	10	20	20	350	2,200	2,800	13,600

Fire, flames, or smoke

Includes deaths from fires, burns, and injuries in conflagrations in the home – such as asphyxiation, falls, and struck by falling objects. Excludes burns from hot objects or liquids.

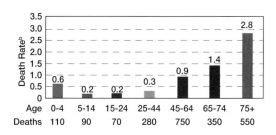

	Total	Change from 2012	Death rate[a]
Deaths	2,200	-4%	0.7

Age	0-4	5-14	15-24	25-44	45-64	65-74	75+
Death Rate[b]	0.6	0.2	0.2	0.3	0.9	1.4	2.8
Deaths	110	90	70	280	750	350	550

See footnotes on page 147.

Type of event and age of victim

Choking

Includes deaths from unintentional ingestion or inhalation of objects or food resulting in the obstruction of respiratory passages.

	Total	Change from 2012	Death rate[a]
Deaths	2,500	-4%	0.8

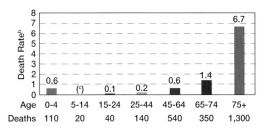

Mechanical suffocation

Includes deaths from smothering by bed clothes, thin plastic materials, etc.; suffocation by cave-ins or confinement in closed spaces; and mechanical strangulation or hanging.

	Total	Change from 2012	Death rate[a]
Deaths	1,500	+7%	0.5

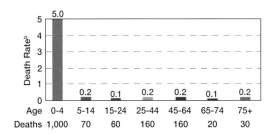

Drowning

Includes drownings of people in or on home premises – such as in swimming pools and bathtubs. Excludes drowning in floods and other cataclysms.

	Total	Change from 2012	Death rate[a]
Deaths	1,000	0%	0.3

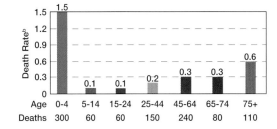

Firearms

Includes firearms injuries in or on home premises – such as while cleaning or playing with guns. Excludes deaths from explosive materials.

	Total	Change from 2012	Death rate[a]
Deaths	400	0%	0.1

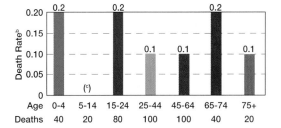

All other home

Most important types included are natural heat and cold, struck by or against objects, machinery, and electric current.

	Total	Change from 2012	Death rate[a]
Deaths	5,800	0%	1.8

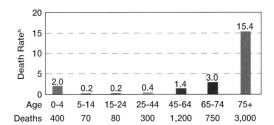

[a]Deaths per 100,000 population.
[b]Deaths per 100,000 population in each age group.
[c]Death rate less than 0.05.

Between 1912 and 2013, public unintentional-injury-related deaths per 100,000 population were reduced 71% from 30 to 8.6 (after adjusting for the 1948 change in classification). In 1912, an estimated 28,000 to 30,000 people died from public non-motor vehicle injuries. In 2013, with the population tripled, and travel and recreational activity greatly increased, 27,200 people died from public unintentional injuries and 10,700,000 suffered injuries serious enough to consult a medical professional. The public class excludes deaths and injuries involving motor vehicles and people at work or at home.

In 2013, the number of public unintentional-injury-related deaths was up 2.3% from the revised 2012 figure of 26,600. The 2013 death rate per 100,000 population increased slightly from 8.5 in 2012 to 8.6.

With an estimated 10,700,000 medically consulted unintentional injuries occurring in public places and a population of over 316 million people, on average about 1 person in 30 experienced such an injury.

The National Safety Council adopted the Bureau of Labor Statistics' Census of Fatal Occupational Injuries count for work-related unintentional-injuries beginning with 1992 data. This affected long-term historical comparisons for the work, home, and public classes. Beginning with 1999 data, deaths are classified according to the 10th revision of the *International Classification of Diseases*. Caution should be used in comparing current data with data classified under prior revisions. See the Technical Appendix for more information.

Deaths...	**27,200**
Medically consulted injuries..	**10,700,000**
Death rate per 100,000 population	**8.6**
Costs	**$124.2 billion**

Public deaths and death rates, United States, 1999-2013

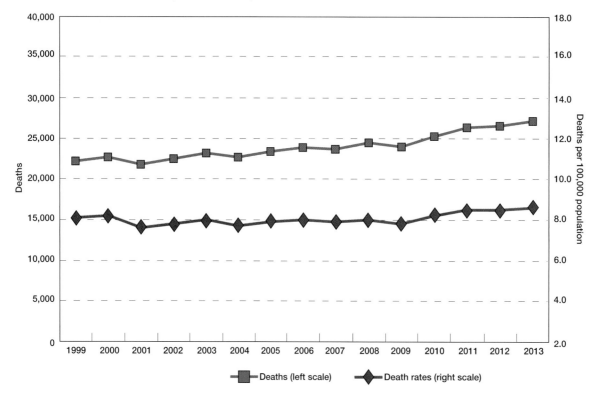

Principal types of public unintentional-injury-related deaths, United States, 1987-2013

Year	Total public[a]	Falls	Poisoning	Drowning	Choking[g]	Fire, flames, or smoke	Firearms	Air transport	Water transport	Rail transport[b]	Mechanical suffocation
1987	18,400	4,000	800	3,200	1,100	500	600	900	800	400	([c])
1988	18,400	4,100	900	3,100	1,100	500	600	700	800	400	([c])
1989	18,200	4,200	900	3,000	1,000	500	600	800	700	400	([c])
1990	17,400	4,300	900	2,800	1,000	400	500	700	800	400	([c])
1991	17,600	4,500	1,000	2,800	900	400	600	700	700	500	([c])
1992	19,000	4,400	1,700	2,500	1,600	200	400	700	700	600	([c])
1993	19,700	4,600	1,900	2,800	1,500	200	400	600	700	600	([c])
1994	19,600	4,700	2,100	2,400	1,500	200	400	600	600	600	([c])
1995	20,100	5,000	2,000	2,800	1,600	200	300	600	700	500	([c])
1996	21,000	5,300	2,100	2,500	1,700	200	300	700	600	500	([c])
1997	21,700	5,600	2,300	2,600	1,700	200	300	500	600	400	([c])
1998	22,600	6,000	2,300	2,900	1,700	200	300	500	600	500	([c])
1999[d]	22,200	4,800	2,800	2,600	2,000	200	300	500	600	400	500
2000	22,700	5,500	2,900	2,400	2,200	200	200	500	500	400	300
2001	21,800	5,600	2,700	2,400	2,100	200	200	700	500	400	300
2002	22,500	5,900	3,600	2,500	2,200	300	200	500	500	400	300
2003	23,200	6,300	3,400	2,400	2,200	300	200	600	500	400	300
2004	22,700	6,700	3,400	2,400	2,200	200	200	400	500	400	200
2005	23,400	6,800	3,500	2,600	2,100	([c])	([c])	400	500	400	200
2006	23,900	7,200	4,100	2,500	2,100	([c])	([c])	400	400	400	200
2007	23,700	7,600	3,900	2,400	2,200	([c])	([c])	400	400	400	200
2008	24,500	8,200	4,200	2,500	2,100	([c])	([c])	400	300	400	200
2009	24,000	8,500	4,200	2,400	2,100	([c])	([c])	400	400	300	200
2010	25,300	8,900	4,100	2,700	2,300	([c])	([c])	300	300	400	200
2011[e]	26,400	9,400	4,700	2,600	2,200	([c])	([c])	300	500	300	200
2012[e]	26,600	10,100	4,800	2,500	2,100	([c])	([c])	300	400	300	200
2013[f]	27,200	10,500	5,000	2,600	2,200	([c])	([c])	300	400	300	200

Source: National Safety Council estimates based on data from the National Center for Health Statistics. The Council adopted the Bureau of Labor Statistics Census of Fatal Occupational Injuries count for work-related unintentional injuries retroactive to 1992 data. Because of the lower work class total resulting from this change, several thousand unintentional-injury-related deaths that had been classified by the Council as work-related had to be reassigned to the home and public classes. For this reason, long-term historical comparisons for these three classes should be made with caution. See the Technical Appendix for an explanation of the methodological changes.
[a]Includes some deaths not shown separately.
[b]Includes subways and elevateds.
[c]Estimates not available.
[d]In 1999, a revision was made in the International Classification of Diseases. See the Technical Appendix for comparability with earlier years.
[e]Revised.
[f]Preliminary.
[g]Inhalation and ingestion of food or other object that obstructs breathing.

Principal types of public unintentional-injury-related deaths, United States, 2013

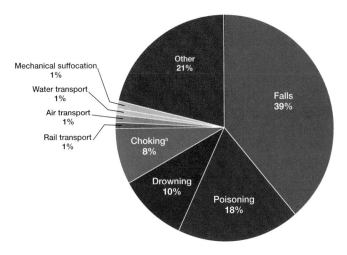

Mechanical suffocation 1%
Water transport 1%
Air transport 1%
Rail transport 1%
Other 21%
Falls 39%
Choking[a] 8%
Drowning 10%
Poisoning 18%

[a]Inhalation and ingestion of food or other object that obstructs breathing.

Type of event and age of victim

All public

Includes deaths in public places and not involving motor vehicles. Most sports, recreation, and transportation deaths are included. Excludes work deaths.

	Total	Change from 2012	Death rate[a]
Deaths	27,200	+2%	8.6

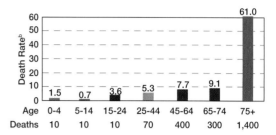

Age	0-4	5-14	15-24	25-44	45-64	65-74	75+
	1.5	0.7	3.6	5.3	7.7	9.1	61.0
Deaths	10	10	10	70	400	300	1,400

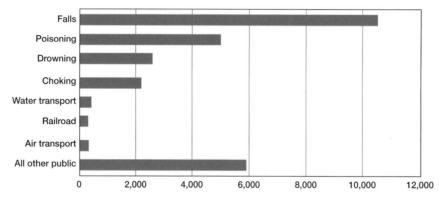

Falls

Includes deaths from falls from one level to another or on the same level in public places. Excludes deaths from falls from moving vehicles.

	Total	Change from 2012	Death rate[a]
Deaths	10,500	+4%	3.3

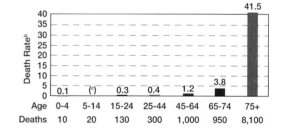

Age	0-4	5-14	15-24	25-44	45-64	65-74	75+
	0.1	(c)	0.3	0.4	1.2	3.8	41.5
Deaths	10	20	130	300	1,000	950	8,100

Poisoning

Includes deaths from drugs, medicines, other solid and liquid substances, and gases and vapors. Excludes poisonings from spoiled foods.

	Total	Change from 2012	Death rate[a]
Deaths	5,000	+4%	1.6

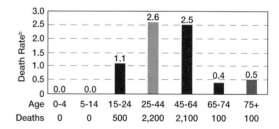

Age	0-4	5-14	15-24	25-44	45-64	65-74	75+
	0.0	0.0	1.1	2.6	2.5	0.4	0.5
Deaths	0	0	500	2,200	2,100	100	100

Drowning

Includes drownings of people swimming or playing in water, or falling into water, except on home premises or at work. Excludes drownings involving boats, which are included in water transportation.

	Total	Change from 2012	Death rate[a]
Deaths	2,600	+4%	0.8

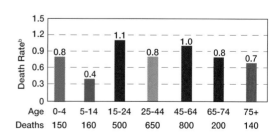

Age	0-4	5-14	15-24	25-44	45-64	65-74	75+
	0.8	0.4	1.1	0.8	1.0	0.8	0.7
Deaths	150	160	500	650	800	200	140

See footnotes on page 151.

Type of event and age of victim

Choking

Includes deaths from unintentional ingestion or inhalation of food or other objects resulting in the obstruction of respiratory passages.

	Total	Change from 2012	Death rate[a]
Deaths	2,200	+5%	0.7

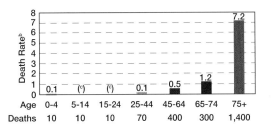

Age	0-4	5-14	15-24	25-44	45-64	65-74	75+
Deaths	10	10	10	70	400	300	1,400

Railroad

Includes deaths arising from railroad vehicles in motion (except involving motor vehicles), subway and elevated trains, and people boarding or alighting from standing trains. Excludes crews and people traveling in the course of employment.

	Total	Change from 2012	Death rate[a]
Deaths	300	0%	0.1

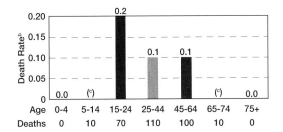

Age	0-4	5-14	15-24	25-44	45-64	65-74	75+
Deaths	0	10	70	110	100	10	0

Water transport

Includes deaths in water transport incidents from falls, burns, etc., as well as drownings. Excludes crews and people traveling in the course of employment.

	Total	Change from 2012	Death rate[a]
Deaths	400	0%	0.1

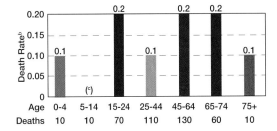

Age	0-4	5-14	15-24	25-44	45-64	65-74	75+
Deaths	10	10	70	110	130	60	10

Air transport

Includes deaths in private flying, passengers in commercial aviation, and deaths of military personnel in the United States. Excludes crews and people traveling in the course of employment.

	Total	Change from 2012	Death rate[a]
Deaths	300	0%	0.1

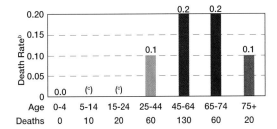

Age	0-4	5-14	15-24	25-44	45-64	65-74	75+
Deaths	0	10	20	60	130	60	20

All other public

Most important types included are mechanical suffocation; excessive natural heat or cold; firearms; fires, flames, or smoke; and machinery.

	Total	Change from 2012	Death rate[a]
Deaths	5,900	-3%	1.9

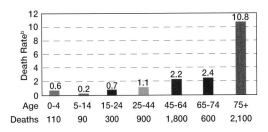

Age	0-4	5-14	15-24	25-44	45-64	65-74	75+
Deaths	110	90	300	900	1,800	600	2,100

[a]Deaths per 100,000 population.
[b]Deaths per 100,000 population in each age group.
[c]Rate less than 0.05.

Sports and Recreational Injuries

■ *In the United States in 2013, bicycle riding and basketball injuries each resulted in more than half a million emergency department visits.*

The table below shows estimates of the number of injuries treated in hospital emergency departments associated with various sports and recreational activities. Because this list of sports is not complete and the frequency and duration of participation is not known, no inference should be made concerning the relative hazard of these sports or rank with respect to risk of injury. Since currently available sports participation estimates do not provide a valid estimate of exposure risk, they are inappropriate for use in rate calculations. Because of this limitation, they are not included in the table below.

Sport injuries, United States, 2013

Sport or activity	Injuries	\multicolumn{5}{c}{Percent of injuries by age}
		Younger than 5	5-14	15-24	25-64	65 or older
Archery	5,153	1.6	15.7	23.4	49.8	9.4
Baseball	143,784	2.2	50.2	26.8	19.8	0.9
Softball	100,010	0.3	30.5	30.9	37.1	1.2
Basketball	533,509	0.4	32.8	47.8	18.8	0.2
Bicycle riding[a]	521,578	4.6	33.4	18.3	39.0	4.7
Billiards, pool	3,698	9.4	25.2	10.8	49.5	5.1
Bowling	16,982	11.9	15.1	11.3	50.6	11.1
Boxing	19,675	0.1	6.3	46.6	46.1	0.9
Cheerleading	36,311	0.1	52.4	47.0	0.5	0.0
Exercise[b]	365,797	1.5	10.6	20.6	56.0	11.3
Fishing	70,541	3.3	16.7	16.6	50.3	13.1
Football	420,581	0.3	51.2	39.5	8.9	0.1
Golf[c]	33,101	1.7	13.7	7.6	39.2	37.8
Gymnastics[d]	36,001	3.0	74.0	17.6	4.6	0.7
Hockey, field	4,241	0.0	25.3	61.6	13.1	0.0
Horseback riding	54,609	1.2	16.9	23.1	53.1	5.6
Horseshoe pitching	1,449	5.4	6.9	12.4	64.7	10.6
Ice hockey	16,871	0.0	37.3	40.4	21.2	1.0
Ice skating[e]	20,443	0.6	47.0	21.7	28.3	2.4
Martial arts	34,395	0.5	29.0	27.8	42.4	0.3
Mountain biking	9,763	0.8	6.5	19.7	70.9	2.1
Mountain climbing	4,307	0.0	17.3	36.2	43.8	2.7
Racquetball, squash & paddleball	4,411	1.9	11.2	32.7	46.4	7.9
Roller skating[f]	57,743	0.8	53.5	12.3	32.9	0.4
Rugby	13,567	0.0	7.3	76.8	15.9	0.0
Scuba diving[g]	1,437	5.0	10.3	22.6	55.2	6.9
Skateboarding	120,424	1.0	35.1	51.3	12.4	0.2
Snowboarding	38,630	0.4	23.8	51.4	24.1	0.3
Snowmobiling	9,270	0.0	7.2	23.3	69.1	0.4
Soccer	229,088	0.8	44.6	37.8	16.4	0.3
Swimming[h]	184,190	9.2	41.7	17.0	27.8	4.4
Tennis	19,292	0.5	16.2	16.3	41.3	25.7
Track & field	29,296	0.0	41.3	43.3	13.8	1.7
Volleyball	50,845	0.0	31.9	44.0	23.1	0.9
Water skiing	5,114	0.0	8.4	43.1	47.6	0.9
Weight lifting	110,188	2.8	8.6	35.8	49.3	3.6
Wrestling	42,633	0.0	42.2	53.4	4.4	0.0

Source: Consumer Product Safety Commission; figures include only injuries treated in hospital emergency departments.
[a]*Excludes mountain biking.*
[b]*Includes exercise equipment (60,546 injuries) and exercise activity (305,251 injuries).*
[c]*Excludes golf carts (15,193 injuries).*
[d]*Excludes trampolines (83,665 injuries).*
[e]*Excludes 7,491 injuries in skating, unspecified.*
[f]*Includes roller skating (46,023 injuries) and in-line skating (11,720 injuries).*
[g]*Data for 2012.*
[h]*Includes injuries associated with swimming, swimming pools, diving or diving boards, and swimming pool equipment.*

Over the past 15 years, the use of cell phones has increased 8-fold in the United States. Research has shown that mobile phone use by pedestrians reduces their situational awareness and distracts their attention in a way similar to its effect on drivers, resulting in unsafe behaviors when talking or texting while walking. A recent study examined National Electronic Injury Surveillance System (NEISS) emergency department (ED) report data from the Consumer Product Safety Commission to describe and quantify injuries and deaths among ambulatory cell phone users between 2000 and 2011. During this time span, an estimated 11,101 injuries resulted from phone-induced distraction while walking.

The majority of patients were female (68%), and most were 40 years old or younger (54%, see chart below). Talking on the phone was the most prevalent activity at the time of injury (62%), while texting accounted for another 12%. Nearly 80% of the injuries occurred as the result of a fall and another 9%

from the pedestrian striking a motionless object (see chart below). The most common injury types included dislocation or fracture (25%), sprain or strain (24%), and concussion or contusion (23%). Over half (52%) of the injuries took place at home (see chart below) and 85% of patients were treated and released from the ED.

National estimates exhibited a statistically significant upward trend in estimated ED visits from 2001 to 2011 (see chart below). Comparisons of the overall trend in the number of cell phone connections and the cell-phone-related distraction injuries showed that the number of injuries per cell phone connection increased approximately 2-fold during the study period.

Source: Smith, D.C., Schreiber, K.M., Saltos, A., Lichenstein, S.B., & Lichenstein, R. (2013, December). Ambulatory cell phone injuries in the United States— An emerging national concern. Journal of Safety Research, 47, 19-23.

Percentages of cell-phone-related injuries by selected demographics, United States, 2000-2011

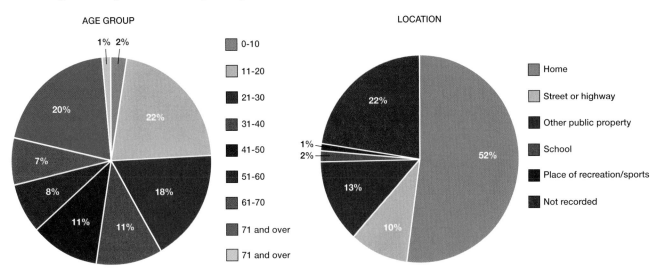

National estimates for cell-phone-related distraction injuries derived from NEISS database, United States, 2000-2011

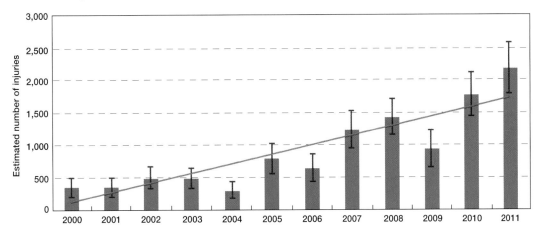

Note: error bars indicate standard deviations.

■ *Weather-related deaths down 4% in 2013.*

Deaths in 2013 are down 4% from 2012. A variety of weather events resulted in 586 deaths in the United States in 2013, compared with 613 deaths in 2012. Temperature extremes accounted for 22% of the deaths, snow and ice accounted for 18%, while floods accounted for 15%. Both 2012 and 2013 experienced typical levels of weather related deaths compared to 2011, which experienced a total of 1,012 deaths dominated by 587 tornado related deaths.

Data on weather-related deaths were compiled by the National Climatic Data Center (NCDC), which is part of the National Oceanic and Atmospheric Administration. NCDC data may differ from data based on death certificates that appear elsewhere in *Injury Facts*.

Weather-related deaths, United States, 2013

Event	Total	Jan.	Feb.	March	April	May	June	July	Aug.	Sept.	Oct.	Nov.	Dec.
Total	586	48	34	23	27	89	65	119	38	21	27	38	57
Thunderstorm/high winds	42	2	1	3	1	7	6	3	5	0	5	9	0
Tornado	55	1	1	0	1	41	1	0	0	0	0	8	2
Temperature extremes	129	12	3	1	0	1	13	80	11	2	0	3	3
Ocean/lake surf/rip current	67	5	2	1	3	7	16	22	4	1	0	2	4
Flood	85	3	1	2	6	28	5	5	8	10	8	1	8
Lightning	25	0	0	0	1	5	2	7	4	6	0	0	0
Avalanche	21	5	1	4	9	0	0	0	0	0	0	0	2
Wild/forest fire	21	0	0	0	0	0	19	0	1	1	0	0	0
Hurricane/tropical storm	1	0	0	0	0	0	1	0	0	0	0	0	0
Snow/ice	104	17	20	9	5	0	0	0	0	0	6	12	35
Fog	15	2	5	3	1	0	0	0	0	0	1	2	1
Precipitation	15	1	0	0	0	0	1	2	3	1	4	1	2
Drought	0	0	0	0	0	0	0	0	0	0	0	0	0
Dust storm	6	0	0	0	0	0	1	0	2	0	3	0	0
Funnel cloud	0	0	0	0	0	0	0	0	0	0	0	0	0
Hail	0	0	0	0	0	0	0	0	0	0	0	0	0
Waterspout	0	0	0	0	0	0	0	0	0	0	0	0	0

Source: National Safety Council analysis of National Climatic Data Center data.

Weather-related fatalities by month, United States, 2013

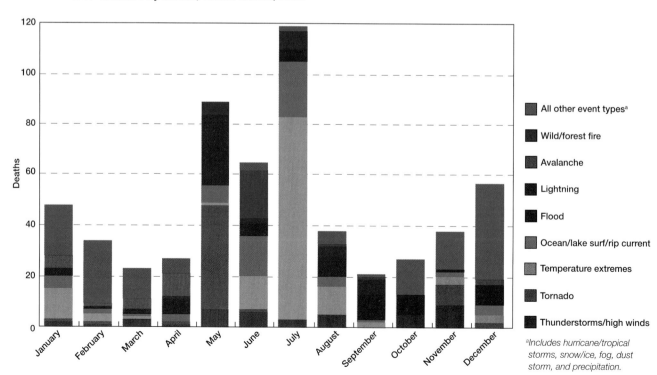

aIncludes hurricane/tropical storms, snow/ice, fog, dust storm, and precipitation.

■ *Unintentional firearms-related deaths were down more than 2% in 2011.*

Firearms-related deaths from unintentional, intentional, and undetermined causes totaled 32,351 in 2011, an increase of 2% from 2010. Suicides accounted for 61.8% of deaths related to firearms – 34.2% were homicides and 1.8% were unintentional deaths. Males dominated all categories of deaths related to firearms and accounted for 86% of the total.

The number of homicide deaths related to firearms decreased by less than 0.5% from 2010 to 2011, representing the fifth consecutive annual decline. Unintentional deaths related to firearms decreased by more than 2.4% in 2011. Suicide deaths related to firearms increased by 3.1% from 2010 to 2011, marking the fifth consecutive annual increase.

Hospital emergency department surveillance data[a] indicate an estimated 17,362 nonfatal unintentional firearms-related injuries occurred in 2012. Assault was related to an estimated 59,077 nonfatal injuries, while the estimated total for intentionally self-inflicted nonfatal injuries was 4,086.

[a]Source: National Center for Injury Prevention and Control injury surveillance data using WISQARS from www.cdc.gov/injury/wisqars/nonfatal.html.

Deaths involving firearms by age and sex, United States, 2011

Type and sex	All ages	Younger than 5	5-14 years	15-19 years	20-24 years	25-44 years	45-64 years	65-74 years	75 or older
Total firearms deaths	**32,351**	**86**	**311**	**2,306**	**3,979**	**11,015**	**9,650**	**2,444**	**2,560**
Male	27,738	56	232	2,041	3,568	9,383	8,003	2,122	2,333
Female	4,613	30	79	265	411	1,632	1,647	322	227
Unintentional	**591**	**29**	**45**	**66**	**64**	**152**	**151**	**46**	**38**
Male	511	22	32	59	55	134	131	44	34
Female	80	7	13	7	9	18	20	2	4
Suicide	**19,990**	**–**	**92**	**758**	**1,410**	**5,577**	**7,622**	**2,159**	**2,372**
Male	17,320	–	81	674	1,262	4,722	6,435	1,916	2,230
Female	2,670	–	11	84	148	855	1,187	243	142
Homicide	**11,068**	**55**	**162**	**1,434**	**2,391**	**4,989**	**1,693**	**210**	**134**
Male	9,270	32	109	1,264	2,142	4,257	1,274	136	56
Female	1,798	23	53	170	249	732	419	74	78
Legal intervention	**454**	**0**	**1**	**28**	**72**	**214**	**121**	**15**	**3**
Male	438	0	0	27	71	208	114	15	3
Female	16	0	1	1	1	6	7	0	0
Undetermined[a]	**248**	**2**	**11**	**20**	**42**	**83**	**63**	**14**	**13**
Male	199	2	10	17	38	62	49	11	10
Female	49	0	1	3	4	21	14	3	3

Source: National Safety Council tabulation of National Center for Health Statistics–Mortality Data for 2011, as compiled from data provided by the 57 vital statistics jurisdictions through the Vital Statistics Cooperative Program.
Note: Dashes (–) indicate category not applicable.
[a]Undetermined means the intentionality of the deaths (unintentional, homicide, suicide) was not determined.

Firearms deaths by intentionality, United States, 1999-2011

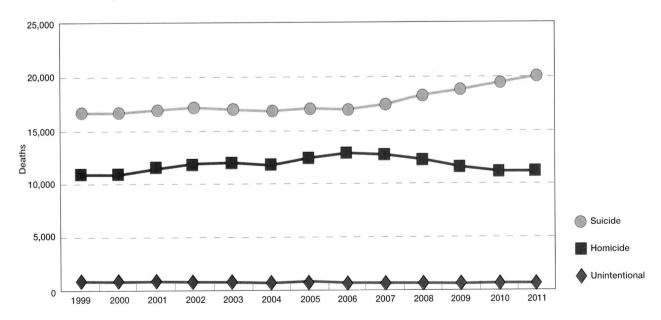

Overall, passenger transportation incidents account for about 2 out of 10 unintentional-injury-related deaths. But the risk of death for the passenger, expressed on a per-mile basis, varies greatly by transportation mode. Highway travel by personal vehicle presents the greatest risk; air, rail, and bus travel have much lower death rates. The tables below show the latest information on passenger transportation deaths and death rates.

In recognition of the current use of vans, sport utility vehicles (SUVs), pickups, and other light trucks as passenger vehicles, the Federal Highway Administration (FHWA) reclassified these vehicles and passenger automobiles as "light duty vehicles" beginning in 2009. Because the data for 2007 and 2008 also meet the requirements of the new FHWA methodology, they are presented with the data for later years in the table below.

The statistics for light duty vehicles shown in the tables below represent all use of such vehicles, both intercity and local. The bus data also include intercity and local (transit) bus travel. Railroad includes both intercity (Amtrak) and local commuting travel. Scheduled airlines includes both large airlines and commuter airlines, but excludes on-demand air taxis and charter operations. In comparing the four modes, drivers of light duty vehicles (except taxis) are considered passengers. Bus drivers and airline or railroad crews are not considered passengers.

Other comparisons are possibly based on passenger trips, vehicle miles, or vehicle trips, but passenger miles is the most commonly used basis for comparing the safety of various modes of travel.

Transportation incident death rates, 2010-2012

Mode of transportation	2012			2010-2012 average death rate
	Passenger deaths	Passenger miles (billions)	Deaths per 100,000,000 passenger miles	
Light duty vehicles[a]	21,669	4,449.6	0.49	0.49
Buses[b]	25	61.3	0.04	0.05
Transit buses	_1_	_22.3_	_<0.01_	_0.01_
Intercity buses	_15_	_39.0_	_0.04_	_0.05_
Railroad passenger trains[c]	5	20.6	0.02	0.02
Scheduled airlines[d]	0	568.7	0.00	0.00

Source: Highway passenger deaths – Fatality Analysis Reporting System data. Railroad passenger deaths and miles – Federal Railroad Administration. Airline passenger deaths – National Transportation Safety Board. Airline passenger miles – Bureau of Transportation Statistics. Passenger miles for transit buses – American Public Transit Association. All other figures – National Safety Council estimates.
[a]_Includes passenger cars, light trucks, vans, and SUVs regardless of wheelbase. Includes taxi passengers. Drivers of light duty vehicles are considered passengers._
[b]_Figures exclude school buses but include "other" and "unknown" bus types._
[c]_Includes Amtrak and commuter rail service._
[d]_Includes large airlines and scheduled commuter airlines; excludes charter, cargo, on-demand services, and suicide/sabotage._

Passenger deaths and death rates, United States, 2007-2012

Year	Light duty vehicles[a]		Buses		Railroad passenger trains		Scheduled airlines	
	Deaths	Rate[b]	Deaths	Rate[b]	Deaths	Rate[b]	Deaths	Rate[b]
2007	29,075	0.66	18	0.03	5	0.03	0	0.00
2008	25,457	0.59	50	0.08	24	0.13	0	0.00
2009	23,441	0.53	21	0.04	3	0.02	49	0.01
2010	22,271	0.50	28	0.05	3	0.02	0	0.00
2011	21,221	0.48	35	0.06	6	0.03	0	0.00
2012	21,669	0.49	25	0.04	5	0.02	0	0.00

Source: See table above.
[a]_Includes passenger cars, light trucks, vans, and SUVs regardless of wheelbase. Includes taxi passengers. Drivers of light duty vehicles are considered passengers._
[b]_Deaths per 100,000,000 passenger miles._

Passenger death rates, United States, 2010-2012

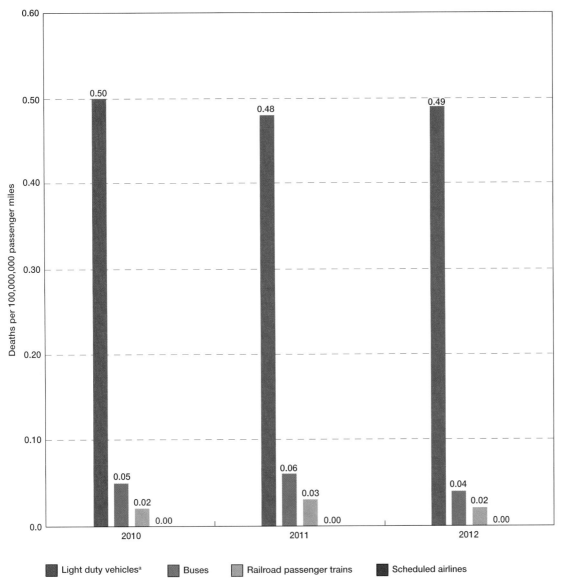

ᵃWith the exception of taxi drivers, drivers of these vehicles are considered passengers.

The total number of incidents involving United States registered civil aviation decreased from 1,539 in 2012 to a preliminary estimate of 1,297 in 2013. However, large airlines experienced the first fatalities since 2009. Please note that the three fatalities resulting from the crash of Asiana Airlines flight 214 are not included below because the carrier is not registered in the United States.

U.S. civil aviation incidents, deaths, and death rates, 2008-2013

| | Incidents | | | Incident rates | | | |
| | | | | Per 100,000 flight hours | | Per million miles flown | |
Year	Total	Fatal	Total deaths[a]	Total	Fatal	Total	Fatal
Large airlines[b]							
2008	20	0	0	0.108	0	0.0026	0
2009	26	1	50	0.151	0.006	0.0036	0.0001
2010	27	0	0	0.157	0	0.0037	0
2011	28	0	0	0.160	0	0.0037	0
2012	27	0	0	0.156	0	0.0036	0
2013	20	1	2	0.117	0.006	0.0027	0.0001
Commuter airlines[b]							
2008	7	0	0	2.357	0	0.1497	0
2009	2	0	0	0.646	0	0.0441	0
2010	6	0	0	1.907	0	0.125	0
2011	4	0	0	1.228	0	0.0821	0
2012	4	0	0	1.25	0	0.0808	0
2013	8	3	6	2.481	0.931	0.1639	0.0615
On-demand air taxis[b]							
2008	58	20	69	1.70	0.59	–	–
2009	47	2	17	1.53	0.07	–	–
2010	30	6	17	0.96	0.19	–	–
2011	50	16	41	–	–	–	–
2012	35	7	9	0.99	0.2	–	–
2013	44	10	27	1.24	0.28	–	–
General aviation[b]							
2008[c]	1,569	277	496	6.87	1.21	–	–
2009[c]	1,480	275	479	7.08	1.32	–	–
2010[c]	1,440	270	457	6.63	1.24	–	–
2011[c]	1,470	266	448	–	–	–	–
2012[c]	1,471	273	440	7.04	1.30	–	–
2013[c]	1,222	221	387	5.85	1.05	–	–

Source: National Transportation Safety Board: 2013 preliminary, 2008-2012 revised; exposure data for rates from the Federal Aviation Administration (FAA). Also note that the 2011 exposure estimates are not currently available. The FAA is engaged in re-calibration efforts. Note: Dash (–) indicates data not available.
[a]Includes passengers, crew members, and others such as people on the ground.
[b]Civil aviation incident statistics collected by the National Transportation Safety Board are classified according to federal air regulations under which the flights were made. The classifications are (1) large airlines operating scheduled service under Title 14, Code of Federal Regulations, part 121 (14 CFR 121); (2) commuter carriers operating scheduled service under 14 CFR 135; (3) unscheduled, "on-demand" air taxis under 14 CFR 135; and (4) "general aviation," which includes incidents involving aircraft flown under rules other than 14 CFR 121 and 14 CFR 135. Not shown in the table is nonscheduled air carrier operations under 14 CFR 121 that experienced (8 incidents/3 fatalities) in 2008, (4/2) in 2009, (3/2) in 2010, (3/0) in 2011, (0/0) in 2012, and (3/7) in 2013. Since 1997, "large airlines" includes aircraft with 10 or more seats, formerly operated as commuter carriers under 14 CFR 135.
[c]Suicide/sabotage/terrorism and stolen/unauthorized cases are included in incident and fatality totals but excluded from rates –General Aviation, 2008 (2/0), 2009 (3/0), 2010 (3/2), 2011 (1/0), 2012 (1/1), and 2013 (1/1).

Civil aviation incidence rates, United States, 1991-2013

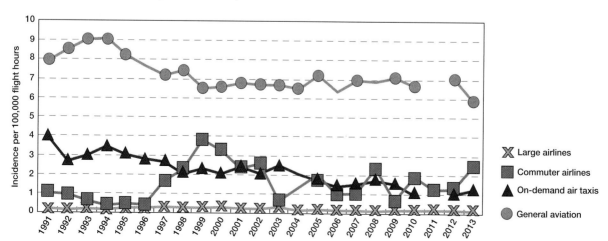

Railroad deaths totaled 752 in 2013, an increase of 8% from the 2012 revised total of 695 but still 5% lower than the 2004-2012 average of 794. From 2012 to 2013, there was a 7% increase in fatalities at highway-rail crossings, and a 9% increase in fatalities involving other types of incidents. The latter included 460 deaths, or 91%, to trespassers. Fourteen employees were killed while on duty, a 12% decrease compared to the 2012 death toll and 30% lower than the 2004-2012 average. Deaths to passengers on trains totaled six, marginally higher than the 2012 total of five deaths and 14% lower than the 2004-2012 average.

The ratio of railroad-related deaths to nonfatal injuries and illnesses is approximately 1:11. In 2013, railroad incidents resulted in 8,585 cases of nonfatal conditions, compared to 8,353 in 2012 and the 2004-2012 average of 8,826. Eleven percent of the total was attributed to highway-rail-crossing incidents, nearly stable from the 2012 total of 960 and was slightly lower than the 2004-2012 average of 989. Of the 4,264 nonfatal occupational railroad injuries and illnesses reported in 2013, 2% were attributed to highway-rail-crossing incidents.

Deaths and nonfatal cases in railroad incidents, United States, 2004-2013

Year	Total	Highway rail-crossing incident?		Occurring in other than highway-rail crossing incident		Employees on duty		Passengers on trains[a]	
						At highway-rail crossing?		At highway-rail crossing?	
		Yes	No	Trespassers	Others	Yes	No	Yes	No
Deaths									
2004	891	371	520	472	48	2	23	0	3
2005	884	359	525	458	67	2	23	0	16
2006	903	369	534	511	23	4	12	0	2
2007	851	339	512	470	42	1	16	0	5
2008	804	290	514	457	57	3	23	0	24
2009	695	248	447	416	31	0	16	0	3
2010	733	260	473	439	34	0	20	0	3
2011	691	250	441	406	35	6	15	4	2
2012	695	232	463	429	34	1	15	0	5
2013	752	249	503	460	43	1	13	0	6
Nonfatal conditions									
2004	9,194	1,094	8,100	406	7,694	116	5,906	28	675
2005	9,550	1,053	8,497	420	8,077	111	5,711	33	924
2006	8,797	1,070	7,727	481	7,246	96	5,179	95	841
2007	9,669	1,059	8,610	407	8,203	105	5,357	72	1,444
2008	9,062	990	8,072	432	7,640	75	4,925	101	1,231
2009	8,022	743	7,279	344	6,935	72	4,431	61	1,130
2010	8,377	888	7,489	390	7,099	80	4,332	114	1,254
2011	8,414	1,043	7,371	369	7,002	71	4,151	245	1,327
2012	8,353	960	7,393	413	6,980	76	3,872	174	1,377
2013	8,585	954	7,631	432	7,199	81	4,183	100	1,524

Source: Federal Railroad Administration.
[a]*Passenger cases include all circumstances, including getting on/off standing trains, stumbling aboard trains, assaults, train incidents, crossing incidents, etc.*

Casualties at public and private highway-rail crossings, United States, 2004-2013

Year	Deaths				Nonfatal conditions			
	Total	Motor vehicle-related	Pedestrians	Others	Total	Motor vehicle-related	Pedestrians	Others
2004	371	289	73	9	1,094	1,058	30	6
2005	359	284	58	17	1,053	1,006	37	10
2006	369	305	53	11	1,070	1,035	29	6
2007	339	265	59	15	1,059	1,018	32	9
2008	290	221	64	5	990	923	54	13
2009	248	182	59	7	743	697	38	8
2010	260	168	80	12	888	820	49	19
2011	250	169	70	11	1,043	984	42	17
2012	232	163	58	11	960	903	40	17
2013	249	161	72	16	954	881	50	23

Source: Federal Railroad Administration.

Unintentional Fatal Poisonings

■ *Poisoning deaths were up 10% from 2010 to 2011.*

Deaths from unintentional poisoning numbered 36,280 in 2011, the latest year for which data are available. The death rate per 100,000 population was 11.6. Males are at greatest risk, with a death rate of 15.2 compared with 8.2 for females. Total poisoning deaths increased 10% from 33,041 in 2010 and are more than 2.5 times the 2001 total. See pages 52-55 for long-term trends.

Thirty-six percent of the poisoning deaths were classified in the "narcotics and psychodysleptics (hallucinogens), not elsewhere classified," category, which includes prescription narcotic analgesics and illegal drugs such as cocaine, heroin, cannabinol, and LSD.

A National Safety Council analysis of National Center for Health Statistics mortality data showed that for all ages, the greatest number of poisoning deaths in 2011 was due to overdoses of prescription drugs, which accounted for 15,417 or over 42% of all unintentional poisoning deaths. Of this total, overdoses of prescription opioids were responsible for 12,267 deaths or 33.8% and overdoses of other prescription drugs for 3,150 deaths or 8.7%. Overdoses of the illegal drugs heroin

or cocaine caused another 5,868 (16.2%) of the deaths, while the combination of heroin, cocaine, and prescription opioids together added another 1,824 (5.0%). Other types of drugs were responsible for 9,962 or 27.4% of poisoning deaths, with the remaining 3,209 or 8.8% due to non-drug poisoning. The chart at the bottom of the opposite page shows the 2011 poisoning deaths by single year of age and illustrates the sizable contribution of prescription drugs to poisoning deaths over a large portion of the life span.

Deaths due to alcohol poisoning increased over 2% from 2010 and totaled 2,155 in 2011. Alcohol poisoning deaths for males outnumbered those for females by more than 3 to 1. The number of alcohol poisoning deaths among males increased by 3% from 2010 to 2011, while the number for females decreased 1%. It should be noted that alcohol also may be present in combination with other drugs.

Carbon monoxide poisoning is included in the category of "other gases and vapors." Additional information on human poisoning exposure cases may be found on pages 162 and 191.

Unintentional poisoning deaths by type, age, and sex, United States, 2011

Type of poison	All ages	Younger than 5	5-14 years	15-19 years	20-24 years	25-44 years	45-64 years	65 or older
Both sexes								
Total poisoning deaths	**36,280**	**49**	**50**	**739**	**2,701**	**15,727**	**15,427**	**1,587**
Deaths per 100,000 population	*11.6*	*0.2*	*0.1*	*3.4*	*12.2*	*19.1*	*18.6*	*3.8*
Total drug-related poisoning deaths	33,071	32	26	688	2,543	14,682	13,898	1,202
Nonopioid analgesics, antipyretics, and antirheumatics (X40)[a]	220	2	0	1	13	72	102	30
Antiepileptic, sedative-hypnotic, antiparkinsonism, and psychotropic drugs, n.e.c. (X41)	2,080	3	4	20	71	778	1,108	96
Narcotics and psychodysleptics (hallucinogens), n.e.c. (X42)	13,214	19	10	347	1,236	5,967	5,336	299
Other drugs acting on the autonomic nervous system (X43)	16	0	0	0	1	6	3	6
Other and unspecified drugs, medicaments, and biological substances (X44)	17,541	8	12	320	1,222	7,859	7,349	771
Alcohol (X45)	2,155	1	1	27	95	705	1,180	146
Organic solvents and halogenated hydrocarbons and their vapors (X46)	82	1	4	3	12	32	28	2
Other gases and vapors (X47)	784	12	18	17	39	240	250	208
Pesticides (X48)	4	0	0	0	0	1	3	0
Other and unspecified chemical and noxious substances (X49)	184	3	1	4	12	67	68	29
Males								
Total poisoning deaths	**23,288**	**30**	**29**	**552**	**2,035**	**10,518**	**9,316**	**808**
Deaths per 100,000 population	*15.2*	*0.3*	*0.1*	*5.0*	*18.0*	*25.5*	*23.1*	*4.5*
Total drug-related poisoning deaths	20,891	18	15	519	1,915	9,709	8,162	553
Nonopioid analgesics, antipyretics, and antirheumatics (X40)	70	0	0	1	8	24	31	6
Antiepileptic, sedative-hypnotic, antiparkinsonism, and psychotropic drugs, n.e.c. (X41)	1,326	0	2	14	45	504	714	47
Narcotics and psychodysleptics (hallucinogens), n.e.c. (X42)	9,311	12	6	272	954	4,367	3,535	165
Other drugs acting on the autonomic nervous system (X43)	7	0	0	0	1	4	1	1
Other and unspecified drugs, medicaments, and biological substances (X44)	10,177	6	7	232	907	4,810	3,881	334
Alcohol (X45)	1,660	1	1	17	75	562	900	104
Organic solvents and halogenated hydrocarbons and their vapors (X46)	63	0	4	2	10	25	20	2
Other gases and vapors (X47)	547	10	8	12	26	175	188	128
Pesticides (X48)	4	0	0	0	0	1	3	0
Other and unspecified chemical and noxious substances (X49)	123	1	1	2	9	46	43	21
Females								
Total poisoning deaths	**12,992**	**19**	**21**	**187**	**666**	**5,209**	**6,111**	**779**
Deaths per 100,000 population	*8.2*	*0.2*	*0.1*	*1.8*	*6.1*	*12.7*	*14.4*	*3.3*
Total drug-related poisoning deaths	12,180	14	11	169	628	4,973	5,736	649
Nonopioid analgesics, antipyretics, and antirheumatics (X40)	150	2	0	0	5	48	71	24
Antiepileptic, sedative-hypnotic, antiparkinsonism, and psychotropic drugs, n.e.c. (X41)	754	3	2	6	26	274	394	49
Narcotics and psychodysleptics (hallucinogens), n.e.c. (X42)	3,903	7	4	75	282	1,600	1,801	134
Other drugs acting on the autonomic nervous system (X43)	9	0	0	0	0	2	2	5
Other and unspecified drugs, medicaments, and biological substances (X44)	7,364	2	5	88	315	3,049	3,468	437
Alcohol (X45)	495	0	0	10	20	143	280	42
Organic solvents and halogenated hydrocarbons and their vapors (X46)	19	1	0	1	2	7	8	0
Other gases and vapors (X47)	237	2	10	5	13	65	62	80
Pesticides (X48)	0	0	0	0	0	0	0	0
Other and unspecified chemical and noxious substances (X49)	61	2	0	2	3	21	25	8

Source: National Safety Council tabulations of National Center for Health Statistics–Mortality Data for 2011, as compiled from data provided by the 57 vital statistics jurisdictions through the Vital Statistics Cooperative Program.
Note: "n.e.c." means "not elsewhere classified."
[a]Numbers following titles refer to external cause of injury and poisoning classifications in ICD-10.

Unintentional poisoning deaths, United States, 1996-2011

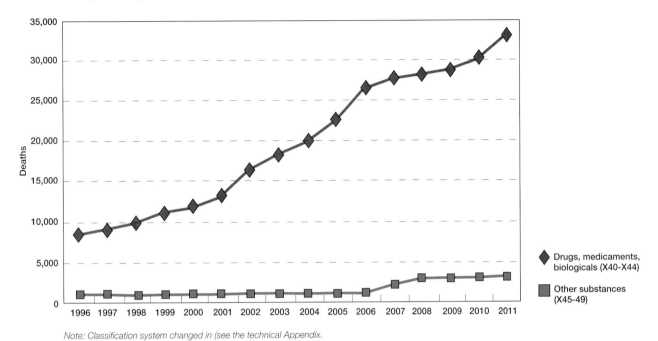

Note: Classification system changed in (see the technical Appendix.

Unintentional poisoning deaths by drug type and age, United States, 2011

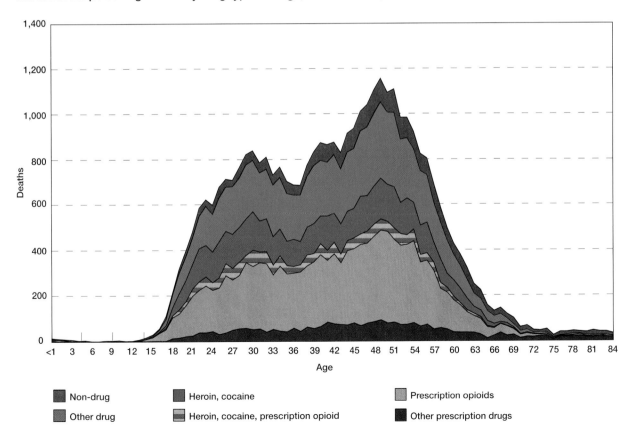

Fatal Versus Nonfatal Unintentional Poisoning

Most people think of poisoning as a childhood issue. That is true for poisonings exposures, but not for nonfatal and fatal poisonings. The pie charts below show the distribution of poisoning exposures, nonfatal poisonings, and fatal poisonings by age groups. The poisoning exposure data are from the American Association of Poison Control Centers and represent the calls received by poison control centers. The nonfatal data represent emergency department visits, while the fatality data are from death certificates.

Nonfatal exposures occur predominantly among young children, whereas nonfatal and fatal poisonings are overwhelmingly among adults. While slightly less than half of the poisoning exposures involve children 5 or younger, nearly 87% of the nonfatal poisonings and nearly 98% of the fatalities occur among adults 19 and older.

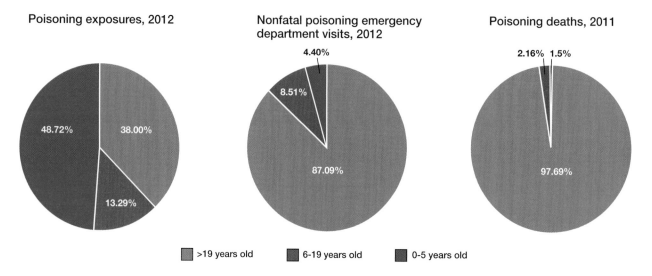

Poisoning exposures, 2012

48.72% 38.00% 13.29%

Nonfatal poisoning emergency department visits, 2012

4.40% 8.51% 87.09%

Poisoning deaths, 2011

2.16% 1.5% 97.69%

■ >19 years old　　■ 6-19 years old　　■ 0-5 years old

For the first time in three years nonfatal poisonings have decreased, while fatal poisonings continue to increase, showing a nearly 10% increase from 2010. The charts below illustrate the trends for both categories of poisonings starting in 2002.

Nonfatal unintentional poisoning trend, 2002-2012

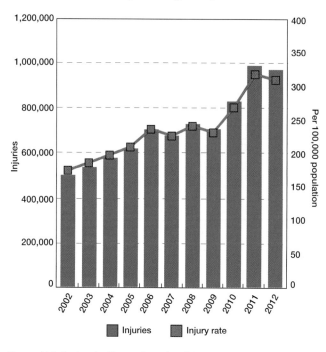

■ Injuries　　■ Injury rate

Fatal unintentional poisoning trend[a], 2002-2011

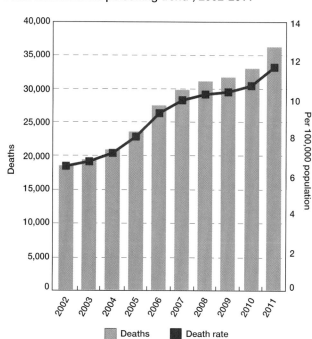

■ Deaths　　■ Death rate

Source: U.S. Centers for Disease Control and Prevention, NEISS-AIP, WISQARS
[a]2011 is the latest official data available. National Safety Council estimates for 2012 and 2013 are available on pages 53 and 55.

The impact of unintentional falls on the older adult population has been highlighted in numerous editions of *Injury Facts* (2010-2014, 2008, 2007, etc.).

Recent research shows that adults with arthritis are at increased risk for experiencing falls and being injured from falling. Among adults 45 years of age or older who report having arthritis, 15.5% report falling once, 21.3% report falling two or more times, while 16.2% report being injured from falls in the past 12 months. In contrast, among adults without arthritis, 12.1% reported falling once, 9% report falling two or more times, while 6.5% report being injured by a fall in the last 12 months (see graph below). It is also projected that the number of adults with arthritis is likely to increase steadily through at least 2030, putting more adults at higher risk for falls and fall injuries.

Percentage of adults aged 45 or older who report experiencing a fall or fall injury in the past months with and without arthritis, United States, 2012

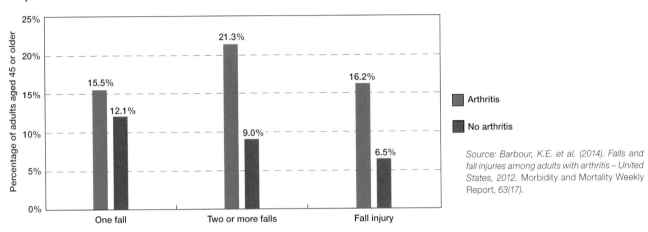

Source: Barbour, K.E. et al. (2014). Falls and fall injuries among adults with arthritis – United States, 2012. Morbidity and Mortality Weekly Report, 63(17).

Looking at 2011, 22,901 fatalities occurred among adults age 65 or older. From 1999 to 2011, the number of fall-related deaths among individuals 65 or older has increased 127%, while the population death rate has increased 91%. At this same time, the number of fall deaths among individuals younger than 65 increased 50% and the death rate increased 35% (see chart below).

As reported in the 2014 edition of *Injury Facts*, it is likely that a substantial proportion of the increase in older adult fall deaths is a result of improved death certificate coding and that the more recent estimates more accurately reflect the full extent of the problem.

Fall deaths and death rates, United States, 1999-2011

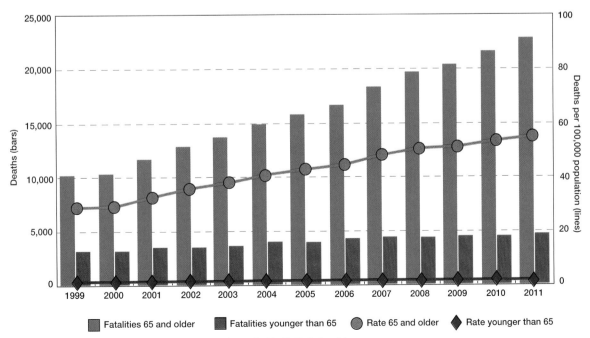

Source: National Safety Council tabulations of National Center for Health Statistics data.

Approximately 366,600 home structure fires occur in the United States each year resulting in an average of 2,570 deaths. According to the National Fire Protection Association, the percentage of homes with at least one smoke alarm has plateaued at around 96% since 2004. This plateau follows a period of dramatic growth. From 1977 through 1995, the percentage of homes with smoke alarms grew from 22% to 92%. Although only about 4% of homes do not currently have smoke alarms, 27% of the home structure fires occurred in these homes accounting for 37% of the deaths. In contrast,

52% of home fires occur in homes with functioning smoke alarms but account for only 40% of the deaths. Surprisingly, when smoke alarms are present but do not function correctly a disproportionate number of deaths appear to occur. While smoke alarms fail to operate correctly in only about 8% of home fires, these fires account for fully 23% of the deaths. It is unclear why this disparity exists. However, it is known that most smoke alarm failures result from missing, disconnected, or dead batteries.

Percent of reported home structure fires and fire deaths by smoke alarm performance, 2007-2011

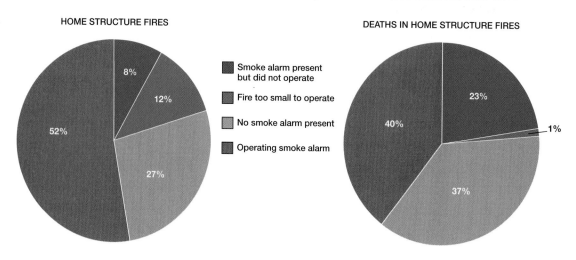

The risk of dying in home fires is cut in half in homes with working smoke alarms. The death rate per 100 home fires is 1.18 in homes with no smoke alarm present or when alarms did not function compared to 0.53 deaths per 100 fires in homes with functioning smoke alarms.

Death rate per 100 reported home structure fires by smoke alarm status, 2007-2011

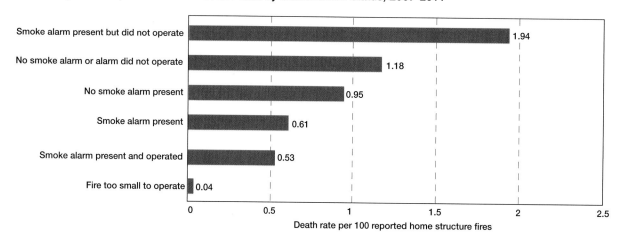

Source: Ahrens, M. (2014). Smoke alarms in U.S. home fires. Quincy, MA: National Fire Protection Association.

Pedalcycles

The estimated number of deaths from collisions between pedalcycles and motor vehicles increased from about 750 in 1940 to 1,200 in 1980, and then declined to about 1,000 in 2013.

In 2011, 601 pedalcyclists died in motor vehicle crashes and 272 in other incidents, according to National Center for Health Statistics mortality data. Males accounted for 87% of all pedalcycle deaths, nearly 7 times the female fatalities.

Emergency department-treated injuries associated with bicycles and bicycle accessories were estimated to total 556,660 in 2012 and 531,340 in 2013, according to the Consumer Product Safety Commission (also see page 168).

A meta-analysis of bicycle helmet efficacy by Attewell, Glase, and McFadden (2001) estimated that bicycle helmets reduce the risk of head injury by 60% and brain injury by 58%. As of July 2014, 21 states, the District of Columbia, and more than 201 localities had bicycle helmet-use laws, according to the Bicycle Helmet Safety Institute.

Source: National Safety Council estimates and tabulations of National Center for Health Statistics mortality data obtained via WISQARS at www.cdc.gov/injury/wisqars/index.html. Population data for rates are from the U.S. Census Bureau. Data from Bicycle Helmet Safety Institute was retrieved September 18, 2014, from www.bhsi.org.

Attewell, R.G., Glase, K., & McFadden, M. (2001). Bicycle helmet efficacy: A meta-analysis. Accident Analysis & Prevention, Vol. 33, No. 3, pp. 345-352.

Pedalcycle deaths and death rates by sex and age group, United States, 2011

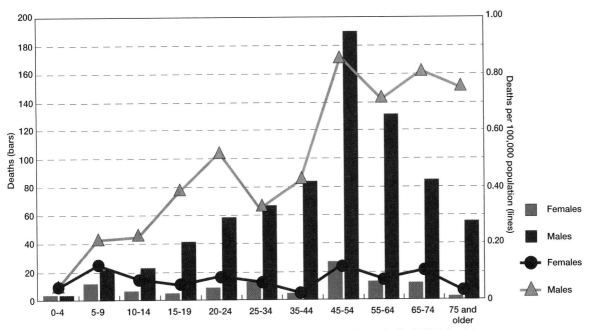

Source: National Safety Council tabulations based on U.S. Census Bureau and National Center for Health Statistics data.

Pedalcycle fatalities by month, United States, 2011

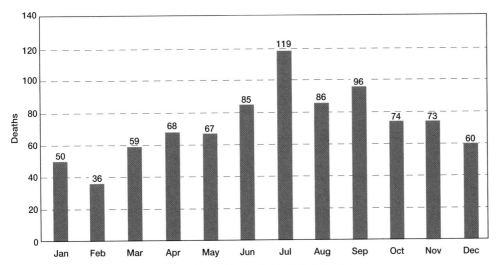

Source: National Safety Council tabulations of National Center for Health Statistics data.

The leading risks for unintentional injury vary with age and are different for deaths and nonfatal injuries. The tables here and on the next page list, for eight age groups, the five leading causes of unintentional-injury-related deaths and the five leading causes of hospital emergency department visits, which is one measure of nonfatal injuries.

For all ages, the five leading causes account for 85% of all unintentional-injury-related deaths and 74% of unintentional-injury-related emergency department visits. Only motor vehicle crashes and falls are common to both lists. Motor vehicle crashes rank second for unintentional-injury-related deaths and fourth for unintentional-injury-related emergency department visits. Falls rank third for unintentional-injury-related deaths and first for emergency department unintentional-injury-related visits.

The five leading causes of unintentional-injury-related deaths account for between 80% and 93% of such deaths depending on the age group. The leading causes of unintentional-injury-related emergency department visits account for between 72% and 88% of such hospital visits.

For deaths, poisoning; motor vehicle crashes; falls; fire, flames, or smoke; and drowning are most often among the top five, with choking, firearms, and mechanical suffocation sometimes included. For emergency department visits, falls; struck by or against; overexertion; motor vehicle occupant injuries; and cut or pierce injuries are most often in the top five. In the younger age groups, bites and stings (except dog bites); foreign body injuries; and struck by or against are among the leading risks.

Leading unintentional-injury risks, all ages, United States, 2011

Rank	Unintentional-injury-related deaths				Unintentional-injury-related emergency department visits			
	Event	Number	Percent	Rate[a]	Event	Number	Percent	Rate[a]
–	Total	126,438	100.0%	40.6	Total	30,024,936	100.0%	9,636
1	Poisoning	36,280	28.7%	11.6	Falls	9,256,761	30.8%	2,971
2	Motor vehicle crashes	35,303	27.9%	11.3	Struck by or against	4,619,897	15.4%	1,483
3	Falls	27,483	21.7%	8.8	Overexertion	3,440,314	11.5%	1,104
4	Choking[b]	4,708	3.7%	1.5	Motor vehicle occupant	2,686,589	8.9%	862
5	Drowning	3,556	2.8%	1.1	Cut or pierce	2,165,207	7.2%	695

Leading unintentional-injury risks, young children (ages 0-4), United States, 2011

Rank	Unintentional-injury-related deaths				Unintentional-injury-related emergency department visits			
	Event	Number	Percent	Rate[a]	Event	Number	Percent	Rate[a]
–	Total	2,540	100.0%	12.6	Total	2,428,579	100.0%	12,045
1	Mechanical suffocation	887	34.9%	4.4	Falls	1,127,911	46.4%	5,594
2	Motor vehicle crashes	520	20.5%	2.6	Struck by or against	416,758	17.2%	2,067
3	Drowning	490	19.3%	2.4	Bite or sting (except dog)	189,222	7.8%	939
4	Choking[b]	153	6.0%	0.8	Foreign body	154,957	6.4%	769
5	Fire, flames, or smoke	150	5.9%	0.7	Cut or pierce	100,807	4.2%	500

Leading unintentional-injury risks, children and young adolescents (ages 5-14), United States, 2011

Rank	Unintentional-injury-related deaths				Unintentional-injury-related emergency department visits			
	Event	Number	Percent	Rate[a]	Event	Number	Percent	Rate[a]
–	Total	1,635	100.0%	4.0	Total	4,031,125	100.0%	9,823
1	Motor vehicle crashes	881	53.9%	2.1	Falls	1,283,186	31.8%	3,127
2	Drowning	235	14.4%	0.6	Struck by or against	1,045,227	25.9%	2,547
3	Fire, flames, or smoke	123	7.5%	0.3	Overexertion	392,716	9.7%	957
4	Mechanical suffocation	53	3.2%	0.1	Cut or pierce	254,172	6.3%	619
5	Poisoning	50	3.1%	0.1	Pedalcyclist	194,806	4.8%	475

Leading unintentional-injury risks, teens (ages 15-19), United States, 2011

Rank	Unintentional-injury-related deaths				Unintentional-injury-related emergency department visits			
	Event	Number	Percent	Rate[a]	Event	Number	Percent	Rate[a]
–	Total	4,298	100.0%	19.9	Total	2,579,059	100.0%	11,916
1	Motor vehicle crashes	2,863	66.6%	13.2	Struck by or against	618,335	24.0%	2,857
2	Poisoning	739	17.2%	3.4	Falls	465,832	18.1%	2,152
3	Drowning	245	5.7%	1.1	Overexertion	384,543	14.9%	1,777
4	Falls	75	1.7%	0.3	Motor vehicle occupant	293,530	11.4%	1,356
5	Firearms	66	1.5%	0.3	Cut or pierce	198,515	7.7%	917

See footnotes on page 167.

Leading unintentional-injury risks, young adults (ages 20-24), United States, 2011

Rank	Unintentional-injury-related deaths				Unintentional-injury-related emergency department visits			
	Event	Number	Percent	Rate[a]	Event	Number	Percent	Rate[a]
–	Total	8,032	100.0%	36.3	Total	2,569,583	100.0%	11,599
1	Motor vehicle crashes	4,242	52.8%	19.1	Falls	456,126	17.8%	2,059
2	Poisoning	2,701	33.6%	12.2	Struck by or against	421,446	16.4%	1,902
3	Drowning	298	3.7%	1.3	Motor vehicle occupant	410,286	16.0%	1,852
4	Falls	130	1.6%	0.6	Overexertion	339,867	13.2%	1,534
5	Fire, flames, or smoke	88	1.1%	0.4	Cut or pierce	261,613	10.2%	1,181

Leading unintentional-injury risks, adults (ages 25-44), United States, 2011

Rank	Unintentional-injury-related deaths				Unintentional-injury-related emergency department visits			
	Event	Number	Percent	Rate[a]	Event	Number	Percent	Rate[a]
–	Total	30,748	100.0%	37.3	Total	7,756,003	100.0%	9,411
1	Poisoning	15,727	51.1%	19.1	Falls	1,626,016	21.0%	1,973
2	Motor vehicle crashes	10,352	33.7%	12.6	Overexertion	1,264,601	16.3%	1,534
3	Drowning	856	2.8%	1.0	Struck by or against	1,149,061	14.8%	1,394
4	Falls	803	2.6%	1.0	Motor vehicle occupant	984,577	12.7%	1,195
5	Fire, flames, or smoke	374	1.2%	0.5	Cut or pierce	713,555	9.2%	866

Leading unintentional-injury risks, adults (ages 45-64), United States, 2011

Rank	Unintentional-injury-related deaths				Unintentional-injury-related emergency department visits			
	Event	Number	Percent	Rate[a]	Event	Number	Percent	Rate[a]
–	Total	35,907	100.0%	43.4	Total	6,217,242	100.0%	7,511
1	Poisoning	15,427	43.0%	18.6	Falls	1,894,224	30.5%	2,288
2	Motor vehicle crashes	9,866	27.5%	11.9	Overexertion	754,916	12.1%	912
3	Falls	3,509	9.8%	4.2	Struck by or against	699,511	11.3%	845
4	Choking[b]	969	2.7%	1.2	Motor vehicle occupant	620,201	10.0%	749
5	Fire, flames, or smoke	926	2.6%	1.1	Cut or pierce	488,363	7.9%	590

Leading unintentional-injury risks, older adults (ages 65-74), United States, 2011

Rank	Unintentional-injury-related deaths				Unintentional-injury-related emergency department visits			
	Event	Number	Percent	Rate[a]	Event	Number	Percent	Rate[a]
–	Total	10,014	100.0%	44.5	Total	1,538,629	100.0%	6,844
1	Falls	3,149	31.4%	14.0	Falls	735,815	47.8%	3,273
2	Motor vehicle crashes	2,913	29.1%	13.0	Struck by or against	130,758	8.5%	582
3	Poisoning	945	9.4%	4.2	Overexertion	117,047	7.6%	521
4	Choking[b]	652	6.5%	2.9	Motor vehicle occupant	114,574	7.4%	510
5	Fire, flames, or smoke	389	3.9%	1.7	Cut or pierce	92,064	6.0%	410

Leading unintentional-injury risks, elderly (age 75 or older), United States, 2011

Rank	Unintentional-injury-related deaths				Unintentional-injury-related emergency department visits			
	Event	Number	Percent	Rate[a]	Event	Number	Percent	Rate[a]
–	Total	33,264	100.0%	175.9	Total	2,313,501	100.0%	12,233
1	Falls	19,754	59.4%	104.4	Falls	1,667,331	72.1%	8,816
2	Motor vehicle crashes	3,666	11.0%	19.4	Struck by or against	138,662	6.0%	733
3	Choking[b]	2,634	7.9%	13.9	Overexertion	86,000	3.7%	455
4	Fire, flames, or smoke	649	2.0%	3.4	Motor vehicle occupant	80,104	3.5%	424
5	Poisoning	642	1.9%	3.4	Cut or pierce	56,002	2.4%	296

Source: National Safety Council analysis of National Center for Health Statistics–Mortality Data for 2011, as compiled from data provided by the 57 vital statistics jurisdictions through the Vital Statistics Cooperative Program. Rates are National Safety Council estimates based on data from the National Center for Health Statistics and the U.S. Census Bureau. Emergency department data are from NEISS-AIP.
[a]*Deaths or emergency department visits per 100,000 population.*
[b]*Inhalation and ingestion of food or other object obstructing breathing.*

Injuries Associated With Consumer Products

■ *More than 1.4 million injury-related emergency department visits each year are associated with floors or flooring materials.*

The following list of items found in and around the home was selected from the Consumer Product Safety Commission's National Electronic Injury Surveillance System (NEISS) for 2013. NEISS estimates are calculated from a statistically representative sample of hospitals in the United States. Injury totals represent estimates of the number of hospital emergency department-treated cases nationwide associated with various products. However, product involvement may or may not be the cause of the injury.

Consumer product-related injuries treated in hospital emergency departments, 2013
(excluding most sports and sports equipment; also see page 152)

Description	Injuries
Home workshop equipment	
Saws (hand or power)	80,900
Hammers	30,776
Tools, not specified	29,745
Workshop grinders, buffers, or polishers	22,219
Packaging or containers, household	
Household containers and packaging	231,008
Bottles and jars	81,419
Bags	54,004
Paper products	31,317
Housewares	
Knives	381,354
Tableware and flatware (excluding knives)	103,047
Drinking glasses	70,557
Waste containers, trash baskets, etc.	45,758
Cookware, bowls, and canisters	37,080
Manual cleaning equipment (excluding buckets)	32,653
Scissors	24,840
Other kitchen gadgets	21,425
Home furnishing, fixtures, or accessories	
Beds	705,933
Chairs	380,288
Tables, n.e.c.[a]	330,155
Bathtubs and showers	324,698
Household cabinets, racks, and shelves	292,212
Sofas, couches, davenports, divans, etc.	189,781
Ladders	175,790
Rugs and carpets	161,509
Other furniture[b]	115,348
Toilets	112,662
Stools	60,671
Miscellaneous decorating items	39,393
Benches	38,091
Sinks	33,167
Mirrors or mirror glass	27,150
Home structures or construction materials	
Floors or flooring materials	1,452,269
Stairs or steps	1,248,421
Ceilings and walls	360,936
Other doors[c]	303,794
Porches, balconies, or open-side floors	148,937
Nails, screws, tacks, or bolts	123,094
Fences or fence posts	113,537
Windows	110,291
Door sills or frames	65,350
Counters or countertops	58,461
Handrails, railings, or banisters	53,192
Poles	47,127
Glass doors	27,337
General household appliances	
Refrigerators	39,561
Ranges or ovens, not specified	33,931
Vacuum cleaners	20,830
Heating, cooling, or ventilating equipment	
Pipes (excluding smoking pipes)	29,899

Description	Injuries
Home communication or entertainment equipment	
Televisions	49,526
Computers (equipment and electronic games)	30,915
Telephones or telephone accessories	24,845
Personal use items	
Footwear	206,837
Jewelry	109,893
Daywear	78,901
Razors and shavers	54,142
Other clothing[d]	50,590
Coins	40,261
Desk supplies	32,056
Luggage	28,312
Hair grooming equipment and accessories	24,987
Yard and garden equipment	
Lawn mowers	86,620
Pruning, trimming & edging equipment	46,449
Other unpowered garden tools[e]	28,203
Manual snow or ice removal tools	26,779
Chainsaws	25,848
Sports and recreation	
Bicycles	531,340
Skateboards	120,424
Swimming pools	85,145
Trampolines	83,665
Monkey bars or other playground climbing equipment	83,356
Aquariums and other pet supplies	62,461
Dancing	62,461
Scooters (unpowered)	61,036
Swings or swing sets	56,808
Minibikes or trailbikes	56,090
Slides or sliding boards	50,680
Other playground equipment[f]	46,019
Sleds	22,655
Miscellaneous products	
Carts	55,116
Hot water	43,545
Elevators, escalators, moving walks	23,567
Household chemicals	
Soaps (excluding laundry soaps or detergents)	24,562
Detergents	24,506

Source: U.S. Consumer Product Safety Commission, National Electronic Injury Surveillance System, Product Summary Report, All Products, CY2013.
Note: Products are listed above if the estimate was greater than 20,500 cases.
"n.e.c." = not elsewhere classified.
[a]Excludes baby changing tables (5,593 injuries), billiard or pool tables (3,698 injuries), and television tables or stands (14,180 injuries).
[b]Excludes household cabinets, racks, shelves, desks, bureaus, chests, buffets, etc. (292,212 injuries).
[c]Excludes glass doors (27,337 injuries) and garage doors (15,259 injuries).
[d]Excludes costumes, masks, day wear (78,901 injuries); footwear (206,837 injuries); nightwear (6,563 injuries); and outerwear (7,794 injuries).
[e]Includes cultivators, hoes, pitchforks, rakes, shovels, spades, and trowels.
[f]Excludes monkey bars (83,356 injuries), see-saws (4,232 injuries), slides (50,680 injuries), and swings (56,808 injuries).

Home and Community, 1987-2013

Principal types of home and community unintentional-injury-related deaths, United States, 1987-2013

Year	Total home and community[a]	Falls	Drowning	Poisoning	Choking[b]	Fire, flames, or smoke	Firearms	Mechanical suffocation	Air transport	Water transport	Rail transport[c]	Other
1987	39,800	10,300	3,900	4,900	3,600	4,400	1,400	(d)	900	800	400	9,200
1988	41,100	10,700	3,800	5,700	3,700	4,600	1,400	(d)	700	800	400	9,300
1989	40,700	10,800	3,700	5,900	3,500	4,400	1,400	(d)	800	700	400	9,100
1990	38,900	11,000	3,700	5,400	3,300	3,800	1,300	(d)	700	800	400	8,500
1991	39,700	11,400	3,700	6,000	3,100	3,800	1,400	(d)	700	700	500	8,400
1992	43,000	12,100	3,400	6,900	3,100	3,900	1,400	(d)	700	700	600	10,200
1993	45,800	12,500	3,700	8,400	3,200	3,900	1,500	(d)	600	700	600	10,700
1994	45,900	12,800	3,300	8,900	3,100	3,900	1,300	(d)	600	600	600	10,800
1995	47,300	13,400	3,700	9,000	3,100	3,700	1,200	(d)	600	700	500	11,400
1996	48,500	14,300	3,400	9,400	3,200	3,700	1,100	(d)	700	600	500	11,600
1997	49,400	14,700	3,500	10,100	3,200	3,400	1,000	(d)	500	600	400	12,000
1998	51,600	15,500	3,900	10,700	3,500	3,100	900	(d)	500	600	500	12,400
1999[e]	52,700	12,400	3,500	12,100	3,900	3,200	900	1,600	500	600	400	13,600
2000	51,900	12,600	3,400	12,700	4,300	2,900	800	1,300	500	500	400	12,500
2001	55,000	14,200	3,300	14,000	4,100	3,200	800	1,400	700	500	400	12,400
2002	58,700	15,600	3,400	17,500	4,100	3,100	700	1,400	500	500	400	11,500
2003	61,800	16,600	3,200	19,300	4,300	3,200	700	1,300	600	500	400	11,700
2004	64,200	18,000	3,300	20,900	4,400	3,100	600	1,400	400	500	400	11,200
2005	69,600	18,800	3,500	23,500	4,400	3,100	(d)	1,500	400	500	400	13,500
2006	73,300	20,000	3,500	27,400	4,400	3,000	(d)	1,600	400	400	400	12,200
2007	77,200	21,800	3,400	29,700	4,300	3,200	(d)	1,600	400	400	400	12,000
2008	79,700	23,300	3,400	31,000	4,400	2,800	(d)	1,700	400	300	400	12,000
2009	79,800	24,200	3,400	31,700	4,400	2,700	(d)	1,500	400	400	300	10,800
2010	83,200	25,400	3,700	32,900	4,500	2,700	(d)	1,600	300	300	400	11,400
2011[f]	88,800	26,800	3,500	36,100	4,700	2,600	(d)	1,600	300	500	300	12,400
2012[f]	89,400	28,000	3,500	36,200	4,700	2,700	(d)	1,600	300	400	300	11,700
2013[g]	93,200	29,500	3,600	38,600	4,700	2,400	(d)	1,700	300	400	300	11,700

Source: National Safety Council estimates based on data from National Center for Health Statistics and state vital statistics departments. The Council adopted the Bureau of Labor Statistics' Census of Fatal Occupational Injuries count for work-related unintentional injuries retroactive to 1992 data. Because of the lower work class total resulting from this change, several thousand unintentional-injury-related deaths that had been classified by the Council as work-related had to be reassigned to the home and public classes. For this reason, long-term historical comparisons for these three classes should be made with caution. See the Technical Appendix for an explanation of the methodological changes.
[a]*Includes some deaths not shown separately.*
[b]*Inhalation and ingestion of food or other object that obstructs breathing.*
[c]*Includes subways and elevateds.*
[d]*Estimates for both home and public are not available.*
[e]*In 1999, a revision was made in the* International Classification of Diseases. *See the Technical Appendix for comparability with earlier years.*
[f]*Revised.*
[g]*Preliminary.*

Leading types of home and community unintentional-injury-related deaths, United States, 2001-2013

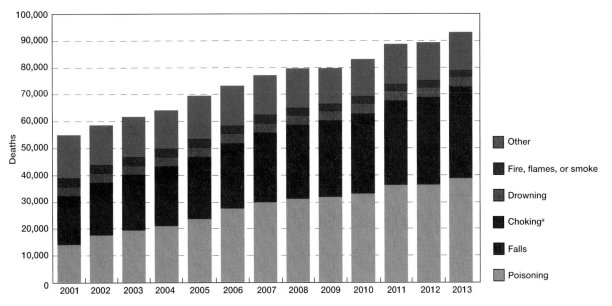

[a]*Inhalation and ingestion of food or other objects that obstructs breathing.*

State Data

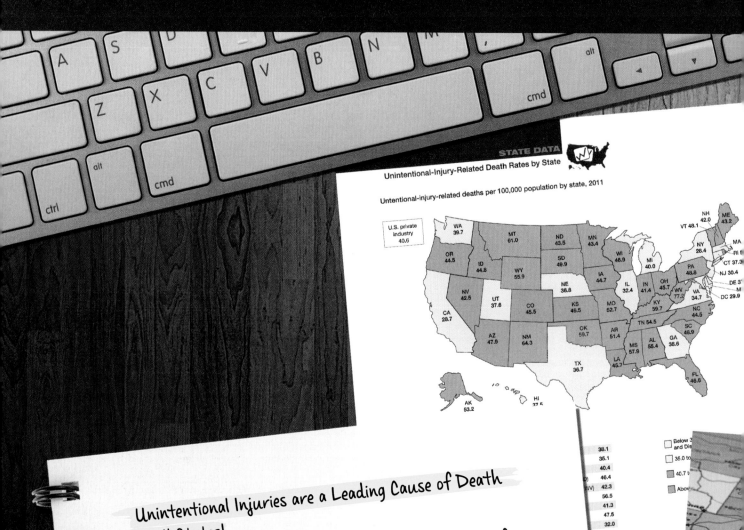

Unintentional-Injury-Related Death Rates by State

Untentional-injury-related deaths per 100,000 population by state, 2011

U.S. private industry 40.6

WA 39.7
OR 44.5
ID 44.8
NV 42.5
CA 28.7
UT 37.6
AZ 47.9
MT 61.0
WY 55.9
CO 45.5
NM 64.3
ND 43.5
SD 49.9
NE 36.8
KS 46.5
OK 59.7
TX 36.7
MN 43.4
IA 44.7
MO 52.7
AR 51.4
LA 45.7
WI 46.9
IL 32.4
MI 40.0
IN 41.4
KY 59.7
TN 54.5
MS 57.9
AL 55.4
GA 38.6
OH 45.7
WV 77.2
VA 34.7
NC 44.5
SC 48.9
FL 46.6
PA 48.8
NY 26.4
VT 48.1
NH 42.0
ME 43.2
MA
RI 5
CT 37.3
NJ 30.4
DE 3
M
DC 29.9
AK 53.2
HI 37.5

38.1
35.1
40.4
46.4
42.3
56.5
41.3
47.5
32.0

Below 3 and Dis
35.0 to
40.7 t
Above

ss--Mortality Data for 2011, as compiled
Safety Council estimates based on data

Unintentional Injuries are a Leading Cause of Death in all States!

Unintentional injuries are the third leading cause of death in 10 states, the fourth leading cause in 17 states and the District of Columbia, and the sixth leading cause in 4 states.

In 2011, poisonings were the leading cause of unintentional-injury-related deaths in 23 states and the District of Columbia. Motor vehicle crashes were the leading cause in 18 states. Falls were the leading cause in nine states.

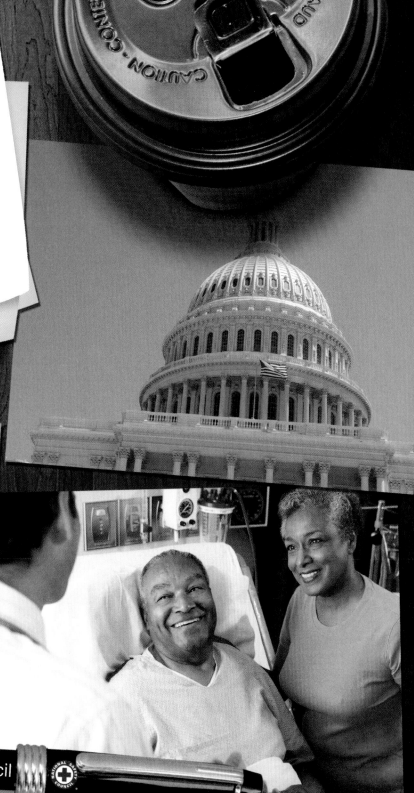

National Safety Council

■ *Poisonings are the leading cause of unintentional-injury-related deaths in 23 states and the District of Columbia.*

This section on state-level data includes data for occupational and motor vehicle injuries, as well as general injury mortality.

Death rates by state of residence for unintentional injuries can vary greatly from one type of injury to the next and from state to state. The graph on the next page shows for each state the death rates (per 100,000 population) for total unintentional-injury-related deaths and the four leading types of unintentional-injury-related deaths nationally – poisonings, motor vehicle crashes, falls, and choking (inhalation or ingestion of food or other object that obstructs breathing).

The map on page 174 shows graphically the overall unintentional-injury-related death rates by state of residence. Rates by region were lowest in Middle Atlantic and highest in East South Central states.

The charts on pages 175-177 show the total unintentional-injury-related deaths by state of residence and where unintentional injuries rank as a cause of death in each state, as well as the five leading causes of unintentional-injury-related deaths in each state.

Unintentional injuries as a whole are the fifth leading cause of death in the United States and in 19 states. Unintentional injuries are the third leading cause of death in 10 states, the fourth leading cause in 17 states and the District of Columbia, and the sixth leading cause in four states.

In 2011, poisonings were the leading cause of unintentional-injury-related deaths in 23 states and the District of Columbia. Motor vehicle crashes were the leading cause in 18 states. Falls were the leading cause in nine states.

The second leading cause of unintentional-injury-related deaths was motor vehicle crashes in 21 states, while poisoning was the second leading cause in 16 states. Falls were second in 13 states and the District of Columbia.

The most common third leading cause of unintentional-injury-related deaths was falls, in 28 states, while motor vehicle crashes were the third leading cause in 11 states and the District of Columbia. Poisoning ranked third in 11 states.

Choking was the fourth leading cause of unintentional-injury-related deaths in 36 states, while the fourth ranking cause was drowning in 11 states; and natural heat or cold was the fourth ranked cause in two states and the District of Columbia. Fire, flames, or smoke was the fourth ranked cause in two states.

Drowning was the fifth leading unintentional-injury-related cause of death in 23 states. Fire, flames, or smoke was fifth in 14 states and choking ranked fifth in nine states and the District of Columbia. Natural heat or cold was the fifth leading cause in three states. Mechanical suffocation ranked fifth in Nebraska. (States with ties for fifth leading causes were included in multiple counts.)

The table on pages 178-179 shows the number of unintentional-injury-related deaths by state of occurrence for the 15 most common types of injury events. State populations also are shown to facilitate computation of detailed death rates.

The table on page 180 consists of a four-year state-by-state comparison of unintentional-injury-related deaths by state of residence and death rates for 2008 through 2011.

Page 181 shows fatal occupational injuries by state and counts of deaths for some of the principal types of events – transportation incidents, assaults or violent acts, contact with objects or equipment, falls, exposure to harmful substances or environments, and fires or explosions.

Nonfatal occupational injury and illness incidence rates for most states are shown in the table on page 182 and graphically in the map on page 183. States not shown do not have state occupational safety and health plans.

Pages 184 and 185 show motor vehicle-related deaths and death rates by state both in tables and maps. The maps show death rates based on population, vehicle miles traveled, and registered vehicles.

Unintentional-injury-related death rates by state of residence, United States, 2011

Deaths per 100,000 population

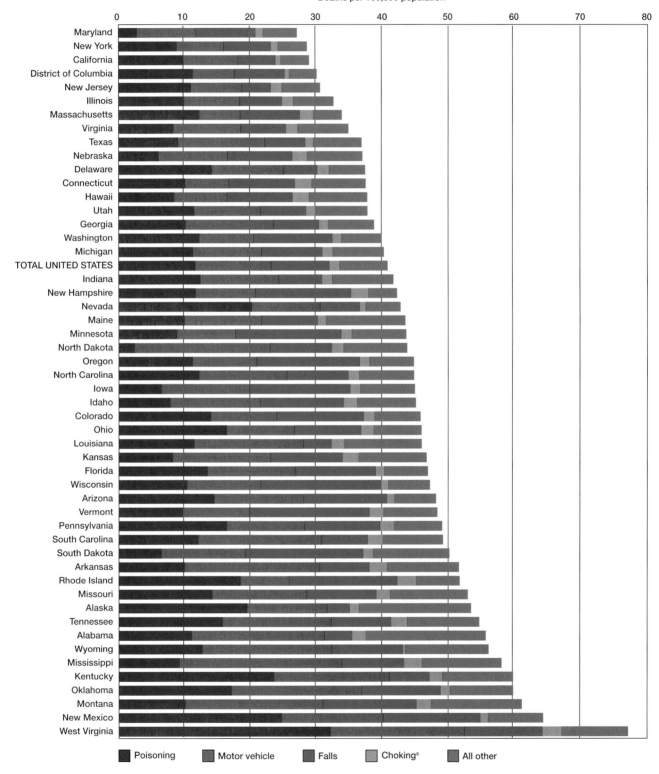

Poisoning   Motor vehicle   Falls   Choking[a]   All other

[a]Suffocation by ingestion or inhalation of food or other object.

Unintentional-Injury-Related Death Rates by State

Untentional-injury-related deaths per 100,000 population by state, 2011

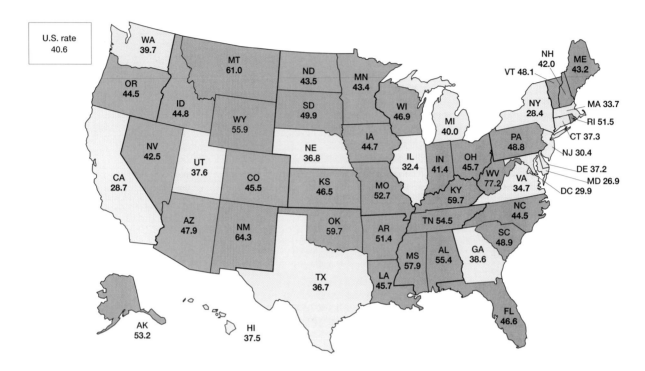

U.S. rate
40.6

WA 39.7 / MT 61.0 / ND 43.5 / MN 43.4 / NH 42.0 / ME 43.2 / VT 48.1 / OR 44.5 / ID 44.8 / WY 55.9 / SD 49.9 / WI 46.9 / NY 28.4 / MA 33.7 / RI 51.5 / CT 37.3 / NJ 30.4 / DE 37.2 / MD 26.9 / DC 29.9 / NV 42.5 / UT 37.6 / NE 36.8 / IA 44.7 / MI 40.0 / PA 48.8 / IL 32.4 / IN 41.4 / OH 45.7 / WV 77.2 / VA 34.7 / CA 28.7 / CO 45.5 / KS 46.5 / MO 52.7 / KY 59.7 / NC 44.5 / AZ 47.9 / NM 64.3 / OK 59.7 / AR 51.4 / TN 54.5 / SC 48.9 / MS 57.9 / AL 55.4 / GA 38.6 / TX 36.7 / LA 45.7 / FL 46.6 / AK 53.2 / HI 37.5

REGIONAL RATES

NEW ENGLAND (CT, ME, MA, NH, RI, VT)	38.1
MIDDLE ATLANTIC (NJ, NY, PA)	35.1
EAST NORTH CENTRAL (IL, IN, MI, OH, WI)	40.4
WEST NORTH CENTRAL (IA, KS, MN, MO, NE, ND, SD)	46.4
SOUTH ATLANTIC (DE, DC, FL, GA, MD, NC, SC, VA, WV)	42.3
EAST SOUTH CENTRAL (AL, KY, MS, TN)	56.5
WEST SOUTH CENTRAL (AR, LA, OK, TX)	41.3
MOUNTAIN (AZ, CO, ID, MT, NV, NM, UT, WY)	47.5
PACIFIC (AK, CA, HI, OR, WA)	32.0

Below 35.0 — 7 states and District of Columbia ⎤
35.0 to 40.6 — 9 states ⎦ Below or at national average

40.7 to 48.0 — 17 states ⎤
Above 48.0 — 17 states ⎦ Above national average

Source: National Safety Council analysis of National Center for Health Statistics–Mortality Data for 2011, as compiled from data provided by the 57 vital statistics jurisdictions through the Vital Statistics Cooperative Program. Rates are National Safety Council estimates based on data from the National Center for Health Statistics and the U.S. Census Bureau.

Unintentional-Injury-Related Deaths by State

The following series of tables is a state-by-state ranking of the five leading causes of deaths due to unintentional injuries based on 2011 data. The data are classified by state of residence. The first line of each section gives the rank of unintentional-injury-related deaths among all causes of death, the total number of unintentional-injury-related deaths, and the rate of unintentional-injury-related deaths per 100,000 population in the state. The following lines list the five leading types of unintentional-injury-related deaths in the state, along with the number and rate for each type.

2011

UNITED STATES

Rank	Cause	Deaths	Rate
5	All unintentional injuries	126,438	40.6
1	Poisoning[a]	36,280	11.6
2	Motor vehicle	35,303	11.3
3	Falls	27,438	8.8
4	Choking[b]	4,708	1.5
5	Drowning[c]	3,556	1.1

ALABAMA

Rank	Cause	Deaths	Rate
4	All unintentional injuries	2,662	55.4
1	Motor vehicle	956	19.9
2	Poisoning[a]	531	11.1
3	Falls	203	4.2
4	Choking[b]	101	2.1
5	Fire, flames or smoke	98	2.0

ALASKA

Rank	Cause	Deaths	Rate
3	All unintentional injuries	385	53.2
1	Poisoning[a]	140	19.4
2	Motor vehicle	87	12.0
3	Falls	25	3.5
4	Natural heat or cold	22	3.0
5	Drowning[c]	20	2.8

ARIZONA

Rank	Cause	Deaths	Rate
4	All unintentional injuries	3,096	47.9
1	Poisoning[a]	935	14.5
2	Motor vehicle	866	13.4
3	Falls	815	12.6
4	Drowning[c]	91	1.4
5	Natural heat or cold	78	1.2

ARKANSAS

Rank	Cause	Deaths	Rate
5	All unintentional injuries	1,510	51.4
1	Motor vehicle	595	20.2
2	Poisoning[a]	294	10.0
3	Falls	223	7.6
4	Choking[b]	77	2.6
5	Drowning[c]	54	1.8

CALIFORNIA

Rank	Cause	Deaths	Rate
6	All unintentional injuries	10,824	28.7
1	Poisoning[a]	3,727	9.9
2	Motor vehicle	3,041	8.1
3	Falls	2,145	5.7
4	Drowning[c]	363	1.0
5	Choking[b]	286	0.8

COLORADO

Rank	Cause	Deaths	Rate
3	All unintentional injuries	2,330	45.5
1	Poisoning[a]	714	13.9
2	Falls	675	13.2
3	Motor vehicle	503	9.8
4	Choking[b]	84	1.6
5	Drowning[c]	44	0.9

CONNECTICUT

Rank	Cause	Deaths	Rate
4	All unintentional injuries	1,339	37.3
1	Poisoning[a]	364	10.1
2	Falls	356	9.9
3	Motor vehicle	233	6.5
4	Choking[b]	91	2.5
5	Drowning[c]	41	1.1

DELAWARE

Rank	Cause	Deaths	Rate
5	All unintentional injuries	338	37.2
1	Poisoning[a]	128	14.1
2	Motor vehicle	98	10.8
3	Falls	46	5.1
4	Choking[b]	16	1.8
5	Natural heat or cold	–	–

DISTRICT OF COLUMBIA

Rank	Cause	Deaths	Rate
4	All unintentional injuries	185	29.9
1	Poisoning[a]	70	11.3
2	Falls	47	7.6
3	Motor vehicle	38	6.1
4	Natural heat or cold	–	–
5	Choking[b]	–	–

FLORIDA

Rank	Cause	Deaths	Rate
4	All unintentional injuries	8,901	46.6
1	Poisoning[a]	2,562	13.4
2	Motor vehicle	2,512	13.2
3	Falls	2,325	12.2
4	Drowning[c]	359	1.9
5	Choking[b]	242	1.3

GEORGIA

Rank	Cause	Deaths	Rate
4	All unintentional injuries	3,785	38.6
1	Motor vehicle	1,289	13.1
2	Poisoning[a]	1,000	10.2
3	Falls	674	6.9
4	Choking[b]	139	1.4
5	Drowning[c]	125	1.3

HAWAII

Rank	Cause	Deaths	Rate
4	All unintentional injuries	517	37.5
1	Falls	136	9.9
2	Poisoning[a]	117	8.5
3	Motor vehicle	108	7.8
4	Drowning[c]	56	4.1
5	Choking[b]	34	2.5

IDAHO

Rank	Cause	Deaths	Rate
4	All unintentional injuries	710	44.8
1	Motor vehicle	212	13.4
2	Falls	200	12.6
3	Poisoning[a]	125	7.9
4	Choking[b]	33	2.1
5	Drowning[c]	20	1.3

ILLINOIS

Rank	Cause	Deaths	Rate
5	All unintentional injuries	4,166	32.4
1	Poisoning[a]	1,282	10.0
2	Motor vehicle	1,063	8.3
3	Falls	820	6.4
4	Choking[b]	212	1.6
5	Fire, flames or smoke	113	0.9

INDIANA

Rank	Cause	Deaths	Rate
5	All unintentional injuries	2,699	41.4
1	Poisoning[a]	808	12.4
2	Motor vehicle	762	11.7
3	Falls	428	6.6
4	Choking[b]	100	1.5
5	Drowning[c]	78	1.2

IOWA

Rank	Cause	Deaths	Rate
6	All unintentional injuries	1,369	44.7
1	Falls	467	15.2
2	Motor vehicle	402	13.1
3	Poisoning[a]	201	6.6
4	Choking[b]	47	1.5
5	Drowning[c]	36	1.2

KANSAS

Rank	Cause	Deaths	Rate
5	All unintentional injuries	1,333	46.5
1	Motor vehicle	419	14.6
2	Falls	311	10.8
3	Poisoning[a]	238	8.3
4	Choking[b]	71	2.5
5	Fire, flames or smoke	36	1.3

See source and footnotes on page 177.

Unintentional-Injury-Related Deaths by State (cont.)

2011

KENTUCKY

Rank	Cause	Deaths	Rate
4	All unintentional injuries	2,608	59.7
1	Poisoning[a]	1,023	23.4
2	Motor vehicle	757	17.3
3	Falls	267	6.1
4	Choking[b]	84	1.9
5	Drowning[c]	61	1.4

LOUISIANA

Rank	Cause	Deaths	Rate
3	All unintentional injuries	2,091	45.7
1	Motor vehicle	747	16.3
2	Poisoning[a]	525	11.5
3	Falls	196	4.3
4	Drowning[c]	89	1.9
5	Choking[b]	87	1.9

MAINE

Rank	Cause	Deaths	Rate
5	All unintentional injuries	574	43.2
1	Motor vehicle	152	11.4
2	Poisoning[a]	133	10.0
3	Falls	113	8.5
4	Drowning[c]	19	1.4
5	Fire, flames or smoke	18	1.4

MARYLAND

Rank	Cause	Deaths	Rate
5	All unintentional injuries	1,569	26.9
1	Falls	522	8.9
2	Motor vehicle	516	8.8
3	Poisoning[a]	167	2.9
4	Choking[b]	63	1.1
5	Drowning[c]	61	1.0

MASSACHUSETTS

Rank	Cause	Deaths	Rate
5	All unintentional injuries	2,224	33.7
1	Poisoning[a]	811	12.3
2	Falls	594	9.0
3	Motor vehicle	399	6.0
4	Choking[b]	133	2.0
5	Drowning[c]	40	0.6

MICHIGAN

Rank	Cause	Deaths	Rate
5	All unintentional injuries	3,951	40.0
1	Poisoning[a]	1,115	11.3
2	Motor vehicle	1,009	10.2
3	Falls	908	9.2
4	Choking[b]	156	1.6
5	Drowning[c]	106	1.1

MINNESOTA

Rank	Cause	Deaths	Rate
3	All unintentional injuries	2,319	43.4
1	Falls	854	16.0
2	Poisoning[a]	477	8.9
3	Motor vehicle	462	8.6
4	Choking[b]	86	1.6
5	Drowning[c]	54	1.0

MISSISSIPPI

Rank	Cause	Deaths	Rate
3	All unintentional injuries	1,724	57.9
1	Motor vehicle	726	24.4
2	Falls	280	9.4
3	Poisoning[a]	275	9.2
4	Fire, flames or smoke	83	2.8
5	Choking[b]	81	2.7

MISSOURI

Rank	Cause	Deaths	Rate
4	All unintentional injuries	3,169	52.7
1	Poisoning[a]	850	14.1
2	Motor vehicle	849	14.1
3	Falls	637	10.6
4	Choking[b]	123	2.0
5	Drowning[c]	79	1.3

MONTANA

Rank	Cause	Deaths	Rate
4	All unintentional injuries	609	61.0
1	Motor vehicle	206	20.6
2	Falls	141	14.1
3	Poisoning[a]	101	10.1
4	Choking[b]	22	2.2
5	Drowning[c]	19	1.9

NEBRASKA

Rank	Cause	Deaths	Rate
5	All unintentional injuries	678	36.8
1	Motor vehicle	189	10.3
2	Falls	180	9.8
3	Poisoning[a]	113	6.1
4	Choking[b]	41	2.2
5	Mechanical suffocation	16	0.9

NEVADA

Rank	Cause	Deaths	Rate
4	All unintentional injuries	1,155	42.5
1	Poisoning[a]	546	20.1
2	Motor vehicle	279	10.3
3	Falls	164	6.0
4	Drowning[c]	31	1.1
5	Choking[b]	24	0.9

NEW HAMPSHIRE

Rank	Cause	Deaths	Rate
4	All unintentional injuries	553	42.0
1	Falls	191	14.5
2	Poisoning[a]	154	11.7
3	Motor vehicle	117	8.9
4	Choking[b]	35	2.7
5	Fire, flames or smoke	–	–

NEW JERSEY

Rank	Cause	Deaths	Rate
5	All unintentional injuries	2,685	30.4
1	Poisoning[a]	971	11.0
2	Motor vehicle	669	7.6
3	Falls	386	4.4
4	Choking[b]	145	1.6
5	Drowning[c]	57	0.6

NEW MEXICO

Rank	Cause	Deaths	Rate
3	All unintentional injuries	1,336	64.3
1	Poisoning[a]	511	24.6
2	Motor vehicle	317	15.3
3	Falls	307	14.8
4	Drowning[c]	31	1.5
5	Choking[b]	24	1.2

NEW YORK

Rank	Cause	Deaths	Rate
5	All unintentional injuries	5,537	28.4
1	Poisoning[a]	1,733	8.9
2	Falls	1,393	7.1
3	Motor vehicle	1,352	6.9
4	Choking[b]	201	1.0
5	Fire, flames or smoke	140	0.7

NORTH CAROLINA

Rank	Cause	Deaths	Rate
5	All unintentional injuries	4,297	44.5
1	Motor vehicle	1,263	13.1
2	Poisoning[a]	1,177	12.2
3	Falls	901	9.3
4	Choking[b]	160	1.7
5	Drowning[c]	120	1.2

NORTH DAKOTA

Rank	Cause	Deaths	Rate
6	All unintentional injuries	298	43.5
1	Motor vehicle	139	20.3
2	Falls	64	9.3
3	Poisoning[a]	17	2.5
4	Choking[b]	12	1.8
5	Fire, flames or smoke	–	–

See source and footnotes on page 177.

2011

OHIO

Rank	Cause	Deaths	Rate
5	All unintentional injuries	5,275	45.7
1	Poisoning[a]	1,882	16.3
2	Falls	1,173	10.2
3	Motor vehicle	1,171	10.1
4	Choking[b]	218	1.9
5	Fire, flames or smoke	96	0.8

OKLAHOMA

Rank	Cause	Deaths	Rate
4	All unintentional injuries	2,261	59.7
1	Motor vehicle	745	19.7
2	Poisoning[a]	643	17.0
3	Falls	449	11.9
4	Drowning[c]	62	1.6
4	Fire, flames or smoke	62	1.6

OREGON

Rank	Cause	Deaths	Rate
5	All unintentional injuries	1,722	44.5
1	Falls	604	15.6
2	Poisoning[a]	434	11.2
3	Motor vehicle	369	9.5
4	Choking[b]	57	1.5
5	Drowning[c]	56	1.4

PENNSYLVANIA

Rank	Cause	Deaths	Rate
5	All unintentional injuries	6,216	48.8
1	Poisoning[a]	2,080	16.3
2	Motor vehicle	1,484	11.6
3	Falls	1,464	11.5
4	Choking[b]	260	2.0
5	Fire, flames or smoke	154	1.2

RHODE ISLAND

Rank	Cause	Deaths	Rate
3	All unintentional injuries	541	51.5
1	Poisoning[a]	193	18.4
2	Falls	172	16.4
3	Motor vehicle	76	7.2
4	Choking[b]	30	2.9
5	Drowning[c]	10	1.0
5	Fire, flames or smoke	10	1.0

SOUTH CAROLINA

Rank	Cause	Deaths	Rate
5	All unintentional injuries	2,285	48.9
1	Motor vehicle	864	18.5
2	Poisoning[a]	565	12.1
3	Falls	327	7.0
4	Choking[b]	105	2.2
5	Fire, flames or smoke	67	1.4

SOUTH DAKOTA

Rank	Cause	Deaths	Rate
6	All unintentional injuries	411	49.9
1	Falls	147	17.8
2	Motor vehicle	103	12.5
3	Poisoning[a]	54	6.6
4	Natural heat or cold	15	1.8
5	Choking[b]	12	1.5

TENNESSEE

Rank	Cause	Deaths	Rate
4	All unintentional injuries	3,485	54.5
1	Motor vehicle	1,044	16.3
2	Poisoning[a]	1,004	15.7
3	Falls	578	9.0
4	Choking[b]	155	2.4
5	Fire, flames or smoke	90	1.4

TEXAS

Rank	Cause	Deaths	Rate
3	All unintentional injuries	9,410	36.7
1	Motor vehicle	3,304	12.9
2	Poisoning[a]	2,333	9.1
3	Falls	1,574	6.1
4	Drowning[c]	361	1.4
5	Choking[b]	306	1.2

UTAH

Rank	Cause	Deaths	Rate
3	All unintentional injuries	1,058	37.6
1	Poisoning[a]	324	11.5
2	Motor vehicle	277	9.8
3	Falls	194	6.9
4	Choking[b]	40	1.4
5	Drowning[c]	34	1.2

VERMONT

Rank	Cause	Deaths	Rate
4	All unintentional injuries	301	48.1
1	Falls	114	18.2
2	Motor vehicle	62	9.9
3	Poisoning[a]	61	9.7
4	Choking[b]	13	2.1
5	Drowning[c]	11	1.8

VIRGINIA

Rank	Cause	Deaths	Rate
5	All unintentional injuries	2,809	34.7
1	Motor vehicle	811	10.0
2	Poisoning[a]	679	8.4
3	Falls	554	6.8
4	Choking[b]	140	1.7
5	Drowning[c]	74	0.9

WASHINGTON

Rank	Cause	Deaths	Rate
5	All unintentional injuries	2,709	39.7
1	Poisoning[a]	834	12.2
2	Falls	813	11.9
3	Motor vehicle	552	8.1
4	Choking[b]	89	1.3
5	Drowning[c]	80	1.2

WEST VIRGINIA

Rank	Cause	Deaths	Rate
4	All unintentional injuries	1,432	77.2
1	Poisoning[a]	593	32.0
2	Motor vehicle	376	20.3
3	Falls	222	12.0
4	Choking[b]	54	2.9
5	Fire, flames or smoke	24	1.3

WISCONSIN

Rank	Cause	Deaths	Rate
3	All unintentional injuries	2,680	46.9
1	Falls	1,043	18.3
2	Motor vehicle	623	10.9
3	Poisoning[a]	594	10.4
4	Choking[b]	60	1.1
5	Drowning[c]	59	1.0

WYOMING

Rank	Cause	Deaths	Rate
4	All unintentional injuries	317	55.9
1	Motor vehicle	110	19.4
2	Poisoning[a]	72	12.7
3	Falls	61	10.8
4	Drowning[c]	14	2.5
5	Natural heat or cold	–	–

Source: National Safety Council analysis of National Center for Health Statistics (NCHS)–Mortality Data for 2011, as compiled from data provided by the 57 vital statistics jurisdictions through the Vital Statistics Cooperative Program. Rates are National Safety Council estimates based on data from NCHS and the U.S. Census Bureau. Dashes (–) indicate data values less than 10 as per NCHS publication guidelines.

[a]*Solid, liquid, gas, and vapor poisoning.*
[b]*Inhalation or ingestion of food or other objects.*
[c]*Excludes transport drownings.*

Unintentional-Injury-Related Deaths
by State and Event

Unintentional-injury-related deaths by state of occurrence and type of event, United States, 2011

State	Population (000)	Total[a]	Poisoning	Motor vehicle[b]	Falls	Choking[c]	Drowning[d]	Fire, flames, or smoke	Mechanical suffocation
Total U.S.	311,592	126,438	36,280	35,303	27,483	4,708	3,556	2,746	1,534
Alabama	4,802	2,613	525	934	187	99	68	102	25
Alaska	723	388	138	84	28	–	21	10	–
Arizona	6,469	3,124	925	878	827	73	93	34	28
Arkansas	2,939	1,464	280	586	210	79	52	39	15
California	37,669	10,795	3,757	3,014	2,134	284	362	176	83
Colorado	5,118	2,393	733	512	692	87	50	31	35
Connecticut	3,589	1,340	361	238	359	94	39	23	–
Delaware	908	360	132	105	47	19	–	–	–
District of Columbia	620	281	87	50	86	–	–	12	–
Florida	19,083	9,016	2,580	2,560	2,346	242	406	91	132
Georgia	9,810	3,787	999	1,288	668	140	116	138	36
Hawaii	1,377	549	119	112	134	34	79	–	–
Idaho	1,584	688	115	202	200	33	20	–	10
Illinois	12,856	3,977	1,292	973	766	204	84	112	74
Indiana	6,516	2,677	795	768	421	103	79	63	45
Iowa	3,064	1,340	198	390	458	48	23	35	12
Kansas	2,870	1,276	234	413	293	69	23	37	16
Kentucky	4,367	2,543	998	742	245	85	61	57	25
Louisiana	4,575	2,113	532	748	193	90	94	71	52
Maine	1,328	583	133	153	112	19	22	18	–
Maryland	5,840	1,485	131	519	493	61	53	39	15
Massachusetts	6,606	2,214	809	387	590	136	43	31	–
Michigan	9,875	3,815	1,094	946	868	155	103	97	95
Minnesota	5,347	2,274	474	432	866	82	57	45	34
Mississippi	2,978	1,674	268	717	265	80	51	74	10
Missouri	6,010	3,296	863	888	682	123	82	78	65
Montana	998	639	101	231	142	21	18	13	–
Nebraska	1,842	704	112	205	186	43	13	10	16
Nevada	2,718	1,258	578	297	193	31	33	20	13
New Hampshire	1,318	522	151	93	193	33	–	–	–
New Jersey	8,837	2,629	948	671	366	141	59	46	12
New Mexico	2,078	1,384	528	362	297	22	29	19	18
New York	19,503	5,392	1,732	1,269	1,359	191	103	141	59
North Carolina	9,651	4,359	1,180	1,297	916	158	121	122	37
North Dakota	685	363	16	162	78	19	–	–	–
Ohio	11,550	5,231	1,882	1,152	1,154	217	75	99	85
Oklahoma	3,786	2,236	631	757	441	45	68	61	–
Oregon	3,868	1,731	443	367	606	54	52	43	17
Pennsylvania	12,741	6,195	2,083	1,463	1,468	265	93	155	62
Rhode Island	1,050	586	202	88	187	32	10	12	–
South Carolina	4,674	2,223	558	854	307	101	59	59	31
South Dakota	824	453	55	131	157	13	12	11	–
Tennessee	6,398	3,753	1,010	1,129	680	164	74	96	52
Texas	25,641	9,421	2,336	3,301	1,590	309	345	213	103
Utah	2,815	1,056	322	275	193	40	31	12	21
Vermont	626	291	60	66	113	–	–	–	–
Virginia	8,106	2,810	687	820	562	140	65	56	33
Washington	6,821	2,639	826	512	810	93	74	48	35
West Virginia	1,855	1,472	602	400	236	52	22	19	–
Wisconsin	5,709	2,670	590	627	1,021	60	65	44	51
Wyoming	567	356	75	135	58	–	11	–	–

See source and footnotes on page 179.

Unintentional-injury-related deaths by state of occurrence and type of event, United States, 2011

State	Natural heat or cold	Struck by or against	Machinery	Firearms	Water transportation	Air transportation	Rail transportation	Electric current	All other incidents
Total U.S.	1,259	827	610	591	533	494	394	308	9,812
Alabama	11	17	11	25	–	14	–	–	576
Alaska	23	–	–	–	13	21	–	–	28
Arizona	86	11	–	–	10	19	–	–	120
Arkansas	27	17	–	10	11	–	–	–	112
California	55	41	38	26	34	48	53	31	659
Colorado	13	–	–	12	11	18	–	–	179
Connecticut	18	–	–	–	–	–	–	–	186
Delaware	–	–	–	–	–	–	–	–	30
District of Columbia	–	–	–	–	–	–	–	–	21
Florida	19	40	21	30	46	23	20	30	430
Georgia	28	28	20	27	10	16	10	12	251
Hawaii	–	–	–	–	–	11	–	–	44
Idaho	–	12	–	–	12	15	–	–	46
Illinois	41	19	15	20	11	15	34	13	304
Indiana	29	28	19	12	–	–	–	–	288
Iowa	11	11	26	–	–	–	–	–	116
Kansas	28	12	12	–	–	–	–	–	110
Kentucky	20	22	17	15	–	–	13	–	226
Louisiana	22	10	17	52	23	–	–	13	189
Maine	–	–	–	–	–	–	–	–	90
Maryland	18	15	–	–	–	–	–	–	107
Massachusetts	22	–	–	–	–	–	–	–	162
Michigan	52	26	27	11	16	16	–	12	294
Minnesota	16	18	17	–	12	–	–	–	201
Mississippi	20	14	–	31	14	–	–	–	111
Missouri	55	23	17	23	16	11	–	–	358
Montana	11	–	–	–	10	–	–	–	58
Nebraska	–	–	–	–	–	–	–	–	82
Nevada	15	–	–	–	–	19	–	–	46
New Hampshire	–	–	–	–	–	–	–	–	16
New Jersey	28	14	–	–	–	–	13	–	303
New Mexico	20	–	–	–	–	10	–	–	52
New York	68	43	20	–	19	12	19	13	335
North Carolina	22	33	29	38	14	13	14	–	357
North Dakota	–	–	–	–	–	–	–	–	50
Ohio	27	38	18	18	10	15	12	12	417
Oklahoma	32	–	13	19	–	–	–	–	136
Oregon	–	19	–	–	12	13	–	–	84
Pennsylvania	50	34	30	19	14	–	17	11	426
Rhode Island	–	–	–	–	–	–	–	–	44
South Carolina	14	–	–	17	14	–	–	–	180
South Dakota	15	–	–	–	–	11	–	–	28
Tennessee	22	39	15	30	14	–	13	–	400
Texas	160	75	49	54	27	32	30	31	766
Utah	12	–	–	–	–	11	–	–	120
Vermont	–	–	–	–	–	–	–	–	15
Virginia	32	24	18	–	17	10	–	–	322
Washington	18	16	15	–	16	13	11	–	141
West Virginia	16	14	12	12	–	–	–	–	57
Wisconsin	29	21	24	–	19	11	–	–	95
Wyoming	–	–	–	–	–	–	–	–	44

Source: National Safety Council analysis of National Center for Heatlh Statistics (NCHS)–Mortality Data for 2011, as compiled from data provided by the 57 vital statistics jurisdictions through the Vital Statistics Cooperative Program. Dashes (–) indicate data values less than 10 as per NCHS publication guidelines.
aDeaths are by place of occurrence and exclude nonresident aliens.
bSee page 184 for motor vehicle deaths by place of residence.
cSuffocation by inhalation or ingestion of food or object obstructing breathing.
dExcludes water transport drownings.

Nationwide, from 2008 to 2011, unintentional-injury-related deaths increased nearly 4% and the death rate increased by over 1%. By state, the greatest decrease in the number of unintentional-injury-related deaths occurred in Louisiana (-13%), while the greatest decrease in the death rate occurred in North Dakota (-18%). The greatest increase in unintentional-injury-related deaths and death rates occurred in Hawaii (+27% and +18%, respectively).

The table below shows the trend in unintentional-injury-related deaths and death rates by state over the most recent four years for which data are available.

Unintentional-injury-related deaths by state of residence, United States, 2008-2011

State	Deaths[a]				Deaths per 100,000 population			
	2011[b]	2010	2009	2008	2011[b]	2010	2009	2008
Total U.S.	126,438	120,859	118,021	121,902	40.6	39.0	38.4	40.0
Alabama	2,662	2,394	2,351	2,509	55.4	50.0	49.9	53.7
Alaska	385	366	340	332	53.2	51.3	48.7	48.4
Arizona	3,096	3,018	2,919	2,956	47.9	47.1	44.3	45.5
Arkansas	1,510	1,461	1,473	1,477	51.4	50.0	51.0	51.5
California	10,824	10,435	10,860	10,761	28.7	28.0	29.4	29.5
Colorado	2,330	2,106	2,144	2,172	45.5	41.7	42.7	44.1
Connecticut	1,339	1,337	1,293	1,386	37.3	37.4	36.8	39.6
Delaware	338	357	333	352	37.2	39.7	37.6	40.1
District of Columbia	185	212	145	160	29.9	35.0	24.2	27.1
Florida	8,901	8,875	8,746	8,939	46.6	47.1	47.2	48.6
Georgia	3,785	3,745	3,812	3,774	38.6	38.5	38.8	38.9
Hawaii	517	432	436	406	37.5	31.7	33.7	31.7
Idaho	710	654	670	649	44.8	41.6	43.3	42.5
Illinois	4,166	3,997	3,961	4,218	32.4	31.1	30.7	32.9
Indiana	2,699	2,534	2,577	2,558	41.4	39.0	40.1	40.1
Iowa	1,369	1,273	1,255	1,266	44.7	41.7	41.7	42.3
Kansas	1,333	1,317	1,273	1,174	46.5	46.1	45.2	42.0
Kentucky	2,608	2,632	2,394	2,379	59.7	60.6	55.5	55.5
Louisiana	2,091	1,999	2,142	2,409	45.7	44.0	47.7	54.1
Maine	574	540	602	628	43.2	40.7	45.7	47.6
Maryland	1,569	1,446	1,415	1,465	26.9	25.0	24.8	25.9
Massachusetts	2,224	2,060	2,076	2,040	33.7	31.4	31.5	31.2
Michigan	3,951	3,770	3,682	3,685	40.0	38.2	36.9	36.9
Minnesota	2,319	2,103	2,037	2,010	43.4	39.6	38.7	38.4
Mississippi	1,724	1,685	1,658	1,693	57.9	56.8	56.2	57.6
Missouri	3,169	2,975	2,939	2,997	52.7	49.6	49.1	50.4
Montana	609	548	619	592	61.0	55.3	63.5	61.2
Nebraska	678	700	683	714	36.8[b]	38.3	38.0	40.1
Nevada	1,155	1,088	1,025	1,134	42.5	40.2	38.8	43.4
New Hampshire	553	517	482	488	42.0	39.3	36.4	36.9
New Jersey	2,685	2,486	1,875	2,436	30.4	28.2	21.5	28.1
New Mexico	1,336	1,233	1,281	1,366	64.3	59.7	63.7	68.8
New York	5,537	5,004	4,891	5,042	28.4	25.8	25.0	25.9
North Carolina	4,297	4,144	4,136	4,313	44.5	43.4	44.1	46.7
North Dakota	298	285	324	342	43.5	42.3	50.1	53.4
Ohio	5,275	5,124	4,012	5,093	45.7	44.4	34.8	44.2
Oklahoma	2,261	2,288	2,284	2,119	59.7	60.9	61.9	58.2
Oregon	1,722	1,566	1,598	1,674	44.5	40.8	41.8	44.3
Pennsylvania	6,216	5,751	5,477	5,787	48.8	45.2	43.5	46.1
Rhode Island	541	475	428	480	51.5	45.1	40.6	45.4
South Carolina	2,285	2,274	2,229	2,285	48.9	49.1	48.9	50.8
South Dakota	411	393	349	381	49.9	48.1	43.0	47.4
Tennessee	3,485	3,539	3,231	3,250	54.5	55.7	51.3	52.1
Texas	9,410	9,212	9,349	9,189	36.7	36.5	37.7	37.8
Utah	1,058	970	899	881	37.6	35.0	32.3	32.3
Vermont	301	298	308	306	48.1	47.6	49.5	49.3
Virginia	2,809	2,527	2,622	2,820	34.7	31.5	33.3	36.2
Washington	2,709	2,609	2,696	2,727	39.7	38.7	40.5	41.5
West Virginia	1,432	1,234	942	1,253	77.2	66.6	51.8	69.0
Wisconsin	2,680	2,525	2,449	2,484	46.9	44.4	43.3	44.1
Wyoming	317	346	299	351	55.9	61.3	54.9	65.9

Source: Deaths are from the National Center for Health Statistics (NCHS)–Mortality Data for 2011, as compiled from data provided by the 57 vital statistics jurisdictions through the Vital Statistics Cooperative Program. Rates are National Safety Council estimates based on data from NCHS and the U.S. Census Bureau. See Technical Appendix for comparability.
[a]Deaths for each state are by state of residence and exclude nonresident aliens.
[b]Latest official figures.

Fatal Occupational Injuries by State

In general, states with the largest number of people employed have the largest number of work-related fatalities. The four largest states – California, Texas, New York, and Florida – accounted for 29% of the total 2013 work-related fatalities in the United States. Each state's industry mix, geographic features, age of population, and other characteristics of the workforce must be considered when evaluating state fatality profiles. Overall, the six leading events or exposures accounted for all but 18 of the 4,405 total occupational fatalities in all states in 2013.

Fatal occupational injuries by state and event or exposure, United States, 2012-2013

State	Total fatal injuries[a] 2012[c]	Total fatal injuries[a] 2013[d]	Transportation incidents[e]	Violence and other injuries by persons or animals[f]	Contact with objects and equipment	Falls, slips, or trips	Exposure to harmful substances or environments	Fire and explosions
Total	4,628	4,405	1,740	753	717	699	330	148
Alabama	84	66	32	11	8	10	4	–
Alaska	31	32	19	6	–	–	3	–
Arizona	60	90	22	25	8	11	5	19
Arkansas	63	62	28	2	10	11	8	3
California	375	385	133	76	64	63	38	10
Colorado	82	65	28	11	7	9	9	–
Connecticut	36	26	7	7	5	6	–	–
Delaware	14	11	3	–	2	3	–	–
District of Columbia	11	24	–	19	–	–	–	1
Florida	218	234	84	47	26	56	19	–
Georgia	101	70	24	10	17	14	3	–
Hawaii	20	11	4	–	–	4	–	–
Idaho	19	29	14	–	5	5	3	–
Illinois	146	172	63	32	35	21	14	6
Indiana	115	123	58	26	16	9	10	3
Iowa	97	71	28	4	16	13	8	1
Kansas	76	54	30	3	8	6	4	3
Kentucky	91	82	33	12	13	13	9	–
Louisiana	116	114	42	15	17	21	14	–
Maine	19	19	6	2	4	4	–	–
Maryland	72	78	22	17	12	17	7	3
Massachusetts	44	55	12	20	6	11	5	1
Michigan	137	133	42	40	25	16	7	2
Minnesota	70	67	32	6	12	11	4	–
Mississippi	63	64	32	8	9	9	3	3
Missouri	88	113	45	23	17	18	7	3
Montana	34	28	12	5	5	4	–	1
Nebraska	48	39	21	4	9	4	1	–
Nevada	42	42	15	7	4	6	–	8
New Hampshire	14	14	1	–	6	4	–	1
New Jersey	92	101	36	28	11	16	8	–
New Mexico	39	53	34	4	6	6	3	–
New York	202	160	49	34	29	33	11	3
North Carolina	146	104	41	20	23	11	7	–
North Dakota	65	55	31	3	13	5	–	3
Ohio	161	148	51	23	30	33	7	4
Oklahoma	97	86	51	5	8	12	7	–
Oregon	43	49	19	4	12	8	5	1
Pennsylvania	194	178	70	29	31	25	19	4
Rhode Island	8	10	–	–	3	–	–	–
South Carolina	63	72	27	14	9	13	8	1
South Dakota	31	19	12	–	1	2	1	–
Tennessee	101	93	39	15	18	12	8	–
Texas	536	493	213	66	76	73	31	32
Utah	39	39	11	7	11	5	–	–
Vermont	11	7	4	–	–	–	–	–
Virginia	149	126	54	27	16	21	6	–
Washington	67	56	23	8	11	10	3	–
West Virginia	49	60	24	6	15	5	3	7
Wisconsin	114	96	40	11	15	23	6	–
Wyoming	35	26	13	–	9	–	–	–

Source: Bureau of Labor Statistics (BLS). National Census of Fatal Occupational Injuries in 2013 (preliminary results), accessed September 15, 2014, from www.bls.gov/news.release/cfoi.nr0.htm.

Note: Dashes (–) indicate no data or data that do not meet publication criteria.

[a]*State totals include other events and exposures, such as bodily reaction, in addition to those shown separately.*

[b]*Based on the BLS Occupational Injury and Illness Classification System 2.01, implemented for 2011 data forward.*

[c]*Data for 2012 are revised and final.*

[d]*Data for 2013 are preliminary and include three fatal injuries that occurred within the territorial boundaries of the United States, but a State of incident could not be determined.*

[e]*Includes highway, nonhighway, air, water, and rail fatal injuries, and fatal injuries resulting from being struck by a vehicle.*

[f]*Includes violence by persons, self-inflicted injuries, and attacks by animals.*

Nonfatal occupational injury and illness rates[a] by state, private industry, 2012

State	Total recordable cases	Cases with days away from work[b]	Cases with job transfer or restriction	Other recordable cases
Private industry[c]	3.4	1.0	0.7	1.6
Alabama	3.3	0.9	0.8	1.6
Alaska	4.6	1.7	0.4	2.5
Arizona	3.2	0.9	0.7	1.6
Arkansas	3.2	0.8	0.7	1.7
California	3.5	1.1	1.0	1.4
Colorado	–	–	–	–
Connecticut	3.9	1.4	0.8	1.7
Delaware	2.8	0.9	0.4	1.5
District of Columbia	1.6	0.7	0.1	0.8
Florida	–	–	–	–
Georgia	2.8	0.8	0.6	1.4
Hawaii	3.8	2.0	0.3	1.5
Idaho	–	–	–	–
Illinois	3.2	1.0	0.7	1.5
Indiana	3.9	0.9	1.1	1.9
Iowa	4.5	1.2	1.2	2.2
Kansas	3.6	0.9	0.9	1.8
Kentucky	4.1	1.1	0.9	2.0
Louisiana	2.3	0.7	0.4	1.2
Maine	5.6	1.3	1.6	2.7
Maryland	3.1	1.2	0.4	1.5
Massachusetts	3.1	1.4	0.3	1.4
Michigan	4.0	1.0	1.0	2.0
Minnesota	3.8	1.0	0.8	2.0
Mississippi	–	–	–	–
Missouri	3.3	0.8	0.9	1.7
Montana	5.0	1.6	0.6	2.8
Nebraska	3.9	1.1	0.8	2.0
Nevada	4.1	1.1	1.2	1.7
New Hampshire	–	–	–	–
New Jersey	3.1	1.2	0.5	1.4
New Mexico	3.9	1.1	0.8	2.0
New York	2.5	1.2	0.2	1.1
North Carolina	2.9	0.8	0.7	1.4
North Dakota	–	–	–	–
Ohio	3.2	0.9	0.6	1.7
Oklahoma	3.6	1.1	0.8	1.7
Oregon	3.9	1.5	0.8	1.7
Pennsylvania	3.9	1.1	0.8	2.0
Rhode Island	–	–	–	–
South Carolina	3.0	0.9	0.6	1.5
South Dakota	–	–	–	–
Tennessee	3.5	0.9	0.9	1.7
Texas	2.7	0.7	0.8	1.2
Utah	3.4	0.7	0.7	2.0
Vermont	5.0	1.4	0.9	2.7
Virginia	2.7	0.9	0.5	1.3
Washington	4.8	1.5	0.9	2.3
West Virginia	4.1	1.6	0.5	1.9
Wisconsin	4.0	1.1	0.9	2.0
Wyoming	3.5	1.3	0.4	1.8

Source: Bureau of Labor Statistics, U.S. Department of Labor.
Note: Because of rounding, components may not add to totals. Dashes (–) indicate data not available.
[a]Incidence rates represent the number of injuries and illnesses per 100 full-time workers using 200,000 hours as the equivalent.
[b]Days-away-from-work cases include those that result in days away from work with or without job transfer or restriction.
[c]Data cover all 50 states.

Nonfatal Occupational Incidence Rates by State (cont.)

Nonfatal occupational injury and illness incidence rates[a] for total recordable cases by state, private industry, 2012

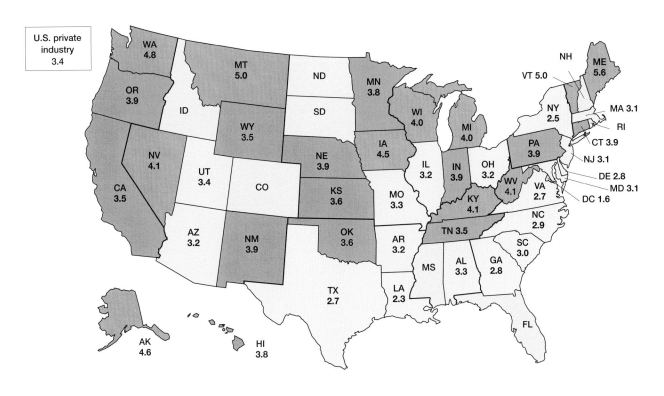

U.S. private industry
3.4

WA 4.8
MT 5.0
ND
MN 3.8
NH
VT 5.0
ME 5.6
OR 3.9
ID
WY 3.5
SD
WI 4.0
MI 4.0
NY 2.5
MA 3.1
RI
NV 4.1
UT 3.4
CO
NE 3.9
IA 4.5
IL 3.2
IN 3.9
OH 3.2
PA 3.9
CT 3.9
NJ 3.1
CA 3.5
KS 3.6
MO 3.3
KY 4.1
WV 4.1
VA 2.7
DE 2.8
MD 3.1
DC 1.6
AZ 3.2
NM 3.9
OK 3.6
AR 3.2
TN 3.5
NC 2.9
SC 3.0
MS
AL 3.3
GA 2.8
TX 2.7
LA 2.3
FL
AK 4.6
HI 3.8

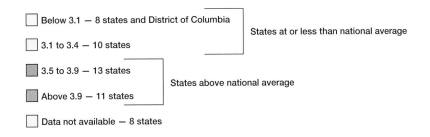

☐ Below 3.1 — 8 states and District of Columbia
☐ 3.1 to 3.4 — 10 states

States at or less than national average

▨ 3.5 to 3.9 — 13 states
▨ Above 3.9 — 11 states

States above national average

☐ Data not available — 8 states

[a]Incidence rates represent the number of injuries and illnesses per 100 full-time workers using 200,000 hours as the equivalent.

Motor Vehicle Deaths by State

Motor vehicle deaths by state, United States, 2010-2013

State	Motor vehicle traffic deaths (Place of incident)				Total motor vehicle deaths[a] (Place of residence)			
	Number		Mileage rate[b]		Number		Population rate[b]	
	2013	2012	2013	2012	2011[c]	2010	2011	2010
Total U.S.[a]	35,500	36,415	1.2	1.4	35,303	35,332	11.3	11.4
Alabama	852	865	1.3	1.3	956	931	19.9	19.5
Alaska	51	59	1.1	1.3	87	71	12.0	9.9
Arizona	845	821	1.4	1.4	866	792	13.4	12.4
Arkansas	484	552	1.4	1.7	595	608	20.2	20.8
California	3,211	3,050	1.0	0.9	3,041	2,922	8.1	7.8
Colorado	481	472	1.0	1.0	503	483	9.8	9.6
Connecticut	289	264	0.9	0.8	233	331	6.5	9.3
Delaware	101	116	1.1	1.3	98	111	10.8	12.3
District of Columbia	29	19	0.8	0.5	38	38	6.1	6.3
Florida	2,374	2,427	1.2	1.3	2,512	2,536	13.2	13.5
Georgia	1,184	1,198	1.1	1.1	1,289	1,324	13.1	13.6
Hawaii	102	125	1.0	1.2	108	124	7.8	9.1
Idaho	213	184	1.3	1.2	212	214	13.4	13.6
Illinois	991	956	0.9	0.9	1,063	1,033	8.3	8.0
Indiana	784	779	1.0	1.0	762	768	11.7	11.8
Iowa	317	365	1.0	1.2	402	400	13.1	13.1
Kansas	350	405	1.1	1.3	419	482	14.6	16.9
Kentucky	638	746	1.3	1.5	757	821	17.3	18.9
Louisiana	703	722	1.5	1.5	747	718	16.3	15.8
Maine	146	164	1.0	1.1	152	171	11.4	12.9
Maryland	466	506	0.8	0.9	516	513	8.8	8.9
Massachusetts	350	376	0.6	0.7	399	387	6.0	5.9
Michigan	965	936	1.0	1.0	1,009	1,051	10.2	10.6
Minnesota	387	395	0.7	0.7	462	515	8.6	9.7
Mississippi	613	582	1.6	1.5	726	682	24.4	23.0
Missouri	757	826	1.1	1.2	849	871	14.1	14.5
Montana	229	205	1.9	1.8	206	192	20.6	19.4
Nebraska	211	212	1.1	1.1	189	211	10.3	11.5
Nevada	265	259	1.1	1.1	279	286	10.3	10.6
New Hampshire	135	106	1.0	0.8	117	135	8.9	10.3
New Jersey	542	589	0.7	0.8	669	579	7.6	6.6
New Mexico	308	371	1.2	1.4	317	331	15.3	16.0
New York	1,188	1,163	0.9	0.9	1,352	1,323	6.9	6.8
North Carolina	1,293	1,262	1.2	1.2	1,263	1,383	13.1	14.5
North Dakota	148	170	1.5	1.9	139	97	20.3	14.4
Ohio	989	1,123	0.9	1.0	1,171	1,251	10.1	10.8
Oklahoma	678	708	1.4	1.5	745	716	19.7	19.0
Oregon	315	336	0.9	1.0	369	324	9.5	8.4
Pennsylvania	1,208	1,310	1.2	1.3	1,484	1,441	11.6	11.3
Rhode Island	65	64	0.8	0.8	76	91	7.2	8.6
South Carolina	767	863	1.6	1.8	864	812	18.5	17.5
South Dakota	133	133	1.5	1.5	103	144	12.5	17.6
Tennessee	995	1,015	1.4	1.4	1,044	1,099	16.3	17.3
Texas	3,385	3,398	1.4	1.4	3,304	3,331	12.9	13.2
Utah	220	217	0.8	0.8	277	272	9.8	9.8
Vermont	69	77	1.0	1.1	62	76	9.9	12.1
Virginia	741	776	0.9	1.0	811	724	10.0	9.0
Washington	439	437	0.8	0.8	552	549	8.1	8.1
West Virginia	332	339	1.7	1.8	376	310	20.3	16.7
Wisconsin	527	601	0.9	1.1	623	620	10.9	10.9
Wyoming	85	120	0.9	1.3	110	138	19.4	24.5

Source: Motor vehicle traffic deaths are provisional counts from state traffic authorities; total motor vehicle deaths are from the National Center for Health Statistics (also see page 178).

[a]Includes both traffic and nontraffic motor vehicle deaths. See definitions of motor vehicle traffic and nontraffic incidents on page 207. The total U.S. figure for 2012 is from NCHS.

[b]The mileage death rate is deaths per 100,000,000 vehicle miles; the population death rate is deaths per 100,000 population. Death rates are National Safety Council estimates.

[c]Latest year available. See Technical Appendix for comparability.

Mileage deaths rates, 2013
Motor vehicle traffic deaths per 100,000,000 vehicle miles

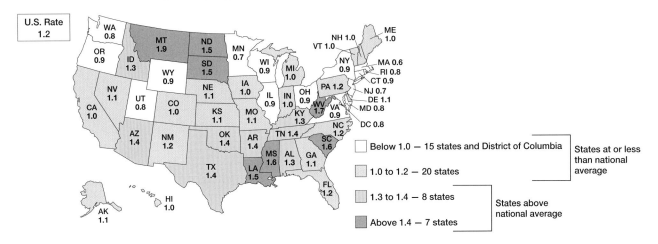

U.S. Rate
1.2

Below 1.0 — 15 states and District of Columbia

1.0 to 1.2 — 20 states

1.3 to 1.4 — 8 states

Above 1.4 — 7 states

States at or less than national average

States above national average

Registration death rates, 2013
Motor vehicle traffic deaths per 10,000 motor vehicles

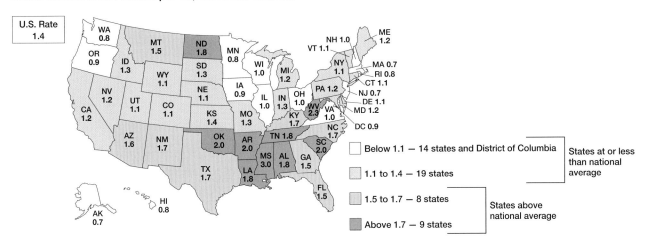

U.S. Rate
1.4

Below 1.1 — 14 states and District of Columbia

1.1 to 1.4 — 19 states

1.5 to 1.7 — 8 states

Above 1.7 — 9 states

States at or less than national average

States above national average

Population death rates, 2013
Motor vehicle traffic deaths per 100,000 population

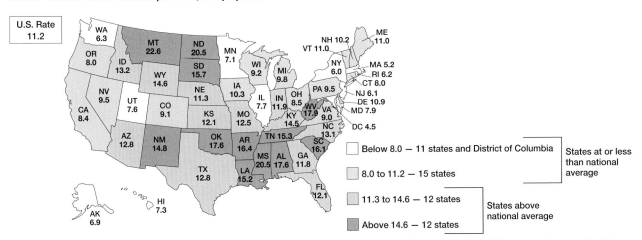

U.S. Rate
11.2

Below 8.0 — 11 states and District of Columbia

8.0 to 11.2 — 15 states

11.3 to 14.6 — 12 states

Above 14.6 — 12 states

States at or less than national average

States above national average

Source: Rates estimated by National Safety Council based on data from state traffic authorities, National Center for Health Statistics, Federal Highway Administration, and the U.S. Census Bureau.

International Data

INTERNATIONAL

International Unintentional-Injury-Related Deaths and Death Rates

The term "Accidents and Adverse Effects" used in the International Classification of Diseases (ICD) system refers to all causes of unintentional-injury-related deaths, including transportation incidents; unintentional poisonings; falls; fires; burns; natural and environmental factors; drowning; suffocation; medical and surgical complications and misadventures; and other causes, such as those involving machinery, firearms, or electric current. The data presented in the table below are identified by codes

V01-X59 and Y85-Y86 of the 10th revision of ICD (where noted). World-wide unintentional-injury-related totaled 3,600,000 in 2011, resulting in a death rate of 100,000 population.

The table below and those on pages 190 through 19 the number of injury-related deaths and the unadjuste rates for 52 countries for which mortality data and pop estimates were obtained.

Unintentional-injury-related deaths and death rates by age group, latest year available

Country	Year	Deaths Total	Deaths % male	All ages	0 to 4	5 to 14	15 to 24	25 to 44	45 to 64	6
Argentina	2010	10,187	73%	24.6	15.8	6.6	25.7	24.3	27.7	
Argentina	2012	401	82%	13.3	4.3	4.2	10.6	16.7	16.8	
Armenia	2011	5,898	60%	26.1	5.2	3.0	13.8	17.6	18.2	
Australia	2011	2,469	58%	29.4	1.8	2.0	13.2	9.7	19.0	
Austria	2011	4,113	54%	37.9	5.7	2.1	17.3	17.5	24.8	
Belgium	2010	70,002	78%	35.7	13.1	7.9	36.1	38.1	41.6	
Brazil	2010	1,848	76%	26.3	11.3	4.7	19.4	18.9	33.3	
Bulgaria	2012	1,270	73%	27.8	9.8	4.9	17.8	26.4	32.5	
Costa Rica	2011	2,068	57%	48.5	4.2	5.2	17.1	22.5	31.7	
Croatia	2012	4,830	53%	43.5	7.9	5.4	12.3	15.7	26.5	
Cuba	2010	225	72%	26.3	4.1	1.1	18.1	21.9	16.2	
Cyprus	2011	3,753	63%	35.7	3.9	1.9	16.7	18.6	34.9	
Czech Republic	2012	1,408	56%	25.3	2.8	1.2	10.6	12.0	17.2	
Denmark	2011	2,083	84%	21.2	10.4	4.4	25.3	30.2	24.7	
Dominican Republic	2010	5,755	79%	36.9	23.5	12.4	37.1	41.8	51.2	
Ecuador	2010				13.5	8.7	16.3	17.0	17.9	

						7.7	1.5	37.1	71.5	83.8
						2.6	2.4	17.9	24.6	57.2
						4.4	2.1	16.4	15.9	24.5
						2.5	1.7	10.2	7.4	12.9
						0.4	0.9	1.8	5.9	8.4
						4.5	3.6	9.9	14.8	36.7
						4.3	1.8	9.2	7.8	11.8
						2.6	1.8	15.7	12.7	13.2
						11.0	5.7	11.6	12.9	31.1
						37.9	21.3	77.2	149.0	165.5
						6.7	7.2	25.8	16.3	19.
						35.6	9.2	21.8	63.0	81
						8.8	6.3	19.5	44.6	9
						13.9	6.4	29.6	55.9	12
						17.7	7.4	30.1	34.1	
						1.7	1.7	3.6	3.3	
						2.8	1.2	7.4	6.2	
						14.9	4.2	16.9	23.3	
						1.9	1.3	11.1	15.7	
						23.3	8.2	37.2	33.4	
						26.1	7.6	18.5	26.9	
						4.3	4.0	24.0	26.9	
						3.3	1.3	12.9	11.4	
						12.2	5.7	26.7	16.2	
						6.0	2.9	9.8	12.2	
						28.3	13.4	31.6	42.5	
						17.9	8.5	19.8	23.1	
						27.0	16.8	93.3	183.9	
						3.0	4.3	14.6	13.6	
						8.5	6.0	18.7	22.9	
						2.5	1.3	10.2	11.2	
						0.9	1.4	10.1	10.1	
						3.1	2.0	18.2	23.4	
						21.3	10.9	55.8	98.	
						3.4	1.7	12.5	14	
						11.7	4.1	28.7	35	

data.
ternational Data Base).

Older adults at highest risk!

The charts on pages 189-193 provide the unintentional-injury-related deaths and death rates for 52 countries. The most current year of mortality data available is reported for motor vehicle, poisonings, falls, drowning, and overall unintentional-injury-related deaths. Looking at overall age trends across the world, the 65-and-older age group has the highest rate of unintentional-injury-related deaths per 100,000 population, while the 5- to 14-year-old age group has the lowest.

National Safety Council

■ *WHO Reports Little Improvement in Road Safety.*

This section on international injury and fatalities includes data for occupational and motor vehicle injuries, as well as general unintentional injury and mortality. The two primary data sources used in this section are the World Health Organization (WHO) and the International Labour Organization.

Looking at specific causes, road traffic incidents are the leading cause of unintentional fatalities for each region in the world. To address the growing road traffic safety issue, *"A Decade of Action for Road Safety 2011-2020 – Saving Millions of Lives"* was officially proclaimed by the United Nations General Assembly in March 2010. This proclamation has been drawn to guide efforts at global, regional, national, and local levels with the goal to stabilize and then reduce the forecasted level of road traffic fatalities around the world.

In addition, *WHO's Global Status Report on Road Safety 2013* found that since the start of the decade there has been no overall reduction in the number of people killed on the world's roads.

Another global unintentional injury issue that is often overlooked is drowning. A recent WHO report, *Global report on drowning: preventing a leading killer*, reports that drowning is the third most prevalent unintentional injury death event after motor vehicle and fall deaths. The WHO estimates about 372,000 drowning deaths occur every year. More than 90% of these drowning deaths take place in low- and middle-income countries.

Drowning is in the top 10 leading causes of death among children and young people in every region of the world. Over half of the drowning deaths occur among individuals under the age of 25 with children under the age of 5 at greatest risk.

Data limitations is making it hard to estimate the full extent of the drowning problem. Data collection in many low- and middle- income countries is limited. In addition, current injury coding standards exclude deaths from flood disasters and water transport incidents. Data on non-fatal drowning is often not collected at all in many parts of the developing world.

The WHO identified several risk factors associated with drowning deaths. These risk factors include:

- Lack of physical barriers controlling between people and water
- Lack of or inadequate supervision of young children
- Uncovered or unprotected water supplies and lack of safe water crossings
- Lack of water safety awareness and risky behavior around water
- Travelling on water, especially on overcrowded or poorly maintained vessels
- Flood disasters, whether from extreme rainfall, storm surges, tsunamis or cyclones.

The charts on pages 189-193 provide the unintentional-injury-related deaths and death rates for 52 countries. The most current year of mortality data available is reported for motor vehicle, poisonings, falls, drowning, and overall unintentional-injury-related deaths. Looking at overall age trends across the world, the 65-and-older age group has the highest rate of unintentional-injury-related deaths per 100,000 population, while the 5- to 14-year-old age group has the lowest. Death rates for all causes except poisonings peak for those 65 and older. The poisoning death rate peaks for the 45-to-64 age group. Because of differences in recordkeeping, comparisons among countries are not recommended.

The International Labour Organization has implemented a new occupational injury database. Because of the database change, comparisons prior to 2009 are not recommended. The charts on pages 194 and 195 detail the occupational deaths and death rates by country for the past two years. Because of the wide range of recordkeeping standards used in the world, countries with similar recordkeeping practices are grouped together. Although comparison among countries is not recommended even within these recordkeeping groupings, trends are evident. Of the 43 countries listed on page 195 reporting at least two years of data, 18 show improvement in the occupational death rates while another 14 countries held stable across the reported years. Eleven of the countries show an increased death rate.

The charts on pages 196 and 197 detail occupational injuries and injury rates by country. Of the 41 countries listed on page 197 reporting at least two years of data, 31 show improvement in occupational injury rates while the remaining 10 countries reported increases in injury rates. Because of differences in injury definitions among countries, comparisons between countries is not recommended.

Source: International Transport Forum. (2013). Road Safety Annual Report 2013. Downloaded from: http://www.trb.org/main/blurbs/169052.aspx on Sep. 10, 2013. World Health Organization. (2011). A Decade of Action for Road Safety 2011-2020 – Saving Millions of Lives. Geneva: Author. Downloaded from www.who.int/violence_injury_prevention/publications/road_traffic/decade_booklet/en/index.html on Nov. 7, 2012. World Health Organization. (2013). Global Status Report on Road Safety 2013. Geneva: Author: Downloaded from: http://www.who.int/violence_injury_prevention/road_safety_status/2013/en/index.html on Sep. 10, 2013. World Health Organization. (2014). Global report on drowning: preventing a leading killer. Downloaded from: http://www.who.int/violence_injury_prevention/publications/drowning_global_report/Final_report_full_web.pdf?ua=1 on December 8, 2014.

International Unintentional-Injury-Related Deaths and Death Rates

The term "Accidents and Adverse Effects" used in the International Classification of Diseases (ICD) system refers to all causes of unintentional-injury-related deaths, including transportation incidents; unintentional poisonings; falls; fires; burns; natural and environmental factors; drowning; suffocation; medical and surgical complications and misadventures; and other causes, such as those involving machinery, firearms, or electric current. The data presented in the table below are identified by codes V01-X59 and Y85-Y86 of the 10th revision of ICD (except where noted). World-wide unintentional-injury-related deaths totaled 3,600,000 in 2011, resulting in a death rate of 52 per 100,000 population.

The table below and those on pages 190 through 193 show the number of injury-related deaths and the unadjusted death rates for 52 countries for which mortality data and population estimates were obtained.

Unintentional-injury-related deaths and death rates by age group, latest year available

Country	Year	Deaths		Deaths per 100,000 population[a]						
		Total	% male	All ages	0 to 4	5 to 14	15 to 24	25 to 44	45 to 64	65 or older
Argentina	2010	10,187	73%	24.6	15.8	6.6	25.7	24.3	27.7	53.3
Armenia	2012	401	82%	13.3	4.3	4.2	10.6	16.7	16.8	15.7
Australia	2011	5,898	60%	26.1	5.2	3.0	13.8	17.6	18.2	101.1
Austria	2011	2,469	58%	29.4	1.8	2.0	13.2	9.7	19.0	110.8
Belgium	2010	4,113	54%	37.9	5.7	2.1	17.3	17.5	24.8	139.3
Brazil	2010	70,002	78%	35.7	13.1	7.9	36.1	38.1	41.6	107.1
Bulgaria	2012	1,848	76%	26.3	11.3	4.7	19.4	18.9	33.3	46.1
Costa Rica	2011	1,270	73%	27.8	9.8	4.9	17.8	26.4	32.5	131.0
Croatia	2012	2,068	57%	48.5	4.2	5.2	17.1	22.5	31.7	170.3
Cuba	2010	4,830	53%	43.5	7.9	5.4	12.3	15.7	26.5	256.3
Cyprus	2011	225	72%	26.3	4.1	1.1	18.1	21.9	16.2	95.1
Czech Republic	2012	3,753	63%	35.7	3.9	1.9	16.7	18.8	34.9	110.9
Denmark	2011	1,408	56%	25.3	2.8	1.2	10.6	12.0	17.2	93.3
Dominican Republic	2010	2,083	84%	21.2	10.4	4.4	25.3	30.2	24.7	30.4
Ecuador	2010	5,755	79%	38.9	23.5	12.4	37.1	41.8	51.2	111.4
Egypt	2011	12,213	81%	15.2	13.5	8.7	16.3	17.0	17.9	25.4
Estonia	2012	798	78%	60.0	7.7	1.5	37.1	71.5	83.8	71.9
Finland	2011	2,766	67%	51.3	2.6	2.4	17.9	24.6	57.2	147.7
France	2010	25,414	55%	40.4	4.4	2.1	16.4	15.9	24.5	161.8
Germany	2012	19,642	54%	24.0	2.5	1.7	10.2	7.4	12.9	81.6
Hong Kong SAR	2011	669	67%	9.5	0.4	0.9	1.8	5.9	8.4	35.1
Hungary	2012	3,750	59%	37.8	4.5	3.6	9.9	14.8	36.7	127.8
Israel	2011	1,173	62%	15.1	4.3	1.8	9.3	7.8	11.8	84.4
Italy	2010	19,077	54%	31.5	2.6	1.8	15.7	12.7	13.2	111.0
Japan	2011	61,517	55%	48.8	11.0	5.7	11.6	12.9	31.1	148.2
Kazakhstan[b]	2010	17,746	78%	108.7	37.9	21.3	77.2	149.0	165.5	142.4
Kuwait	2011	609	84%	16.8	8.7	7.2	25.8	16.3	19.4	44.2
Kyrgyzstan	2010	2,376	77%	43.6	35.6	9.2	21.8	63.0	81.4	63.0
Latvia	2012	1,168	74%	57.4	8.8	6.3	19.5	44.6	97.3	82.2
Lithuania	2010	2,384	76%	72.5	13.9	6.4	29.6	55.9	128.6	110.3
Mexico	2010	36,372	77%	31.9	17.7	7.4	30.1	34.1	39.1	108.8
Morocco	2011	1,010	80%	3.2	1.7	1.7	3.6	3.3	3.6	6.8
Netherlands	2011	3,985	49%	23.9	2.8	1.2	7.4	6.2	9.9	114.8
Nicaragua	2011	1,204	79%	21.2	14.9	4.2	16.9	23.3	31.3	97.7
Norway	2012	1,874	53%	37.3	1.9	1.3	11.1	15.7	24.4	161.6
Paraguay	2010	1,987	79%	31.2	23.3	8.2	37.2	33.4	37.0	74.6
Peru	2010	7,021	74%	24.3	26.1	7.6	18.5	25.9	32.5	62.0
Poland	2011	14,480	73%	37.6	4.3	4.0	24.0	26.9	47.0	92.7
Portugal	2011	1,823	71%	17.3	3.3	1.3	12.9	11.4	17.3	40.2
Qatar	2011	327	89%	18.9	12.2	5.7	26.7	16.2	28.4	62.5
Republic of Korea	2011	13,004	70%	26.0	6.0	2.9	9.8	12.2	30.3	107.1
Republic of Moldova	2012	2,056	75%	57.8	28.3	13.4	31.6	42.5	96.1	112.7
Romania	2011	7,525	76%	34.4	17.9	8.5	19.8	23.1	49.5	70.0
Russian Federation[b]	2010	216,867	77%	151.8	27.0	16.8	93.3	183.9	205.9	182.0
Serbia	2012	1,547	75%	21.5	3.0	4.3	14.6	13.6	23.9	48.7
Slovakia	2010	1,738	78%	32.0	8.5	6.0	18.7	22.9	49.6	63.6
Spain	2011	10,253	61%	22.2	2.5	1.3	10.2	11.2	15.5	77.7
Sweden	2010	2,970	58%	31.7	0.9	1.4	10.1	10.1	18.9	123.9
Switzerland[b]	2010	3,566	59%	45.6	3.1	2.0	18.2	23.4	38.8	151.8
Ukraine[b]	2012	41,713	78%	91.9	21.3	10.9	55.8	98.2	129.2	115.4
United Kingdom	2010	14,143	56%	22.7	3.4	1.7	12.5	14.6	15.6	76.6
United States of America	2010	121,053	63%	39.1	11.7	4.1	28.7	35.4	41.8	102.5

Source: National Safety Council tabulations of World Health Organization (WHO) data.
[a]Population estimates based on data from WHO and the U.S. Census Bureau (International Data Base).
[b]Data include deaths due to all external causes, including self-harm and assault.

International Motor Vehicle Injury-Related Deaths and Death Rates

The International Classification of Diseases (ICD) system identifies motor vehicle traffic incidents by codes V02-V04, V09, V12-V14, V19-V79, and V86-V89 of the 10th revision of ICD. A motor vehicle is a mechanically or electrically powered device used in the transportation of people or property on a land highway. A motor vehicle traffic incident involves a motor vehicle in transport (i.e., in motion or on a roadway) on a public highway. World-wide road-injury-related deaths totaled 1,262,000 in 2011, resulting in a death rate of 18 per 100,000 population.

Motor vehicle injury-related deaths and death rates by age group, latest year available

Country	Year	Deaths Total	Deaths % male	Deaths per 100,000 population[a] All ages	0 to 4	5 to 14	15 to 24	25 to 44	45 to 64	65 or older
Argentina	2010	4,432	78%	10.7	2.6	2.7	14.1	13.3	13.5	13.1
Armenia	2012	211	84%	7.0	0.5	2.2	5.7	11.2	7.8	5.0
Australia	2011	1,328	73%	5.9	1.8	1.6	8.7	6.1	5.5	9.0
Austria	2011	269	76%	3.2	0.3	0.5	4.9	2.8	2.9	5.5
Belgium	2010	824	75%	7.6	1.3	1.2	13.7	9.9	6.1	8.3
Brazil	2010	34,220	82%	17.5	2.6	2.9	24.0	23.0	19.6	24.8
Bulgaria	2012	359	79%	5.1	0.3	0.9	8.0	5.1	5.8	5.7
Costa Rica	2011	541	81%	11.8	4.9	2.2	11.5	15.3	16.2	15.8
Croatia	2012	387	86%	9.1	0.9	2.1	10.0	10.5	9.6	11.6
Cuba	2010	852	77%	7.7	1.6	2.4	6.3	7.7	9.9	13.2
Cyprus	2011	83	83%	9.7	0.0	1.1	13.6	11.9	8.1	14.2
Czech Republic	2012	547	76%	5.2	0.5	0.7	7.7	6.0	5.0	6.5
Denmark	2011	196	75%	3.5	0.9	0.7	5.5	2.6	3.6	6.2
Dominican Republic	2010	1,408	85%	14.3	3.7	2.6	19.8	21.2	16.0	17.1
Ecuador	2010	1,071	81%	7.2	1.9	2.1	9.3	9.4	8.8	12.5
Egypt	2011	7,064	83%	8.8	5.3	4.4	8.6	10.5	12.6	17.7
Estonia	2012	67	81%	5.0	1.3	0.0	9.9	5.9	5.7	3.4
Finland	2011	264	73%	4.9	0.3	1.0	9.1	4.2	4.1	8.1
France	2010	3,821	77%	6.1	1.0	1.1	11.6	6.9	5.1	7.6
Germany	2012	3,179	74%	3.9	0.4	0.7	7.3	3.5	3.5	5.1
Hong Kong SAR	2011	86	66%	1.2	0.0	0.0	0.5	1.0	1.1	3.6
Hungary	2012	702	73%	7.1	1.3	1.7	5.0	7.1	9.6	9.4
Israel	2011	244	79%	3.1	0.5	0.4	6.4	3.5	3.2	4.6
Italy	2010	4,058	79%	6.7	0.8	0.9	11.7	7.5	5.6	8.7
Japan	2011	6,142	67%	4.9	1.0	0.8	4.5	2.7	4.1	10.7
Kazakhstan[b]	2010	3,379	73%	20.7	5.8	6.9	19.2	29.4	26.3	21.2
Kuwait	2011	399	88%	11.0	2.0	3.4	21.7	10.2	13.3	26.5
Kyrgyzstan	2010	615	75%	11.3	2.5	2.3	8.2	19.0	18.3	13.6
Latvia	2012	178	71%	8.7	1.0	2.6	9.1	9.7	9.6	11.1
Lithuania	2010	305	75%	9.3	1.2	1.8	12.0	8.6	10.7	12.7
Mexico	2010	10,699	79%	9.4	3.2	2.1	12.2	12.2	11.5	14.9
Morocco	2011	423	83%	1.3	0.4	0.4	1.3	1.5	1.8	3.2
Netherlands	2011	577	71%	3.5	0.8	0.9	5.3	2.7	2.7	7.5
Nicaragua	2011	430	84%	7.6	1.6	1.0	7.0	11.5	12.3	16.9
Norway	2012	153	75%	3.0	0.6	0.5	4.2	3.3	3.5	3.8
Paraguay	2010	1,071	81%	16.8	6.4	3.5	26.0	22.0	18.8	16.6
Peru	2010	775	77%	2.7	1.1	0.8	1.9	3.4	4.4	5.4
Poland	2011	3,948	78%	10.2	1.4	1.9	14.8	10.4	11.1	13.2
Portugal	2011	811	77%	7.7	1.0	0.6	10.8	7.7	8.2	10.6
Qatar	2011	225	91%	13.0	2.0	3.8	19.0	11.3	20.0	52.1
Republic of Korea	2011	6,146	74%	12.3	2.2	1.5	7.7	7.4	15.1	40.3
Republic of Moldova	2012	453	76%	12.7	3.6	4.2	17.8	14.1	13.9	11.0
Romania	2011	1,840	77%	8.4	1.9	1.8	9.3	7.3	10.4	13.4
Russian Federation[b]	2010	28,558	73%	20.0	3.3	4.2	24.5	26.5	19.9	19.0
Serbia	2012	522	77%	7.3	0.3	1.3	8.1	6.1	8.2	12.2
Slovakia	2010	396	75%	7.3	1.1	2.9	9.9	7.1	7.9	9.7
Spain	2011	2,195	78%	4.8	0.6	0.6	5.7	4.9	4.8	7.6
Sweden	2010	252	73%	2.7	0.4	0.8	4.2	2.4	2.9	3.6
Switzerland[b]	2010	359	77%	4.6	1.0	0.9	5.3	3.7	5.1	8.0
Ukraine[b]	2012	5,905	75%	13.0	2.3	2.5	16.4	16.5	13.8	11.8
United Kingdom	2010	1,967	74%	3.2	0.4	0.7	5.9	3.6	2.7	3.7
United States of America	2010	35,420	70%	11.4	2.5	2.2	16.9	12.6	12.1	16.0

Source: National Safety Council tabulations of World Health Organization (WHO) data.
[a]Population estimates based on data from WHO and the U.S. Census Bureau (International Data Base).
[b]Data include deaths due to all transportation-related causes, ICD codes V01-V99.

International Poisoning Injury-Related Deaths and Death Rates

The International Classification of Diseases (ICD) system identifies unintentional poisonings by codes X40-X49, which include cases of accidental poisoning by drugs, medicaments, biological substances, alcohol, solvents, gases, vapors, and pesticides. Other accidental poisonings by unspecified chemicals and noxious substances also are included. World-wide poisoning-related deaths totaled 192,000 in 2011, resulting in a death rate of 3 per 100,000 population.

Unintentional poisoning injury-related deaths and death rates by age group, latest year available

Country	Year	Deaths Total	Deaths % male	Deaths per 100,000 population[a] All ages	0 to 4	5 to 14	15 to 24	25 to 44	45 to 64	65 or older
Argentina	2010	276	62%	0.7	1.3	0.2	0.2	0.5	1.0	1.5
Armenia	2012	12	67%	0.4	0.0	0.0	0.0	0.3	0.7	1.3
Australia	2011	987	70%	4.4	0.1	0.1	1.9	7.9	5.8	2.8
Austria	2011	21	57%	0.3	0.0	0.0	0.3	0.2	0.3	0.5
Belgium	2010	230	62%	2.1	0.2	0.0	1.1	2.9	2.4	3.2
Brazil	2010	706	76%	0.4	0.1	0.0	0.3	0.5	0.6	0.5
Bulgaria	2012	83	72%	1.2	0.6	0.0	0.9	1.0	1.3	2.1
Costa Rica	2011	58	79%	1.3	0.8	0.0	0.1	2.0	2.5	1.0
Croatia	2012	119	70%	2.8	0.9	0.9	1.4	4.6	2.5	3.0
Cuba	2010	88	88%	0.8	0.2	0.0	0.1	0.6	1.9	1.1
Cyprus	2011	16	81%	1.9	0.0	0.0	1.5	3.1	1.0	3.6
Czech Republic	2012	419	67%	4.0	0.5	0.0	1.2	3.8	7.2	4.4
Denmark	2011	223	74%	4.0	0.0	0.0	3.2	6.6	6.2	1.4
Dominican Republic	2010	1	100%	0.0	0.0	0.0	0.0	0.0	0.0	0.2
Ecuador	2010	196	84%	1.3	0.5	0.2	0.6	1.4	2.5	5.1
Egypt	2011	101	50%	0.1	0.2	0.1	0.2	0.1	0.1	0.1
Estonia	2012	350	84%	26.3	0.0	0.0	19.8	50.5	32.2	7.2
Finland	2011	719	77%	13.3	0.0	0.0	6.8	15.4	24.6	9.3
France	2010	1,847	56%	2.9	0.0	0.1	0.7	2.4	2.7	8.9
Germany	2012	599	70%	0.7	0.0	0.1	0.4	1.0	0.9	0.8
Hong Kong SAR	2011	149	80%	2.1	0.0	0.0	0.6	3.1	2.9	1.1
Hungary	2012	119	72%	1.2	0.0	0.2	1.2	1.1	1.8	1.3
Israel	2011	5	60%	0.1	0.0	0.0	0.0	0.0	0.1	0.4
Italy	2010	449	71%	0.7	0.0	0.0	0.4	1.2	0.6	1.0
Japan	2011	942	62%	0.7	0.1	0.0	0.4	1.1	0.9	0.8
Kazakhstan	2010	2,297	76%	14.1	3.9	1.6	4.3	19.6	27.1	20.0
Kuwait	2011	8	75%	0.2	0.3	0.0	0.0	0.4	0.0	0.0
Kyrgyzstan	2010	489	82%	9.0	1.1	0.0	0.8	13.1	27.6	15.2
Latvia	2012	177	79%	8.7	0.0	0.0	2.8	8.9	17.0	6.8
Lithuania	2010	543	78%	16.5	0.6	0.0	5.1	15.9	33.3	16.4
Mexico	2010	1,051	80%	0.9	0.5	0.1	0.7	1.1	1.6	2.2
Morocco	2011	73	59%	0.2	0.1	0.1	0.3	0.3	0.3	0.2
Netherlands	2011	138	72%	0.8	0.0	0.1	0.6	1.2	1.1	0.9
Nicaragua	2011	67	91%	1.2	1.6	0.1	0.3	1.4	2.7	4.3
Norway	2012	312	71%	6.2	0.0	0.0	4.5	9.1	10.1	3.5
Paraguay	2010	26	85%	0.4	0.3	0.0	0.2	0.3	1.1	1.3
Peru	2010	381	60%	1.3	0.5	0.4	2.3	1.3	1.5	1.6
Poland	2011	1,351	83%	3.5	0.0	0.2	1.1	3.3	6.9	3.2
Portugal	2011	27	63%	0.3	0.2	0.0	0.1	0.2	0.2	0.5
Qatar	2011	2	100%	0.2	0.0	0.0	0.0	0.0	1.1	0.0
Republic of Korea	2011	207	71%	0.4	0.0	0.0	0.0	0.2	0.6	1.4
Republic of Moldova	2012	320	74%	9.0	2.6	1.3	0.8	7.8	17.7	15.3
Romania	2011	898	69%	4.1	2.1	0.6	0.7	2.4	7.4	8.5
Russian Federation	2010	34,518	77%	24.2	2.3	1.2	7.1	31.5	39.0	20.9
Serbia	2012	51	67%	0.7	0.0	0.0	0.5	0.8	0.7	1.4
Slovakia	2010	128	76%	2.4	0.0	0.2	0.4	2.3	4.8	2.4
Spain	2011	757	71%	1.6	0.0	0.0	0.7	2.1	1.6	2.7
Sweden	2010	398	75%	4.2	0.0	0.0	3.1	5.4	6.9	3.5
Switzerland	2010	175	72%	2.2	0.0	0.0	1.7	3.7	2.8	1.1
Ukraine	2012	6,690	79%	14.7	1.5	0.8	3.1	15.6	27.9	12.0
United Kingdom	2010	1,912	69%	3.1	0.1	0.0	1.9	5.5	4.0	1.6
United States of America	2010	33,049	64%	10.7	0.2	0.1	7.4	17.1	17.5	3.5

Source: National Safety Council tabulations of World Health Organization (WHO) data.
[a]Population estimates based on data from WHO and the U.S. Census Bureau (International Data Base).

International Fall Injury-Related Deaths and Death Rates

"Accidental falls" are identified by codes W00-W19 in the 10th revision of the International Classification of Diseases (ICD) system. World-wide fall-related deaths totaled 647,000 in 2011, resulting in a death rate of 9 per 100,000 population.

Unintentional fall injury-related deaths and death rates by age group, latest year available

Country	Year	Deaths Total	% male	Deaths per 100,000 population[a] All ages	0 to 4	5 to 14	15 to 24	25 to 44	45 to 64	65 or older
Argentina	2010	337	63%	0.8	0.2	0.1	0.2	0.4	0.9	4.1
Armenia	2012	13	92%	0.4	0.0	0.0	0.0	0.5	0.5	1.6
Australia	2011	1,845	49%	8.2	0.0	0.0	0.3	0.4	2.3	54.1
Austria	2011	865	54%	10.3	0.3	0.1	0.3	1.5	6.3	45.8
Belgium	2010	1,525	45%	14.1	0.6	0.1	0.5	1.2	7.6	67.7
Brazil	2010	10,426	63%	5.3	0.7	0.3	0.8	2.2	6.2	47.6
Bulgaria	2012	267	72%	3.8	0.9	0.5	0.5	1.6	5.0	9.8
Costa Rica	2011	91	78%	2.0	0.0	0.5	0.2	1.1	2.7	15.8
Croatia	2012	1,043	43%	24.4	0.0	0.0	0.8	1.2	8.2	120.4
Cuba	2010	2,003	45%	18.0	0.2	0.2	0.6	1.2	5.1	143.3
Cyprus	2011	28	61%	3.3	2.1	0.0	0.0	1.2	2.9	16.0
Czech Republic	2012	751	57%	7.1	0.3	0.2	0.8	1.0	5.0	32.6
Denmark	2011	519	46%	9.3	0.0	0.1	0.1	0.8	2.8	48.7
Dominican Republic	2010	30	67%	0.3	0.0	0.0	0.2	0.3	0.5	1.6
Ecuador	2010	423	76%	2.9	1.3	0.5	1.2	2.2	4.1	17.9
Egypt	2011	1,014	73%	1.3	2.5	0.9	1.0	0.9	1.5	3.1
Estonia	2012	99	66%	7.4	0.0	0.8	1.9	5.4	8.0	19.9
Finland	2011	1,212	56%	22.5	0.7	0.0	0.3	1.9	12.5	103.3
France	2010	5,932	49%	9.4	0.2	0.1	0.6	1.1	4.3	46.9
Germany	2012	10,240	46%	12.5	0.4	0.0	0.3	0.7	3.9	53.7
Hong Kong SAR	2011	183	61%	2.6	0.4	0.5	0.2	0.4	1.7	13.9
Hungary	2012	1,802	47%	18.2	0.0	0.0	0.4	1.1	9.3	89.7
Israel	2011	130	62%	1.7	0.3	0.0	0.3	0.5	0.8	13.0
Italy	2010	3,188	54%	5.3	0.3	0.1	0.6	1.0	2.3	21.2
Japan	2011	7,686	58%	6.1	0.3	0.2	0.5	0.7	2.8	21.6
Kazakhstan	2010	538	75%	3.3	2.0	1.0	1.9	4.4	4.5	5.3
Kuwait	2011	53	75%	1.5	1.0	0.8	1.2	1.8	1.2	2.9
Kyrgyzstan	2010	97	85%	1.8	0.8	0.5	1.0	2.1	3.4	5.8
Latvia	2012	183	72%	9.0	1.0	0.5	0.8	5.9	14.5	17.4
Lithuania	2010	305	73%	9.3	0.6	0.3	1.2	4.9	14.0	24.9
Mexico	2010	2,180	79%	1.9	0.7	0.3	0.8	1.3	3.3	11.7
Morocco	2011	45	82%	0.1	0.0	0.1	0.1	0.1	0.1	0.8
Netherlands	2011	1,682	43%	10.1	0.0	0.0	0.2	0.6	3.1	56.6
Nicaragua	2011	184	57%	3.2	1.1	0.4	0.7	1.3	4.2	44.3
Norway	2012	479	50%	9.5	0.3	0.2	0.3	0.6	3.9	53.5
Paraguay	2010	83	81%	1.3	0.5	0.3	0.6	1.0	2.4	6.6
Peru	2010	205	76%	0.7	0.4	0.2	0.3	0.5	1.2	3.8
Poland	2011	4,047	55%	10.5	0.3	0.2	1.3	2.7	8.4	52.4
Portugal	2011	327	60%	3.1	0.0	0.2	0.3	0.7	2.4	11.6
Qatar	2011	25	76%	1.4	2.0	0.0	1.5	1.3	2.9	0.0
Republic of Korea	2011	2,144	75%	4.3	1.0	0.2	0.5	1.5	6.0	18.4
Republic of Moldova	2012	167	75%	4.7	0.5	0.3	1.4	2.5	8.5	14.1
Romania	2011	1,292	79%	5.9	1.1	0.4	1.3	2.6	9.3	17.0
Russian Federation	2010	9,716	72%	6.8	1.7	0.6	3.1	5.9	8.7	15.7
Serbia	2012	295	65%	4.1	0.0	0.0	0.4	0.5	3.8	16.1
Slovakia	2010	460	71%	8.5	0.7	0.2	1.6	3.7	11.3	32.3
Spain	2011	2,112	51%	4.6	0.2	0.1	0.7	0.9	2.3	21.0
Sweden	2010	875	55%	9.3	0.0	0.0	0.3	0.3	2.7	46.6
Switzerland	2010	1,506	43%	19.2	0.0	0.1	1.3	1.2	4.7	103.1
Ukraine	2012	2,506	74%	5.5	1.0	0.2	1.7	4.1	7.7	12.4
United Kingdom	2010	4,496	49%	7.2	0.2	0.0	0.4	1.2	3.3	36.2
United States of America	2010	26,014	50%	8.4	0.2	0.1	0.5	1.0	4.1	53.7

Source: National Safety Council tabulations of World Health Organization (WHO) data.
[a]*Population estimates based on data from WHO and the U.S. Census Bureau (International Data Base).*

International Drowning Injury-Related Deaths and Death Rates

The International Classification of Diseases (ICD) system identifies drowning by codes W65-W74, which include cases of unintentional drowning and submersion while in or following a fall in a bathtub, swimming pool, or natural body of water. Other specified and unspecified cases of drowning and submersion also are included. World-wide drowning-related deaths totaled 359,000 in 2011, resulting in a death rate of 5 per 100,000 population.

Unintentional drowning injury-related deaths and death rates by age group, latest year available

Country	Year	Deaths		Deaths per 100,000 population[a]						
		Total	% male	All ages	0 to 4	5 to 14	15 to 24	25 to 44	45 to 64	65 or older
Argentina	2010	566	82%	1.4	2.7	1.1	2.0	1.0	1.1	1.2
Armenia	2012	26	100%	1.8	0.0	1.0	4.3	2.2	1.2	0.0
Australia	2011	169	80%	0.7	1.4	0.4	0.8	0.6	0.6	1.3
Austria	2011	49	65%	0.6	0.8	0.1	0.5	0.3	0.3	1.6
Belgium	2010	71	76%	0.7	0.8	0.4	0.2	0.4	0.9	1.0
Brazil	2010	5,548	87%	2.8	2.7	2.2	3.5	2.9	2.8	2.9
Bulgaria	2012	135	77%	1.9	1.5	1.4	1.7	1.3	2.1	3.1
Costa Rica	2011	135	84%	2.9	1.6	1.8	3.5	3.2	3.5	3.1
Croatia	2012	100	73%	2.3	0.0	0.7	2.2	1.1	3.4	4.2
Cuba	2010	224	92%	2.0	1.6	1.2	2.2	2.0	2.4	2.1
Cyprus	2011	18	56%	2.1	2.1	0.0	0.0	1.5	1.0	9.8
Czech Republic	2012	151	80%	1.4	0.7	0.1	1.4	1.1	2.1	2.0
Denmark	2011	29	76%	0.5	0.3	0.0	0.7	0.1	0.8	0.9
Dominican Republic	2010	24	92%	0.2	0.1	0.3	0.3	0.3	0.3	0.0
Ecuador	2010	436	81%	2.9	4.8	2.1	3.8	2.3	2.5	4.0
Egypt	2011	1,305	83%	1.6	2.8	1.7	2.5	1.1	0.6	0.8
Estonia	2012	48	71%	3.6	1.3	0.8	3.1	3.0	3.7	7.2
Finland	2011	120	83%	2.2	0.7	0.3	0.6	1.0	3.4	4.9
France	2010	1,046	71%	1.7	1.1	0.2	0.7	1.0	2.2	3.8
Germany	2012	417	71%	0.5	0.4	0.3	0.3	0.3	0.5	1.0
Hong Kong SAR	2011	30	57%	0.4	0.0	0.3	0.3	0.2	0.4	1.3
Hungary	2012	131	85%	1.3	0.4	0.9	1.5	1.3	1.7	1.2
Israel	2011	44	86%	0.6	0.4	0.5	0.3	0.7	0.6	0.9
Italy	2010	374	81%	0.6	0.4	0.3	0.7	0.5	0.6	1.0
Japan	2011	7,356	53%	5.8	0.6	0.5	0.9	0.7	2.5	20.4
Kazakhstan	2010	1,062	84%	6.5	5.9	4.3	6.2	8.2	6.8	4.4
Kuwait	2011	17	76%	0.5	1.3	0.4	0.2	0.3	0.5	1.5
Kyrgyzstan	2010	325	72%	6.0	13.3	3.1	3.9	6.3	6.2	7.0
Latvia	2012	135	79%	6.6	1.9	1.1	3.2	7.2	10.0	7.4
Lithuania	2010	319	82%	9.7	4.2	4.0	5.3	8.6	16.5	10.1
Mexico	2010	2,424	85%	2.1	2.7	1.1	2.7	2.0	2.1	3.5
Morocco	2011	193	83%	0.6	0.7	0.7	1.1	0.3	0.3	0.7
Netherlands	2011	74	84%	0.4	0.3	0.1	0.2	0.4	0.5	1.0
Nicaragua	2011	129	89%	2.3	2.9	0.9	4.1	1.9	1.8	2.0
Norway	2012	45	82%	0.9	0.0	0.2	0.3	0.5	1.4	2.2
Paraguay	2010	144	88%	2.3	4.2	1.6	2.9	1.8	2.2	1.6
Peru	2010	431	74%	1.5	2.7	1.0	1.3	1.3	1.6	1.9
Poland	2011	865	80%	2.2	0.6	0.5	1.7	1.8	3.7	2.6
Portugal	2011	61	79%	0.6	1.0	0.0	0.4	0.4	0.6	1.1
Qatar	2011	22	91%	1.3	4.1	1.3	1.8	0.8	1.3	0.0
Republic of Korea	2011	646	78%	1.3	0.6	0.7	0.8	0.8	1.6	3.5
Republic of Moldova	2012	214	87%	6.0	3.1	6.3	5.9	4.7	8.2	5.9
Romania	2011	692	79%	3.2	2.0	2.5	2.8	2.3	4.0	4.9
Russian Federation	2010	11,981	85%	8.4	2.8	4.1	6.7	11.1	10.2	5.7
Serbia	2012	84	76%	1.2	0.9	2.0	1.2	0.9	1.0	1.4
Slovakia	2010	156	85%	2.9	2.5	1.1	2.1	2.2	4.5	3.6
Spain	2011	461	79%	1.0	0.6	0.2	1.1	0.7	1.1	2.0
Sweden	2010	64	72%	0.7	0.5	0.3	0.5	0.3	0.5	1.9
Switzerland	2010	52	81%	0.7	0.5	0.0	0.8	0.4	0.9	1.1
Ukraine	2012	2,713	85%	6.0	2.4	2.9	4.8	6.7	7.8	5.3
United Kingdom	2011	175	78%	0.3	0.4	0.1	0.3	0.2	0.4	0.3
United States of America	2010	3,814	78%	1.2	2.2	0.6	1.5	1.1	1.3	1.3

Source: National Safety Council tabulations of World Health Organization (WHO) data.
[a]*Population estimates based on data from WHO and the U.S. Census Bureau (International Data Base).*

Occupational Deaths

Counts and rates of fatal work-related injuries are shown on this page and the next. Comparisons between countries should be made with caution and take into account the differences in sources, coverage, and kinds of cases included.

Occupational deaths by country, 2009-2013

Country	Deaths 2009	2010	2011	2012	2013	Source of data	Coverage Worker types[b]	Activities excluded
Injuries only – compensated cases								
Finland	26	33	26	–	–	IR	E	none
France	538	529	–	–	–	IR	I	none
Germany	622	674	664	–	–	IR	I	none
Korea, Republic of	1,300	1,255	1,271	1,292	–	IR	–	none
Lithuania	49	50	53	57	60	LR	–	none
Slovenia	26	–	18	–	–	AR	I	none
South Africa	337	185	–	–	–	AR	–	none
Injuries only – reported cases								
Armenia	16	12	–	–	–	LR	–	none
Austria	–	185	73	98	91	IR	E	none
Belize	122	123	–	–	–	AR	–	none
Bulgaria	88	92	94	77	81	IR	I	none
Cuba	88	88	–	–	–	AR	E	none
Cyprus	9	19	5	9	9	LR	E	none
Czech Republic	–	–	139	105	–	LR	–	none
Estonia	19	17	19	14	20	LR	–	none
Ethiopia	48	46	–	–	–	AR	–	none
Hungary	99	95	80	62	–	LR	E	none
Ireland	43	48	49	–	40	LR	–	none
Kazakhstan	302	322	–	–	266	AR	–	none
Latvia	–	–	34	34	29	LR	E	none
New Zealand	116	118	–	48	–	IR	–	none
Norway	42	46	53	37	48	LR	E	SF, MT, OOE
Panama	15	12	24	24	–	LR	–	none
Poland	406	446	404	348	–	S	–	Priv. Agr
Singapore	70	55	61	56	59	AR	E	PDS
Slovakia	44	48	38	54	53	LR	E	none
Spain	390	342	335	271	–	IR	I	none
Sri Lanka	76	64	–	–	141	LR	E	none
Sweden	41	54	58	45	33	AR	–	none
Trinidad and Tobago	12	9	–	–	–	AR	–	–
Turkey	1,171	1,454	1,710	745	–	IR	I	none
United States[c]	4,551	4,547	4,693	4,383	–	C	E,SE	none
Injuries and commuting accidents – compensated cases								
Croatia	38	38	38	40	–	IR	E, SE	none
Injuries and commuting accidents – reported cases								
Chile	458	–	282	322	–	AR	E, SE	none
El Salvador	102	96	–	–	–	C	E, SE	none
Romania	412	377	297	240	223	LR	E,SE	none
Injuries and diseases – compensated cases								
Malta	8	3	1	6	–	AR	–	none
Injuries and diseases – reported cases								
Argentina	830	871	558	562	–	AR	E,SE	none
Hong Kong, China	165	183	191	196	188	LR	E	none
Nicaragua	38	42	–	–	–	AR	–	none
Injuries, diseases, and commuting accidents – compensated cases								
Thailand	595	619	–	–	–	IR	I	none
Injuries, diseases, and commuting accidents – reported cases								
Mexico	1,368	1,433	1,578	1,534	1,314	IR	–	none

Source: International Labour Organization (ILO), ILO Department of Statistics, accessed September 16, 2014, from http://laborsta.ilo.org.
Note: Dash (–) means data not available. See footnotes on page 195.

Source of Data
AR = Administrative reports
C = Census
IR = Insurance records
LR = Labor inspectorate records
S = Survey

Worker Types
E = Employees
I = Insured persons
SE = Self-employed

Economic Activites
MT = Maritime transport
OOE = Offshore oil extraction
PDS = Private domestic service
Priv. Agr = Private farms in agriculture
SF = Sea fishing

Occupational Death Rates

The International Labour Organization (ILO) estimates that about 2.3 million persons die from work-related incidents and diseases each year, out of which 350,000 are fatal and close to 2 million are work-related diseases. The total equates to about 6,300 worker deaths per day due to an incident or disease from their work, with one worker dying from a work-related incident or disease every 15 seconds. In addition to the human cost of these deaths and injuries, the economic burden of poor safety and health practices is estimated at 4% of global gross domestic product each year.

Source: International Labour Organization. (2014). Accessed November 21, 2014 at http://www.ilo.org/global/topics/safety-and-health-at-work/lang--en/index.htm

Occupational death rates by country, 2009-2013

Country	Coverage[d]	2009	2010	2011	2012	2013
Deaths per 1,000 employees						
Injuries only						
Cuba	RC	0.2	0.2	–	–	–
Ireland	RC	(e)	(e)	(e)	–	–
Slovakia	RC	–	–	–	3	3
Injuries and diseases						
Hong Kong, China	RC	0.1	0.1	0.1	0.1	0.1
Deaths per 100,000 employed persons						
Injuries only						
Australia	CC	2.6	2	2	–	–
Austria	RC	–	–	2.6	2.4	3.1
Cyprus	RC	–	–	1.5	2.8	2.9
Denmark	RC	–	–	2	2	
Estonia	RC	3.2	3	3.1	2.2	3.2
Ethiopia	RC	0.2	0.2	–	–	–
Finland	CC	1.2	1.6	1.2	–	–
Hungary	RC	–	–	2.1	1.6	–
Kyrgyzstan	RC	–	–	–	–	6
Lithuania	RC	–	–	5.4	5.6	5.8
Malaysia	RC	–	–	9	6	–
Netherlands	RC	–	–	0.7	–	–
Norway	RC	1.7	1.8	2.1	1.4	–
Poland[f]	RC	3.5	3.9	–	–	–
Romania	RC	–	–	–	–	4.7
Singapore	RC	2.9	2.2	2.3	2.1	2.1
Slovakia	RC	–	–	2	–	–
Slovenia	CC	–	–	2.2	–	–
Sweden	RC	1	1	1	1	1
Turkey	RC	–	–	15.5	6.2	–
United Kingdom	RC	0.5	0.6	0.6	–	0.5
United States[c,g]	RC	3.5	3.5	3.5	3.2	–
Injuries and commuting accidents						
Brazil	RC	–	–	7.4	–	–
Chile	RC	6.9	–	–	–	–
Croatia	CC	–	–	2.7	2.9	–
Israel	CC	–	–	2.4	2	–
Macau, China	RC	2.2	3.8	4	5.5	–
Romania	RC	8	8.2	6.4	5.1	–
Injuries and diseases						
Malta	CC	5	1.8	0.6	3.5	–
Injuries, diseases, and commuting accidents						
Israel	CC	1.7	2	–	–	–
Luxembourg	RC	–	–	(e)	(e)	(e)
Mexico	RC	10	10	10.5	9.8	8.1
Panama	RC	–	–	1.6	1.5	–
Deaths per 100,000 persons insured						
Injuries only						
Australia	CC	–	–	–	2	1.9
Belize	CC	–	–	4.5	6.7	–
Bulgaria	CC	–	–	3.6	3	3.1
Chile	CC	–	–	5.5	6	–
Czech Republic	RC	2.5	2.8	–	–	–
France	CC	(e)	(e)	–	–	–
Germany	CC	1.6	1.8	–	–	–
Malaysia	RC	–	–	–	–	5
Spain	RC	2.6	2.3	2.3	1.9	–
Thailand	CC	–	–	–	–	(e)
Turkey	RC	20.9	20.8	–	–	–
Injuries and commuting accidents						
El Salvador	RC	0.2	0.1	–	–	–
Injuries and diseases						
Argentina	RC	–	–	67.1	64.9	
Injuries per 1,000,000 Hours Worked						
Injuries only						
Japan[h]	RC	(e)	(e)	–	–	–
Korea, Republic of	CC	(e)	(e)	(e)	(e)	–

See source and limitations of data on page 194.

Note: Dash (–) indicates data not available

[a]*Maximum period between accident and death for death to be counted.*
[b]*Types of workers included in the data.*
[c]*Excludes farms with less than 11 employees.*

[d]*Includes reported cases (RC) and compensated cases (CC) of occupational fatalities*
[e]*Value 0.05 or less.*
[f]*Excludes private farms in agriculture.*
[g]*Excludes federal jurisdictions.*
[h]*Excludes agriculture.*

Counts and rates of nonfatal work-related injuries are shown on this page and the next. Comparisons between countries should be made with caution and take into account the differences in sources, coverage, and kinds of cases included.

Occupational injuries by country, 2009-2013

Country	Nonfatal injuries					Source of data	Coverage	
	2009	2010	2011	2012	2013		Worker types[b]	Economic Activities excluded
Injuries only – compensated cases								
Australia	97,475	92,300	94,714	105,525	100,050	IR	–	none
Chile	–	–	225,535	214,986	–	AR	I	none
Finland	48,308	50,557	51,344	–	–	IR	E	none
France	651,453	658,847	–	–	–	IR	I	none
Germany	974,020	1,045,142	1,007,200	–	–	IR	I	none
Lithuania	2,043	2,305	2,668	2,840	3,082	LR	–	none
Slovenia	17,407	–	15,200	–	–	AR	–	none
Injuries only – reported cases								
Armenia	21	21	–	–	–	LR	E	none
Austria	–	117,775	70,374	68,260	59,464	IR	E	none
Belgium	84,392	86,268	85,329	77,609	71,008	IR	E	–
Belize	2,086	1,804	1,757	1,756	–	AR	–	none
Bulgaria	2,517	2,365	2,279	2,314	2,203	IR	I	none
Cuba	5,397	4,919	–	–	–	AR	E	none
Cyprus	2,218	2,165	2,005	1,732	1,529	LR	E	none
Czech Republic	50,068	51,557	–	–	42,927	AR	I	AF
Denmark	–	–	42,491	41,710	–	AR	–	–
Estonia	2,920	3,198	3,725	4,133	4,160	LR	–	none
Hungary	18,355	19,853	17,215	16,963	–	LR	E	AF
Ireland	31,795	40,583	–	–	–	S	–	AF, Inst.
Latvia	–	–	1,363	1,476	1,566	LR	E	none
Netherlands	–	–	834,200	908,000	831,800	S	E	–
New Zealand	22,526	20,229	–	15,369	–	IR	E, SE	none
Norway	17,739	15,370	12,051	15,198	–	LR	–	SF, MT, OOE
Panama	38	40	22	30	–	LR	–	–
Singapore	10,764	10,264	10,060	11,057	11,842	AR	–	PDS
Slovakia	9,183	9,124	8,789	8,469	8,482	LR	E	none
Spain	615,996	568,080	511,051	407,073	–	IR	–	none
Sri Lanka	1,449	1,456	–	–	–	LR	E	none
Sweden	25,809	28,311	28,702	29,906	30,480	AR	E,SE	none
Trinidad and Tobago	921	833	–	–	–	AR	–	–
Turkey	1,885	2,085	2,216	2,209	–	IR	I	AF, Inst.
United Kingdom	124,654	117,469	113,535	–	79,917	LR	E	–
United States[b]	1,238,490	1,191,100	–	–	–	S	E,SE	Fed., Inst., OT
Injuries and commuting accidents - compensated cases								
Croatia	19,566	15,791	18,116	15,718	–	LR	–	none
Injuries and commuting accidents - reported cases								
Macau, China	3,626	3,759	4,247	3,352	–	LR	E	AF, Inst.
Romania	3,589	3,767	3,264	3,251	3,352	LR	E,SE	AF
Injuries and diseases - compensated cases								
Malta	3,366	3,314	3,024	3,057	–	AR	–	none
Injuries and diseases - reported cases								
Argentina	572,031	568,162	466,086	441,113	–	AR	I	none
Hong Kong, China	39,414	41,724	40,387	39,711	–	LR	E	none
Nicaragua	23,338	25,838	–	–	–	AR	–	none
Switzerland	87,793	–	93,770	–	–	IR	I	none
Injuries, diseases, and commuting accidents - compensated cases								
Israel	61,848	62,519	63,294	–	–	IR	–	none
Thailand	148,846	145,892	–	–	–	IR	I	none
Injuries, diseases, and commuting accidents - reported cases								
Ecuador	–	–	9,338	13,657	–	AR	–	none
Mexico	489,787	506,528	536,322	557,782	542,373	IR	–	none

Source: International Labour Organization, Department of Statistics, accessed November 14, 2014, from http://laborsta.ilo.org.
Note: Dash (–) means data not available. See footnotes on page 197.

Source of Data
AR = Administrative reports
IR = Insurance records
LR = Labor inspectorate records
S = Survey

Worker Types
E = Employees
I = Insured persons
SE = Self-employed

Economic Activites
AF = Armed forces
Agr = Agriculture
Fed. = Federal jurisdictions
Inst. = Institutional population
M = Manufacturing
MT = Maritime transport

OOE = Offshore oil extraction
OT = Overseas territories
PDS = Private domestic service
Priv. Agr = Private farms in agriculture
SF = Sea fishing

Occupational Injury Rates

The International Labour Organization (ILO) estimates that about 313 million nonfatal occupational injuries occur annually, many of which result in extended absences from work. This means that every 15 seconds, 160 workers suffer a work-related injury. Provided below are nonfatal injury and illness rates for 43 countries included in the ILO dataset.

Source: International Labour Organization. (2014). Safety and health at work. Accessed November 21, 2014 from www.ilo.org/global/topics/safety-and-health-at-work/lang--en/index.htm.

Occupational injury rates by country, 2009-2013

Country	Coverage[d]	2009	2010	2011	2012	2013
Injuries per 1,000 employees						
Injuries only						
Cuba	RC	11.2	10.2	–	–	–
Ireland	RC	16.4	21.8	22.5	–	–
Injuries and diseases						
Hong Kong, China	RC	15	15.4	14.5	14	–
Injuries per 1,000 insured employees						
Injuries and diseases						
Argentina	RC	–	–	56.1	50.9	–
Injuries per 100,000 employed persons						
Injuries only						
Australia	CC	986.1	912.5	907.5	–	–
Austria	RC	–	–	2,478	2,368	2,051
Canada	CC	1,339.009	1,256.129	–	–	–
Cyprus	RC	–	–	613.6	534.4	494.4
Denmark	RC	–	–	1,588	1,560	–
Estonia	RC	490.1	560.2	611.6	661.9	669.6
Finland	CC	2,275.7	2,385	2,397	–	–
Hungary	RC	–	–	451.6	437.4	–
Kyrgyzstan	RC	–	–	–	–	38
Lithuania	RC	–	–	269.3	281.1	299.7
Malaysia	RC	–	–	747	703	–
Netherlands	RC	–	–	11,800	12,800	11,900.0
New Zealand	CC	–	–	–	800	–
Norway[d]	RC	707.9	613.1	–	–	–
Qatar[e]	CC	11.1	–	8.9	5.4	3.6[f]
Romania	RC	–	–	–	–	70.5
Slovakia	RC	–	–	452	430	431.2
Slovenia	CC	–	–	1,858.6	–	–
Sweden	RC	601	643	636	662	666
Turkey	RC	–	–	20.1	18.5	–
Ukraine	RC	112.63	112.19	–	–	–
United Kingdom	RC	427.3	402.7	387.8	–	270.1
United States[b,d]	RC	1,172	1,179	–	–	–
Injuries and commuting accidents						
Brazil	RC	–	–	1,609.3	–	–
Croatia	CC	–	–	1,284.6	1,127.3	–
Israel	CC	–	–	2,419.5	–	–
Macau, China[f]	RC	1,142	1,181[g]	1,296.4	976.7	–
Romania	RC	69.8	82.4	70	69.3	–
Injuries and diseases						
Malta	CC	2,086.7	2,013.2	1,792.4	1,770.1	–
Switzerland	RC	–	–	2,437.7	–	–
Injuries, diseases, and commuting accidents						
Israel	CC	2,498.6	2,438.8	–	–	–
Mexico	RC	3,545	3,532	3,582.4	3,559.2	3,343
Panama[f]	RC	–	–	1.4	1.9	–
Injuries per 100,000 persons insured						
Injuries only						
Australia	CC	–	–	–	1,016.4	943.9
Belize	CC	–	–	1,996.9	1,954.4	–
Bulgaria	CC	–	–	88.1	90.2	84.7
Chile	CC	–	–	5,488.3	4,876.2	–
Czech Republic[d]	RC	1,177.2	1,196	–	–	–
France	CC	23.4	23.3	–	–	–
Germany	CC	2,579	2,738	–	–	–
Malaysia[f]	RC	–	–	–	–	681
Spain	RC	4,121	3,861.1	3,504.7	2,838.7	–
Injuries and commuting accidents						
El Salvador	RC	30.09	28.68	–	–	–
Injuries and diseases						
Switzerland	RC	2,270.1	–	–	–	–
Injuries per 1,000,000 Hours Worked						
Injuries only						
Belgium[f]	RC	22	22.2	21.4	19.4	17.6
Injuries, diseases, and commuting accidents						
Luxembourg	RC	–	–	12.5	12.3	12

See source and limitations of data on page 196.
Note: Dash (–) indicates data not available
[a]Types of workers included in the data.
[b]Excludes federal jurisdictions, occpational diseases, and farms with less than 11 employees.

[c]Includes reported cases (RC) and compensated cases (CC) of occupational fatalities.
[d]See activities excluded in table on page 196.
[e]Excluding injuries not resulting in some degree of disability.
[f]Private sector only.
[g]Provisional.

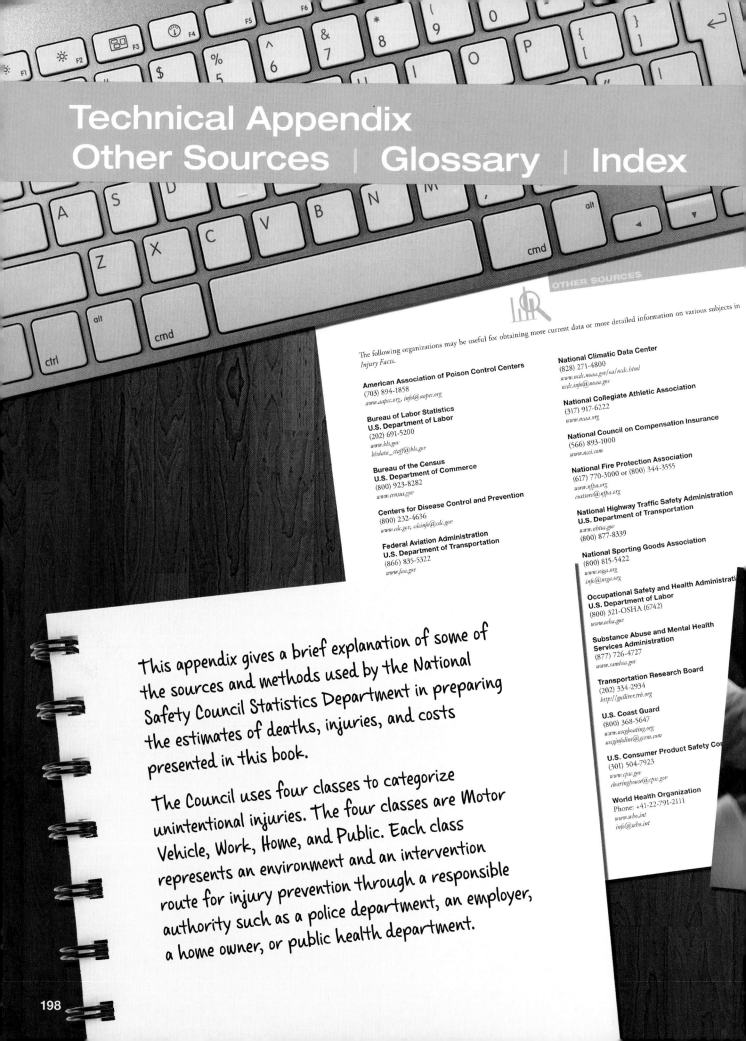

OTHER SOURCES

The following organizations may be useful for obtaining more current data or more detailed information on various subjects in *Injury Facts*.

American Association of Poison Control Centers
(703) 894-1858
www.aapcc.org, info@aapcc.org

Bureau of Labor Statistics
U.S. Department of Labor
(202) 691-5200
www.bls.gov
blsdata_staff@bls.gov

Bureau of the Census
U.S. Department of Commerce
(800) 923-8282
www.census.gov

Centers for Disease Control and Prevention
(800) 232-4636
www.cdc.gov, cdcinfo@cdc.gov

Federal Aviation Administration
U.S. Department of Transportation
(866) 835-5322
www.faa.gov

National Climatic Data Center
(828) 271-4800
www.ncdc.noaa.gov/oa/ncdc.html
ncdc.info@noaa.gov

National Collegiate Athletic Association
(317) 917-6222
www.ncaa.org

National Council on Compensation Insurance
(566) 893-1000
www.ncci.com

National Fire Protection Association
(617) 770-3000 or (800) 344-3555
www.nfpa.org
custserv@nfpa.org

National Highway Traffic Safety Administration
U.S. Department of Transportation
www.nhtsa.gov
(800) 877-8339

National Sporting Goods Association
(800) 815-5422
www.nsga.org
info@nsga.org

Occupational Safety and Health Administration
U.S. Department of Labor
(800) 321-OSHA (6742)
www.osha.gov

Substance Abuse and Mental Health Services Administration
(877) 726-4727
www.samhsa.gov

Transportation Research Board
(202) 334-2934
http://gulliver.trb.org

U.S. Coast Guard
(800) 368-5647
www.uscgboating.org
uscginfoline@gcrm.com

U.S. Consumer Product Safety Commission
(301) 504-7923
www.cpsc.gov
clearinghouse@cpsc.gov

World Health Organization
Phone: +41-22-791-2111
www.who.int
info@who.int

This appendix gives a brief explanation of some of the sources and methods used by the National Safety Council Statistics Department in preparing the estimates of deaths, injuries, and costs presented in this book.

The Council uses four classes to categorize unintentional injuries. The four classes are Motor Vehicle, Work, Home, and Public. Each class represents an environment and an intervention route for injury prevention through a responsible authority such as a police department, an employer, a home owner, or public health department.

National Safety Council

This appendix gives a brief explanation of some of the sources and methods used by the National Safety Council Statistics Department in preparing the estimates of deaths, injuries, and costs presented in this book. Because many of the estimates depend on death certificate data provided by the National Center for Health Statistics (NCHS), it begins with a brief introduction to the certification and classification of deaths.

Certification and classification. The medical certification of death involves entering information on the death certificate about the disease or condition directly leading to death, antecedent causes, and other significant conditions. The death certificate is then registered with the appropriate authority and a code is assigned for the underlying cause of death. The underlying cause is defined as "(a) the disease or injury which initiated the train of morbid events leading directly to death, or (b) the circumstances of the accident or violence which produced the fatal injury" (World Health Organization [WHO], 1992). Deaths are classified and coded on the basis of a WHO standard, the *International Statistical Classification of Diseases and Related Health Problems*, commonly known as the International Classification of Diseases or ICD (WHO, 1992). For deaths due to injury and poisoning, the ICD provides a system of "external cause" codes to which the underlying cause of death is assigned. (See pages 20-21 of *Injury Facts* for a condensed list of external cause codes.)

Comparability across *ICD* revisions. The *ICD* is revised periodically and these revisions can affect comparability from year to year. The sixth revision (1948) substantially expanded the list of external causes and provided for classifying the place of occurrence. Changes in the classification procedures for the sixth revision as well as the seventh (1958) and eighth (1968) revisions classified as diseases some deaths previously classified as injuries. The eighth revision also expanded and reorganized some external cause sections. The ninth revision (1979) provided more detail on the agency involved, the victims' activity, and the place of occurrence. The tenth revision, which was adopted in the United States effective with 1999 data, completely revised the transportation-related categories. Specific external cause categories affected by the revisions are noted in the historical tables.

The table at the end of this appendix (page 203) shows the ICD-9 codes, the ICD-10 codes, and a comparability ratio for each of the principal causes of unintentional injury death. The comparability ratio represents the net effect of the new revision on statistics for the cause of death. The comparability ratio was obtained by classifying a sample of death certificates under both ICD-9 and ICD-10 and then dividing the number of deaths for a selected cause classified under ICD-10 by the number classified to the most nearly comparable ICD-9 cause. A comparability ratio of 1.00 indicates no net change due to the new classification scheme. A ratio less than 1.00 indicates fewer deaths assigned to a cause under ICD-10 than under ICD-9. A ratio greater than 1.00 indicates an increase in assignment of deaths to a cause under ICD-10 compared to ICD-9.

The broad category of "accidents" or "unintentional injuries" under ICD-9 included complications and misadventures of surgical and medical care (E870-E879) and adverse effects of drugs in therapeutic use (E930-E949). These categories are not included in "accidents" or "unintentional injuries" under ICD-10. In 1998, deaths in these two categories numbered 3,228 and 276, respectively.

Under ICD-9, the code range for falls (E880-E888) included a code for "fracture, cause unspecified" (E887). A similar code does not appear in ICD-10 (W00-W19), which probably accounts for the low comparability ratio (0.8409). In 1998, deaths in code E887 numbered 3,679.

Beginning with 1970 data, tabulations published by NCHS no longer include deaths of nonresident aliens. In 2011, there were 710 such unintentional deaths, of which 209 were motor vehicle related.

Fatality estimates. The Council uses four classes and three venues to categorize unintentional injuries. The four classes are Motor Vehicle, Work, Home, and Public. Each class represents an environment and an intervention route for injury prevention through a responsible authority such as a police department, an employer, a home owner, or public health department. The three venues are Transportation, Work, and Home and Community.

Motor vehicle. The Motor Vehicle class can be identified by the underlying cause of death (see the table on page 203).

Work. The National Safety Council adopted the Bureau of Labor Statistics' Census of Fatal Occupational Injuries (CFOI) figure, beginning with the 1992 data year, as the authoritative count of unintentional work-related deaths. The CFOI system is described in detail in Toscano and Windau (1994).

The 2-Way Split. After subtracting the Motor Vehicle and Work figures from the unintentional injury total (ICD-10 codes V01-X59, Y85-Y86), the remainder belong to the Home and Public classes. The Home class can be identified by the "place of occurrence" subclassification (code .0) used with most nontransport deaths; the Public class is the remainder. Missing "place of occurrence" information, however, prevents the direct determination of the Home and Public class totals. Because of this, the Council allocates non-motor vehicle, nonwork deaths into the Home and Public classes based on the external cause, age group, and cases with specified "place of occurrence." This procedure, known as the 2-Way Split, uses the most recent death certificate data available from the NCHS and the CFOI data for the same calendar year. For each cause-code group and age group combination, the Motor Vehicle and Work deaths are subtracted and the remainder, including those with "place of occurrence" unspecified, are allocated to Home and Public in the same proportion as those with "place of occurrence" specified.

The table on page 203 shows the ICD-10 cause-codes and CFOI event codes for the most common causes of unintentional-injury death. The CFOI event codes (BLS, 1992) do not match exactly with ICD cause codes, so there is some error in the allocation of deaths among the classes.

Linking up to current year. The benchmark data published by NCHS are usually two years old and the final CFOI data are usually one year old. Starting with the 2011 edition of *Injury Facts*, an exponential smoothing technique is used to make current year estimates. Exponential smoothing is a statistical technique to make short term forecasts. In exponential smoothing (as opposed to in moving averages smoothing) older data are given progressively less relative weight (importance) whereas newer data are given progressively greater weight. The results of the exponential smoothing is then compared against the latest reported state data for validation.

Revisions of prior years. When the figures for a given year are published by NCHS, the 2-Way Split based on those figures and the CFOI become the final estimate of unintentional injury deaths by class, age group, and type of event or industry. Subsequent years are revised by repeating the exponential smoothing and state data process described above. For example, in the current edition of *Injury Facts*, the 2011 NCHS and CFOI data were used to produce final estimates using the 2-Way Split, the 2012 estimates were revised, and the new 2013 estimates were made with 2013 preliminary CFOI data.

Nonfatal injury estimates. Starting with the 2011 edition of *Injury Facts*, the Council adopted the concept of "medically consulted injury" to define the kinds of injuries included in its estimates. Prior editions of *Injury Facts* used the definition of disabling injury. There is no national injury surveillance system that provides injury estimates on a current basis. The National Health Interview System, a household survey conducted by NCHS (see page 25), produces national estimates using its own definition of medically consulted injury (Adams, Heyman, Vickerie, 2009). A medically consulted injury as defined by NCHS is an injury serious enough that a medical professional was consulted. The Council uses the medically consulted injury estimates from the National Health Interview survey for its motor vehicle, home, and public injury estimates. In addition, the Occupational Safety and Health Administration defines injury or illness using criteria including "Medical treatment beyond first aid." The Council uses the total recordable case estimate defined by OSHA and published by the Bureau of Labor Statistics to estimate the number of workplace injuries. Because BLS's estimate excludes the self-employed, unpaid family workers, and federal government employees, the Council uses total employment estimates, as well as BLS nonfatal estimates, to calculate the total number of nonfatal medically consulted injuries.

Injury-to-death ratios. Because estimates for medically consulted injuries are not available for the current year, the Council uses injury-to-death ratios to estimate nonfatal medically consulted injuries for the current year. Complete documentation of the procedure, effective with the 1993 edition, may be found in Landes, Ginsburg, Hoskin, and Miller (1990). The resulting estimates are not direct measures of nonfatal injuries and should not be compared with prior years.

Population sources. All population figures used in computing rates are estimates taken from various reports published by the Bureau of the Census, U.S. Department of Commerce, on their its website (*www.census.gov*). *Resident* population is used for computing rates.

Costs (pages 6-9). The procedures for estimating the economic losses due to fatal and nonfatal unintentional injuries were extensively revised for the 1993 edition of *Accident Facts*. New components were added, new benchmarks adopted, and a new discount rate assumed. All of these changes resulted in significantly higher cost estimates. For this reason, it must be re-emphasized that the cost estimates should not be compared to those in earlier editions of the book.

The Council's general philosophy underlying its cost estimates is that the figures represent income not received or expenses incurred because of fatal and nonfatal unintentional injuries. Stated this way, the Council's cost estimates are a measure of the economic impact of unintentional injuries and may be compared to other economic measures such as gross domestic product, per capita income, or personal consumption expenditures. (See page 109 and "lost quality of life" [page 202] for a discussion of injury costs for cost-benefit analysis.)

The general approach followed was to identify a benchmark unit cost for each component, adjust the benchmark to the current year using an appropriate inflator, estimate the number of cases to which the component applied, and compute the product. Where possible, benchmarks were obtained for each class: Motor Vehicle, Work, Home, and Public.

Wage and productivity losses include the value of wages, fringe benefits, and household production for all classes, and travel delay for the Motor Vehicle class.

For fatalities, the present value of after-tax wages, fringe benefits, and household production was computed using the human capital method. The procedure incorporates data on life expectancy from the NCHS life tables, employment likelihood from the Bureau of Labor Statistics household survey, and mean earnings from the Bureau of the Census money income survey. The discount rate used was 4%, reduced from 6% used in earlier years. The present value obtained is highly sensitive to the discount rate; the lower the rate, the greater the present value.

For permanent partial disabilities, an average of 17% of earning power is lost (Berkowitz & Burton, 1987). The incidence of permanent disabilities, adjusted to remove intentional injuries, was computed from data on hospitalized cases from the National Hospital Discharge Survey (NHDS) and nonhospitalized cases from the National Health Interview Survey and National Council on Compensation Insurance data on probabilities of disability by nature of injury and part of body injured.

For temporary disabilities, an average daily wage, fringe benefit, and household production loss was calculated and this was multiplied by the number of days of restricted activity from the NHIS.

Travel delay costs were obtained from the Council's estimates of the number of fatal, injury, and property damage crashes and an average delay cost per crash from Miller et al. (1991).

Medical expenses, including ambulance and helicopter transport costs, were estimated for fatalities, hospitalized cases, and nonhospitalized cases in each class.

The incidence of hospitalized cases was derived from the NHDS data adjusted to eliminate intentional injuries. Average length of stay was benchmarked from Miller, Pindus, Douglass, and Rossman (1993b) and adjusted to estimate lifetime length of stay. The cost per hospital day was benchmarked to the National Medical Expenditure Survey (NMES).

Nonhospitalized cases were estimated by taking the difference between total NHIS injuries and hospitalized cases. Average cost per case was based on NMES data adjusted for inflation and lifetime costs.

Medical cost of fatalities was benchmarked to data from the National Council on Compensation Insurance (1989) to which was added the cost of a premature funeral and coroner costs (Miller et al., 1991).

Cost per ambulance transport was benchmarked to NMES data and cost per helicopter transport was benchmarked to data in Miller et al. (1993a). The number of cases transported was based on data from Rice and MacKenzie (1989) and the National Electronic Injury Surveillance System.

Administrative expenses include the administrative cost of private and public insurance, which represents the cost of having insurance, and police and legal costs.

The administrative cost of motor vehicle insurance was the difference between premiums earned (adjusted to remove fire, theft, and casualty premiums) and pure losses incurred, based on data from A. M. Best. Workers' compensation insurance administration was based on A. M. Best data for private carriers and regression estimates using Social Security Administration data for state funds and the self-insured. Administrative costs of public insurance (mainly Medicaid and Medicare) amount to about 4% of the medical expenses paid by public insurance, which were determined from Rice and MacKenzie (1989) and Hensler et al. (1991).

Average police costs for motor-vehicle crashes were taken from Miller et al. (1991) and multiplied by the Council's estimates of the number of fatal, injury, and property damage crashes.

Legal expenses include court costs, and plaintiff's and defendant's time and expenses. Hensler et al. (1991) provided data on the proportion of injured persons who hire a lawyer, file a claim, and get compensation. Kakalik and Pace (1986) provided data on costs per case.

Fire losses were based on data published by the National Fire Protection Association in the *NFPA Journal.* The allocation into the classes was based on the property use for structure fires and other NFPA data for non-structure fires.

Motor vehicle damage costs were benchmarked to Blincoe and Faigin (1992) and multiplied by the Council's estimates of crash incidence.

Employer costs for work injuries is an estimate of the productivity costs incurred by employers. It assumes each fatality or permanent injury resulted in four person-months of disruption, serious injuries one person-month, and minor to moderate injuries two person-days. All injuries to nonworkers were assumed to involve two days of worker productivity loss. Average hourly earnings for supervisors and nonsupervisory workers were computed and then multiplied by the incidence and hours lost per case. Property damage and production delays (except motor vehicle related) are not included in the estimates but can be substantial.

Lost quality of life is the difference between the value of a statistical fatality or statistical injury and the value of after-tax wages, fringe benefits, and household production. Because this does not represent real income not received or expenses incurred, it is not included in the total economic cost figure. If included, the resulting comprehensive costs can be used in cost-benefit analysis because the total costs then represent the maximum amount society should spend to prevent a statistical death or injury.

Work deaths and injuries (page 58). The method for estimating total work-related deaths and injuries is discussed above. The breakdown of deaths by industry division for the current year is obtained from CFOI. The estimate of nonfatal medically consulted injuries by industry division is made using the Survey of Occupational Injury and Illness' estimate of total recordable injury and illness after correcting for the exclusion of self-employed, unpaid family workers, and federal government employees.

Employment. The employment estimates for 1992 to the present were changed for the 1998 edition. Estimates for these years in prior editions are not comparable. The total employment figure used by the Council represents the number of persons in the civilian labor force, aged 16 and older, who were wage or salary workers, self-employed, or unpaid family workers, plus active duty military personnel resident in the United States. The total employment estimate is a combination of three figures – total civilian employment from the Current Population Survey (CPS) as published in Employment and Earnings, plus the difference between total resident population and total civilian population, which represents active duty military personnel.

Employment by industry is obtained from an unpublished Bureau of Labor Statistics table titled "Employed and experience unemployed persons by detailed industry and class of worker, Annual Average [year] (based on CPS)."

Time lost (page 62) is the product of the number of cases and the average time lost per case. Deaths average 150 workdays lost in the current year and 5,850 in future years; permanent disabilities involve 75 and 565 days lost in current and future years, respectively; temporary disabilities involve 17 days lost in the current year only. Off-the-job injuries to workers are assumed to result in similar lost time.

Off-the-job (page 63) deaths and injuries are estimated by assuming that employed persons incur injuries at the same rate as the entire population.

Motor vehicle (pages 104-139). Estimates of miles traveled, registered vehicles and licensed drivers are published by the Federal Highway Administration in *Highway Statistics* and *Traffic Volume Trends*.

Selected unintentional-injury code groupings

Manner of injury	ICD-9 codes[a]	ICD-10 codes[b]	Comparability ratio[c]	OICCS v2.01[d] event codes
Unintentional injuries	E800-E869, E880-E929[e]	V01-X59, Y85-Y86	1.0305 (1.0278-1.0333)[f]	12 - 9999
Railway accident	E800-E807	V05, V15, V80.6, V81(.2-.9)	n/a	22
Motor vehicle accident	E810-E825	V02-V04, V09.0, V09.2, V12-V14, V19.0-V19.2, V19.4-V19.6, V20-V79, V80.3-V80.5, V81.0-V81.1, V82.0-V82.1, V83-V86, V87.0-V87.8, V88.0-V88.8, V89.0, V89.2	0.9754 (0.9742-0.9766)	24, 26, 27
Water transport accident	E830-E838	V90-V94	n/a	25
Air transport accident	E840-E845	V95-V97	n/a	21
Poisoning by solids and liquids	E850-58, E860-66	X40-X49	n/a	55, 59, 1224
Poisoning by gases and vapors	E867-E869			
Falls	E880-E888	W00-W19	0.8409 (0.8313-0.8505)	40, 42-45, 49
Fires and burns	E890-E899	X00-X09	0.9743 (0.9568-0.9918)	31
Drowning[g]	E910	W65-W74	0.9965 (0.9716-1.0213)	561
Choking[h]	E911-E912	W78-W80	n/a	562
Mechanical suffocation	E913	W75-W77, W81-W84	n/a	560, 563, 569
Firearms	E922	W32-W34	1.0579 (1.0331-1.0828)	1211, 1221, 1222

Source: National Safety Council.
Note: n/a means comparability ratio not calculated or does not meet standards of reliability or precision.
[a]*WHO (1977).*
[b]*WHO (1992).*
[c]*Hoyert, Arias, Smith, et al. (2001). Table III.*
[d]*BLS (2012), Occupational Injury and Illness Classification Manual, Version 2.01.*
[e]*The National Safety Council has used E800-E949 for unintentional injuries. The code group in the table omits complications and misadventures of surgical and medical care (E870-E879) and adverse effects of drugs in therapeutic use (E930-E949).*
[f]*Figures in parentheses are the 95% confidence interval for the comparability ratio.*
[g]*Excludes transport.*
[h]*Suffocation by ingestion or inhalation.*

Berkowitz, M., & Burton, J.F., Jr. (1987). *Permanent Disability Benefits in Workers' Compensation*. Kalamazoo, MI: W.E. Upjohn Institute for Employment Research.

Blincoe, L.J., & Faigin, B.M. (1992). *Economic Cost of Motor Vehicle Crashes, 1990*. Springfield, VA: National Technical Information Service.

Bureau of Labor Statistics [BLS]. (2012). *Occupational Injury & Illness Classification Manual Version 2.01*. Downloaded from http://www.bls.gov/iif/oshoiics.htm on August 29, 2013.

Bureau of Labor Statistics [BLS]. (2014, December). *Workplace Injuries and Illnesses in 2013*. Press release USDL-14-2183.

Hensler, D.R., Marquis, M.S., Abrahamse, A.F., Berry, S.H., Ebener, P.A., Lewis, E.D., Lind, E.A., MacCoun, R.J., Manning, W.G., Rogowski, J.A., & Vaiana, M.E. (1991). *Compensation for Accidental Injuries in the United States*. Santa Monica, CA: The RAND Corporation.

Hoyert, D.L., Arias, E., Smith, B.L., Murphy, S.L., & Kochanek, K.D. (2001). Deaths: final data for 1999. *National Vital Statistics Reports, 49*(8).

Kakalik, J.S., & Pace, N. (1986). *Costs and Compensation Paid in Tort Litigation*. R-3391-ICJ. Santa Monica, CA: The RAND Corporation.

Landes, S.R., Ginsburg, K.M., Hoskin, A.F., & Miller, T.A. (1990). *Estimating Nonfatal Injuries*. Itasca, IL: Statistics Department, National Safety Council.

Miller, T., Viner, J., Rossman, S., Pindus, N., Gellert, W., Douglass, J., Dillingham, A., & Blomquist, G. (1991). *The Costs of Highway Crashes*. Springfield, VA: National Technical Information Service.

Miller, T.R., Brigham, P.A., Cohen, M.A., Douglass, J.B., Galbraith, M.S., Lestina, D.C., Nelkin, V.S., Pindus, N.M., & Smith-Regojo, P. (1993a). Estimating the costs to society of cigarette fire injuries. *Report to Congress in Response to the Fire Safe Cigarette Act of 1990*. Washington, DC: U.S. Consumer Product Safety Commission.

Miller, T.R., Pindus, N.M., Douglass, J.B., & Rossman, S.B. (1993b). *Nonfatal Injury Incidence, Costs, and Consequences: A Data Book*. Washington, DC: The Urban Institute Press.

Occupational Safety and Health Administration. (2005). *OSHA recordkeeping handbook*. OSHA 3245-01R.

Rice, D.P., & MacKenzie, E.J. (1989). *Cost of Injury in the United States: A Report to Congress*. Atlanta, GA: Centers for Disease Control and Prevention.

Adams, P.F., Heyman, K.M., Vickerie, J.L. (2009). Summary health statistics for the U.S. population: National health interview survey, 2008. *Vital and Health Statistics, Series 10, No. 243*. Hyattsville, MD: National Center of Health Statistics.

Toscano, G., & Windau, J. (1994). The changing character of fatal work injuries. *Monthly Labor Review, 117*(10), 17-28.

World Health Organization. (1977). *Manual of the International Statistical Classification of Diseases, Injuries, and Causes of Death*. Geneva, Switzerland: Author.

World Health Organization. (1992). *International Statistical Classification of Diseases and Related Health Problems – Tenth Revision*. Geneva, Switzerland: Author.

The following organizations may be useful for obtaining more current data or more detailed information on various subjects in *Injury Facts*.

American Association of Poison Control Centers
(703) 894-1858
www.aapcc.org, info@aapcc.org

Bureau of Labor Statistics
U.S. Department of Labor
(202) 691-5200
www.bls.gov
blsdata_staff@bls.gov

Bureau of the Census
U.S. Department of Commerce
(800) 923-8282
www.census.gov

Centers for Disease Control and Prevention
(800) 232-4636
www.cdc.gov, cdcinfo@cdc.gov

Federal Aviation Administration
U.S. Department of Transportation
(866) 835-5322
www.faa.gov

Federal Highway Administration
U.S. Department of Transportation
(202) 366-4000
www.fhwa.dot.gov
execsecretariat.fhwa@fhwa.dot.gov

Federal Motor Carrier Safety Administration
U.S. Department of Transportation
(800) 832-5660
www.fmcsa.dot.gov

Federal Railroad Administration
U.S. Department of Transportation
(202) 493-6065
www.fra.dot.gov

International Labour Organization
Phone: +41-22-799-6111
Fax: +41-22-798-8685
www.ilo.org
ilo@ilo.org

Mine Safety and Health Administration
(202) 693-9400
www.msha.gov

National Center for Health Statistics
(800) 232-4636
www.cdc.gov/nchs

National Center for Statistics and Analysis
(202) 366-4198 or (800) 934-8517
www.nhtsa.dot.gov
NCSAweb@nhtsa.dot.gov

National Climatic Data Center
(828) 271-4800
www.ncdc.noaa.gov/oa/ncdc.html
ncdc.info@noaa.gov

National Collegiate Athletic Association
(317) 917-6222
www.ncaa.org

National Council on Compensation Insurance
(566) 893-1000
www.ncci.com

National Fire Protection Association
(617) 770-3000 or (800) 344-3555
www.nfpa.org
custserv@nfpa.org

National Highway Traffic Safety Administration
U.S. Department of Transportation
www.nhtsa.gov
(800) 877-8339

National Sporting Goods Association
(800) 815-5422
www.nsga.org
info@nsga.org

Occupational Safety and Health Administration
U.S. Department of Labor
(800) 321-OSHA (6742)
www.osha.gov

Substance Abuse and Mental Health Services Administration
(877) 726-4727
www.samhsa.gov

Transportation Research Board
(202) 334-2934
http://gulliver.trb.org

U.S. Coast Guard
(800) 368-5647
www.uscgboating.org
uscginfoline@gcrm.com

U.S. Consumer Product Safety Commission
(301) 504-7923
www.cpsc.gov
clearinghouse@cpsc.gov

World Health Organization
Phone: +41-22-791-2111
www.who.int
info@who.int

Accident is that occurrence in a sequence of events that produces unintended injury, death, or property damage. Accident refers to the event, not the result of the event (see Unintentional injury). The term "accident" has largely been replaced in the public health community with the term "incident."

Death from incident is a death that occurs within one year of the incident.

Disabling injury is an injury causing death, permanent disability, or any degree of temporary total disability beyond the day of the injury. Starting with the 2012 edition of *Injury Facts*, the definition of disabling injury was replaced by medically consulted injury for all non-fatal injury estimates.

Fatal incident is an incident that results in one or more deaths within one year.

Home is a dwelling and its premises within the property lines including single family dwellings and apartment houses, duplex dwellings, boarding and rooming houses, and seasonal cottages. Excluded from home are barracks, dormitories, and resident institutions.

Incidence rate, as defined by OSHA, is the number of occupational injuries and/or illnesses or lost workdays per 100 full-time employees (see formula on page 76).

Incident is the preferred term for "accident" in the public health community. It refers to the occurrence in a sequence of events that produces unintended injury, death, or property damage. Incident refers to the event, not the result of the event (see Unintentional injury).

Injury is physical harm or damage to the body resulting from an exchange, usually acute, of mechanical, chemical, thermal, or other environmental energy that exceeds the body's tolerance.

Medically consulted injury is an injury serious enough that a medical professional was consulted. For the motor vehicle, home and public venues, the National Safety Council uses the medically consulted injury estimates from the National Health Interview Survey. The Council uses the total recordable case estimate, using OSHA's definition, published by the Bureau of Labor Statistics (BLS) to estimate the number of workplace injuries. Because the BLS estimate excludes self-employed, unpaid family workers, and federal government employees, the Council extrapolates the BLS estimate to reflect the total worker population.

Motor vehicle is any mechanically or electrically powered device not operated on rails, upon which or by which any person or property may be transported upon a land highway. The load on a motor vehicle or trailer attached to it is considered part of the vehicle. Tractors and motorized machinery are included while self-propelled in transit or used for transportation. Non-motor vehicle is any road vehicle other than a motor vehicle, such as a bicycle or animal-drawn vehicle, except a coaster wagon, child's sled, child's tricycle, child's carriage, and similar means of transportation; persons using these latter means of transportation are considered pedestrians.

Motor vehicle incident is an unstabilized situation that includes at least one harmful event (injury or property damage) involving a motor vehicle in transport (in motion, in readiness for motion, or on a roadway but not parked in a designated parking area) that does not result from discharge of a firearm or explosive device and does not directly result from a cataclysm. [See Committee on Motor Vehicle Traffic Accident Classification (1997), *Manual on Classification of Motor Vehicle Traffic Accidents,* ANSI D16.1-1996, Itasca, IL: National Safety Council.]

Motor vehicle traffic incident is a motor vehicle incident that occurs on a trafficway – a way or place, any part of which is open to the use of the public for the purposes of vehicular traffic. A motor vehicle nontraffic incident is any motor vehicle incident that occurs entirely in any place other than a trafficway.

Nonfatal injury incident is an incident in which at least one person is injured and no injury results in death.

Occupational illness is any abnormal condition or disorder other than one resulting from an occupational injury caused by exposure to environmental factors associated with employment. It includes acute and chronic illnesses or diseases that may be caused by inhalation, absorption, ingestion, or direct contact (see also pages 73 and 79).

Occupational injury is any injury such as a cut, fracture, sprain, amputation, etc., that results from a work incident or from a single instantaneous exposure in the work environment (see also page 79).

Pedalcycle is a vehicle propelled by human power and operated solely by pedals; excludes mopeds.

Pedestrian is any person involved in a motor vehicle incident who is not in or upon a motor vehicle or non-motor vehicle. Includes persons injured while using a coaster wagon, child's tricycle, roller skates, etc. Excludes persons boarding, alighting, jumping, or falling from a motor vehicle in transport who are considered occupants of the vehicle.

Permanent disability (or permanent impairment) includes any degree of permanent nonfatal injury. It includes any injury that results in the loss or complete loss of use of any part of the body or in any permanent impairment of functions of the body or a part thereof.

Property damage incident is an incident that results in property damage but in which no person is injured.

Public incident is any incident other than motor vehicle that occurs in the public use of any premises. Includes deaths in recreation (swimming, hunting, etc.), in transportation except motor vehicle, public buildings, etc., and from widespread natural disasters even though some may have happened on home premises. Excludes incidents to people in the course of gainful employment.

Source of injury is the principal object such as tool, machine, or equipment involved in the incident and is usually the object inflicting injury or property damage. Also called agency or agent.

Temporary total disability is an injury that does not result in death or permanent disability but that renders the injured person unable to perform regular duties or activities on one or more full calendar days after the day of the injury.

Total cases include all work-related deaths and illnesses and those work-related injuries that result in loss of consciousness, restriction of work or motion, or transfer to another job, or require medical treatment other than first aid.

Unintentional injury is the preferred term for accidental injury in the public health community. It refers to the result of an incident.

Work hours are the total number of hours worked by all employees. They are usually compiled for various levels, such as an establishment, a company, or an industry. A work hour is the equivalent of one employee working one hour.

Work injuries (including occupational illnesses) are those that arise out of and in the course of gainful employment regardless of where the accident or exposure occurs. Excluded are work injuries to private household workers and injuries occurring in connection with farm chores that are classified as home injuries.

Workers are all persons gainfully employed, including owners, managers, other paid employees, the self-employed, and unpaid family workers but excluding private household workers.

Work/motor vehicle duplication includes work injuries that occur in motor vehicle incidents (see Work injuries and Motor vehicle incident).